Understanding Pre-e

Understanding Pre-eclampsia

a guide for parents and health professionals

Joyce Cowan, Prof Chris Redman,
Isabel Walker

Clearsay Publishing

British Library Cataloguing in Publication Data
A catalogue record for this book is available from the British Library.

ISBN 978-0-9954709-0-3

Typeset by Amolibros, Milverton, Somerset
This book production has been managed by Amolibros
Printed and bound by T J International Ltd, Padstow, Cornwall, UK

CONTENTS

PREFACE

Pre-eclampsia, a pregnancy complication that affects at least three mothers-to-be in every hundred and is a major cause of stillbirth, prematurity, neonatal and even maternal death throughout the world, is one of the great remaining medical mysteries.

Although doctors and midwives have recognised its various features for thousands of years it remains, at heart, an enigma wrapped in a puzzle.

We know that problems within the placenta are the root of the disorder; but we don't know what causes these problems.

We can't accurately predict who will get pre-eclampsia; and even if we could, we can do little to stop them getting it.

We can't halt the illness in its tracks once it's started; and, while we can now prevent many of the worst outcomes through careful management, we can't do anything to cure pre-eclampsia, short of delivering babies who are sometimes too premature to survive or develop normally.

Even so, scientists and clinical researchers have made considerable progress in understanding pre-eclampsia since two of the authors of this book – Professor Chris Redman and Isabel Walker – first wrote about it a quarter of a century ago in *Pre-eclampsia: The Facts*, published by Oxford University Press in 1992.

Crucially, for example, it now seems likely that pre-eclampsia is not just a single illness that affects mothers and babies in varying ways, but an umbrella term for several different conditions that share certain signs and symptoms.

Equally importantly we now know that the main problem with the placenta in pre-eclampsia is a defective blood supply from the mother, technically known as 'malperfusion'; we have a better understanding of how the placenta's response to this problem can make the mother ill; we know that a woman's choice of partner can influence her risk of getting pre-eclampsia; and, finally, we now have confirmation that low-dose aspirin and, in some areas, calcium supplements can reduce the risk to some extent.

This book is not an update of *Pre-eclampsia: The Facts* but an entirely different book, written for a new generation of parents and caregivers.

The fact that it is co-written by Joyce Cowan, an academic midwife based in New Zealand, provides a unique midwifery perspective and a global context.

Throughout the book, we have used first-person accounts from the hundreds of women who responded to our worldwide online questionnaire survey about pre-eclampsia to illustrate our key points. They do so more powerfully than mere description could; and they show – often with distressing poignancy – how women the world over share the same experiences and feelings.

We have written this book so that parents and parents-to-be can understand how they were - or might be - affected by pre-eclampsia and what they can do to help themselves in future pregnancies and to safeguard their health in the long term; and so that midwives and other caregivers can gain deeper insights into the nature of the illness, its effects on their patients and the role they can play in screening, detection, management and aftercare.

It is not uncommon, as we point out at various places in this book, for professionals to misdiagnose or mismanage pre-eclampsia. But that is not surprising, given the extraordinary complexity of the disease and the fact that, with improved antenatal care, the most severe effects are seen much less often than they used to be. We are not out to beat people up for getting it wrong but to help them get it right more often.

Maybe one day the mystery at the heart of pre-eclampsia will be solved. That is certainly the fervent hope of Professor Redman, who has devoted more than 40 years of his life to the search for answers.

In the meantime, there is this book. It offers our personal perspectives as experts based in the UK and New Zealand. We recognise that other perspectives may differ, but probably more in terms of detail than on the overall picture we present.

JC, CR, IW
April 2017

FOREWORD

Pre-eclampsia is a confusing, multifaceted condition. High blood pressure and protein in the urine are the most familiar features, but pre-eclampsia is much more than the sum of these parts. It is a complex mixture of disease and response, as the mother's body fights to protect herself and her unborn child.

With few early symptoms, affected women are often unaware they even have pre-eclampsia. So antenatal care, with its routine testing of blood pressure and urine, is crucial to timely diagnosis, which has led to a massive reduction in maternal deaths in the UK and other developed countries since the 1950s. Nevertheless, pre-eclampsia still causes serious illness in mothers, while babies continue to suffer problems of poor growth and prematurity, with an increased risk of stillbirth or neonatal death.

The distress pre-eclampsia causes to mothers and families is aggravated by widespread ignorance of the condition. Many pregnant women get no advance information about pre-eclampsia and only find out about it if they are unlucky enough to get it.

Former journalist Isabel Walker recognised this information gap 30 years ago after a devastating personal experience of pre-eclampsia; and she worked with world expert Professor Chris Redman to produce the ground-breaking book *Pre-eclampsia: The Facts*, published by Oxford University Press in 1992. The book was such a success that it quickly sold out, and photocopies were subsequently passed around like a sacred text. Its value lay in its ability to present complex medical information in an easily digestible form.

Now, in collaboration with Joyce Cowan, an academic midwife based in New Zealand, Redman and Walker have written this follow-up, *Understanding Pre-eclampsia*, which blends detailed explanations about pre-eclampsia and analysis of the latest research with patient stories gathered from all parts of the world. With their combined experience in patient advocacy, clinical research and practice and midwifery expertise, the three authors offer a unique perspective on pre-eclampsia and have achieved the difficult task of making the current scientific knowledge accessible to parents and professionals alike.

This book covers the amazing intricacies of a normal pregnancy, looks at how and why pre-eclampsia evolves and then considers the challenges of screening, diagnosis, treatment and aftercare. It should help women and their families make sense of what has happened – and what might happen – to them, and give health professionals a deeper insight into the complex nature of this strange condition.

The patient stories enrich the narrative, helping women to realise that they are not alone in their suffering and offering caregivers the understanding they need to support their patients through a time of great uncertainty and stress.

This book is a labour of love, written by people who know about pre-eclampsia and care about its impact on women, families, doctors, midwives and others involved in the care of pregnant women. Everyone who reads it will learn from it to their benefit.

James Walker
Professor of Obstetrics and Gynaecology
University of Leeds, UK

ACKNOWLEDGEMENTS

The authors wish to acknowledge the help of all the women from Europe, Australasia, the United States and other parts of the world who responded to our online survey about personal experiences of pre-eclampsia. Their first-person accounts, sprinkled liberally throughout the book, provide an immediacy and emotional resonance that enriches the explanatory text. We also wish to thank women interviewed for Joyce Cowan's Master's thesis, and members of New Zealand Action on Pre-eclampsia (NZAPEC), who provided some of the case history material used in Chapters 4 and 7.

Thanks also to the following people who read the book before publication and provided very helpful suggestions for improvement: Cheryl Benn, Mark Brown, Jane Butler, Susan Calvert, Andy Etchells, Marianne Johansen, Hilary Gammill, Sandra Lowe, Laura A Magee, Fiona Milne, Wendy Roberts, Sicco Scherjon, Eleni Tsigas.

Finally, we are immensely grateful to Jane Tatam of Amolibros for the skilled support and expert advice she provided throughout the publication process.

ABOUT THE AUTHORS

Professor Chris Redman is a retired physician, the first in the world to be appointed to a full time academic appointment in the new specialty of obstetric medicine, at Oxford University in the UK. Early in his research career he encountered women with the worst forms of pre-eclampsia, which opened his eyes to the suffering it caused to them and their families, and how poorly it was managed - neither humanely nor effectively. The experience inspired him to devote his career to 'understanding pre-eclampsia'. Much has been achieved, but there is still a great deal more to be done. He and Isabel Walker have worked together for 30 years to communicate progress and knowledge to those who need to know more about this uniquely difficult complication of pregnancy.

Joyce Cowan is a midwife and senior lecturer in undergraduate and postgraduate midwifery education, based in Auckland, New Zealand. Her special interest in pre-eclampsia led her in 1994 to co-found, with client Wendy Roberts, the New Zealand Action on Pre-eclampsia patient group (NZ APEC – an offshoot of the UK-based parent organisation). As director of NZ APEC she has helped to raise awareness of pre-eclampsia by organising study days for midwives and doctors and publishing educational materials for women and families. As a midwife she has worked in a variety of settings, from home to specialist hospital units. As an academic, she has published a Master's thesis on women's experience of early-onset pre-eclampsia, while her current doctoral study focuses on detection of fetal growth restriction.

Isabel Walker is a former medical journalist, who lost her first baby as a result of pre-eclampsia in 1987 and went on to co-found the UK patient group Action on Pre-eclampsia (APEC) with Professor Chris Redman. She and Professor Redman also co-wrote the award-winning book *Pre-eclampsia: The Facts*, published by Oxford University Press in 1992. Isabel led APEC as Director until 2000, winning the *Options Magazine* 'Woman of Commitment' award for her work in 1995. A qualified personal performance coach, she currently works with private and not-for-profit sector organisations in the UK and internationally as a consultant and trainer, specialising in communication skills.

TESTIMONIALS

'The International Society for the Study of Hypertension in Pregnancy (ISSHP) has been promoting the need for greater understanding of pre-eclampsia and better information for pregnant women worldwide for more than 35 years. *Understanding Pre-eclampsia* makes a substantial contribution to these goals, with its compelling description of the latest advances in knowledge and treatment, coupled with poignant first-hand accounts from women who have suffered this shocking and sometimes cruel condition. Importantly, the authors highlight the life-long implications of pre-eclampsia. As current and future presidents of the ISSHP, we recommend this book to all who are or have been involved with pre-eclampsia, whether as patients or health professionals.'

Mark Brown and Laura A Magee

'Women who experience hypertensive disorders of pregnancy, sometimes with very bad outcomes, often have scores of unanswered questions, leaving them anxious, angry or uncertain about the future. This book provides many of the answers they seek, with easy-to-understand medical explanations and snippets of various real-life experiences. This information can be empowering at an otherwise fragile time.'

Eleni Z Tsigas, Executive Director, Preeclampsia Foundation (US)

'This is an attractive and very useful piece of work – easy to read, extremely informative and enriched by compelling first-person accounts from women who have experienced the worst this condition has to offer.'

Sicco Scherjon, Professor and Chairman, Department of Obstetrics and Gynecology, University of Groningen, the Netherlands

'A clear, well-researched book that provides in-depth answers to many of the questions women, their families and their caregivers need to ask about this important condition.'

Sandra Lowe, President, International Society of Obstetric Medicine and Co-Editor-in-chief of Obstetric Medicine

'A superb book that I highly recommend for both expectant parents and maternity care providers. As a previous sufferer of HELLP Syndrome I found it informative and easy to read and understand.'

Wendy Roberts, Co-founder of New Zealand Action on Pre-eclampsia (NZAPEC)

'Fantastic book! What a great read! I really enjoyed this book and found it to be very well written, interesting and informative. I believe it will be an important source of information for parents, midwives and junior doctors. The integration of patients' real experiences of pre-eclampsia into the text is achieved with great success and delicacy.'

Marianne Johansen, Senior Consultant in Obstetrics, Rigshospitalet, Copenhagen

'If you have ever come across pre-eclampsia, whether as a patient, a health professional or a carer, this book is a must-read. It sheds a wide beam of light on the very many problems pre-eclampsia continues to cause and offers help and understanding for anyone interested in learning more. Action on Pre-eclampsia welcomes what will very quickly become the go-to reference book on this horrible and unpredictable condition.'

Marcus Green, Chief Executive, Action on Pre-eclampsia (UK)

'Concise and thorough information on the topic....easy to understand for parents, midwives and physicians. This book is a must read for those interested in pre eclampsia.'

Jane Butler, Certified Nurse Midwife, Master's in Public Health, University of California Berkeley

'This unique volume brings together voices with complementary expertise on pre-eclampsia to speak directly to families and front-line caregivers. It offers an integrated view of patient experiences with clinical perspectives and research insights and will serve as an essential resource for those seeking to understand the impact of pre-eclampsia on women and their families.'

Hilary Gammill, Research Assistant Professor, Department of Obstetrics and Gynecology, University of Washington, Seattle

'An easy read with good, accessible up-to-date information, specifically aimed at women and families but also a great resource for midwives and other health professionals working with pregnant women. Highly recommended!'

Cheryl Benn, Midwifery Advisor to Mid Central Health, New Zealand

HOW TO READ THIS BOOK

Since this book is aimed at a dual audience of parents and health professionals, we thought it might be helpful to provide some guidance on the content. While some readers will be happy to read it from cover to cover, others may prefer to dip in and out or to focus solely on the chapters that relate to their specific interests and concerns.

We have inserted references and further reading suggestions at the end of individual chapters, where we think they might be helpful. But since we do not regard the book as an academic text, we have not adopted a slavish approach to referencing.

The main section headings of each chapter are set out on the Contents pages (*pp v-vii*). Here's what you may like to know about each:

Chapter 1 is a scene-setting chapter, focusing on how pre-eclampsia is defined, who it affects and the current and future research challenges.

Chapter 2 paints a comprehensive picture of pre-eclampsia, including risk factors, signs and symptoms and the way the illness develops and progresses.

Chapter 3 focuses on what doctors and midwives can do to keep mothers and babies safe through careful screening and effective treatment. It also looks at prospects for preventing the illness or reducing risk.

Chapter 4 looks at pre-eclampsia through the lens of women's experiences, taking readers on a journey from the earliest signs to birth and beyond. It considers the physical and emotional impact of the illness on women and their partners, and offers advice on what midwives, in those parts of the world where they are responsible for much of the care, can do to help and support them at every stage.

Chapter 5 is all about the vital role of antenatal care in identifying women at risk of pre-eclampsia and ensuring timely detection of the illness through careful monitoring.

Chapter 6 considers the challenges involved in diagnosing pre-eclampsia and looks at all aspects of management up to and beyond the birth.

Chapter 7 is aimed at midwives. It examines their role in assessing risk for pre-eclampsia, detecting the earliest signs, working with specialists to provide care after diagnosis and providing vital support for women and their partners.

Chapter 8 looks at how women can help themselves by understanding their risk of pre-eclampsia and doing what they can to reduce it, recognising and acting on signs and symptoms, and working with health professionals to optimise the outcome for themselves and their babies.

Chapter 9 provides answers to the wide range of questions commonly asked about pre-eclampsia, from causes to feelings, from treatment to research, from signs and symptoms to long-term health implications.

CHAPTER 1: WHAT IS PRE-ECLAMPSIA?

'I had a pretty normal first pregnancy – apart from a small bleed at eight weeks and sickness that went on well beyond the beginning of the second trimester – until 25 weeks, when I had a severe bout of pain just below my ribs that went on for several hours.

'The pain persisted on and off for the next two weeks, when it was variously diagnosed first as a gastric infection, then as heartburn and finally as gallstones.

'No one checked my blood pressure or urine – which had been normal at 24 weeks – until I developed a violent headache at 27 weeks. The results of the tests were so extreme that I was immediately ambulanced to hospital, where doctors tried but failed to stabilise my worsening condition.

'My baby was delivered that same day and was given a 50/50 chance of survival because of the immaturity of his lungs. Heartbreakingly, he died two days later. I went on to make a full recovery.'

Ruth, UK

Ruth had a bad case of pre-eclampsia, an illness that affects about three in every hundred pregnant women in the Western world. Doctors have been aware of the illness – at least in its most severe form – for more than two thousand years. And it is the main reason for regular antenatal (or prenatal) checks in pregnancy. Yet it remains a mysterious and unpredictable condition that continues to baffle and frustrate health professionals and put mothers' and babies' lives at risk.

- It can be so mild that a woman is completely unaware she has it – or bad enough to threaten her life and/or that of her baby.

- It usually starts in late pregnancy and gets better after the baby is born. But some women get it as early as 20 weeks – or even earlier. In contrast, some get it as late as a few days after the birth.
- Signs like rising blood pressure and protein in the urine usually come before symptoms of illness. But some women get seriously ill with no warning signs.
- Often it affects both mother and baby, but sometimes just one or the other.
- Most women get it only once, in their first pregnancy. But some get it for the first time in a later pregnancy. And others get it again – and again.

These complexities and inconsistencies have made it very difficult to *define* pre-eclampsia, let alone study it; and that explains why researchers still don't understand its underlying cause (or causes), doctors cannot reliably predict, prevent or diagnose it, and there is no effective treatment other than delivery, which resolves the problem, usually within a week.

In the next chapter we look at what *is* known about the condition – the risk factors, the signs and symptoms and the way the illness develops and progresses.

In this briefer introductory chapter we have tried to set the broader scene by outlining current definitions of pre-eclampsia, considering the worldwide health burden imposed by the condition, summarising the current research priorities and looking ahead to the challenges of the future.

Pre-eclampsia through the ages

Recognition of eclampsia – one of several late-stage complications of pre-eclampsia – dates back to ancient times. As early as the fourth century BC the Greek physician Hippocrates, sometimes referred to as 'the father of modern medicine', talked about the occurrence of life-threatening convulsions in pregnancy.

After that there was no real progress in understanding until the early nineteenth century when the beginnings of modern biochemistry led to the discovery of proteins. In 1843, the British physician Dr John Lever was able to show that women with eclampsia had large amounts of protein in their urine, technically known as *proteinuria*.

High blood pressure, known as *hypertension*, the sign most commonly associated with pre-eclampsia, was not recognised until about 50 years later, when it became possible to measure pressure in the arteries indirectly by means of the sphygmomanometer devices that are still in standard use today. It soon became clear that blood pressure was raised not just in women with eclampsia but in those with proteinuria who had *not* had convulsions.

The recognition of pre-eclampsia

The concept of a state of *pre*-eclampsia – then known as 'toxaemia of pregnancy' – began to evolve in the early twentieth century, although it was not clearly distinguished from other medical conditions, or from hypertension on its own.

Throughout this time eclampsia continued to exact a very high maternal death toll of up to 40 per cent. Doctors had known since the seventeenth century that the condition was cured after delivering the baby. But that kind of intervention was itself highly dangerous before the development of safer caesarean sections in the middle of the last century.

UK Government enquiries in the 1920s and '30s, prompted by concerns over the high death rate from pre-eclampsia/eclampsia, identified the lack of systematic checks on blood pressure and urine as major factors in these deaths.

The mid-twentieth century saw the introduction of the systematic screening for pre-eclampsia and prompt admission after diagnosis that is the mainstay of care today and that led to a dramatic and sustained fall in maternal deaths throughout the Western world.

The need to define pre-eclampsia

A major obstacle to progress in understanding and managing pre-eclampsia has been a striking lack of consensus on how the condition should be defined.

Disease definitions are important for two main reasons:

1. **Diagnosis and treatment** If an illness is not clearly defined it is impossible to diagnose it accurately and treat it systematically;
2. **Research** If an illness is not clearly defined, different teams of researchers cannot be sure that they are all studying the same condition.

One of the clearest and simplest early definitions of pre-eclampsia was developed in Aberdeen, Scotland, in 1955 in order to study the incidence of the condition in that city. All modern definitions of pre-eclampsia have been derived from this one. It set out two levels of the condition:

- 'mild pre-eclampsia' – raised blood pressure alone, which is now known in most countries as *gestational hypertension*;
- 'severe pre-eclampsia' – raised blood pressure and proteinuria, which we would now call simply 'pre-eclampsia'. Swelling due to water retention was recognised as a feature of some cases of pre-eclampsia but was not part of the definition.

Before 2000 most consensus definitions of pre-eclampsia were based on hypertension and proteinuria appearing for the first time in pregnancy and disappearing after delivery. These included definitions agreed by the American College of Obstetricians and Gynecologists (ACOG) in 1972 and the International Society for the Study of Hypertension in Pregnancy (ISSHP) in 1988.

Pre-eclampsia without proteinuria

In the 1990s ASSHP, the Australasian branch of ISSHP, began to float the idea that pre-eclampsia could exist without proteinuria but with other accompaniments to new hypertension, such as growth restriction of the unborn baby *(fetal growth restriction* or FGR), liver damage (as in the complication known as HELLP syndrome) and convulsions (eclampsia).

This concept, formalised in the ASSHP definition of pre-eclampsia in 2001, was partially adopted by ACOG in 2013 and was accepted by ISSHP in 2015.

However, the ASSHP and ACOG definitions differ in a number of ways. For example, ASSHP includes FGR as a sign of non-proteinuric pre-eclampsia while ACOG does not. And while ACOG focuses on objective measurements of maternal wellbeing, ASSHP[†] includes subjective symptoms such as headache, visual disturbances and abdominal pain.

[†]   ASSHP has now been replaced by the Society of Obstetric Medicine of Australia and New Zealand (SOMANZ), which also incorporates the former Obstetric Medicine Group of Australasia (OMGA).

A broader definition from Canada

The Canadian definition includes more than 30 'adverse conditions' that can identify pre-eclampsia with new hypertension but without proteinuria. These include symptoms like breathlessness, chest pain, nausea and vomiting, signs like a non-reassuring or abnormal CTG (electronic record of the baby's heartbeat before labour) and events such as stillbirth and transfusion of any blood product.

However, these newer, more comprehensive definitions pose problems of their own. For while the traditional narrow definition of pre-eclampsia is now considered inadequate, the later versions are probably too complicated to be used in poorly resourced countries or in busy maternity units with varying levels of expertise. They are also too vague to serve as the basis for research studies.

Can pre-eclampsia exist without hypertension?

All definitions of pre-eclampsia to date have included the presence of new hypertension. But is this an essential element? Or could 'normotensive' pre-eclampsia be yet another variant of the condition?

To answer this question we need to look at what is known about the *cause* of pre-eclampsia. Much of this is still uncertain but what we *do* know is that the condition originates in the placenta, the all-important life support system, which brings oxygen and nutrients from the mother to the baby via the umbilical cord.

Pre-eclampsia appears to develop in two stages:

1.   An inadequate blood supply from the mother to the placenta, known as *placental malperfusion;*
2.   A range of maternal problems produced by abnormal signals from the malperfused or 'stressed' placenta.

Placental malperfusion can have two causes: 'poor placentation', when the placenta fails to develop normally in early pregnancy; and 'limited capacity', when the placenta outgrows what the mother's uterus and blood supply can provide in late pregnancy.

Whatever the cause of the malperfusion, the effect on the mother is similar, although poor placentation leads to earlier illness than limited capacity *(see also Chapter 2, pp 21-25).*

Fetal growth restriction

For the unborn baby placental malperfusion leads to fetal growth restriction (FGR – sometimes called intrauterine growth restriction, or IUGR) because it can't get the nourishment and oxygen it needs from the mother's blood. FGR is associated with pre-eclampsia as currently defined, especially the early-onset form of the condition. But it can also occur in the absence of high blood pressure (so-called 'isolated' or 'normotensive' FGR). And in these cases changes similar to pre-eclampsia are found in the placenta and the mother's systems after the birth.

All of this could point to a much broader concept of a variety of possible maternal responses to placental malperfusion. The key thing to understand here is that it is the malperfusion that is the true disorder – not the hypertension. In other words, pre-eclampsia is essentially a placental disorder.

The worldwide health burden of pre-eclampsia

As mentioned at the start of this chapter, pre-eclampsia affects about three in every 100 white pregnant women in developed countries. In some other countries it appears to be more common: for example, Nicaragua has an incidence of 7.67 per cent, Mongolia 6.71 per cent and Brazil 4.60 per cent.

Pre-eclampsia is also more common in some races, such as black Africans and Polynesians, for reasons that are not well understood. Differences in genetic evolution, diet, education, housing and income may all be important factors.

However, the known incidence of pre-eclampsia between and within populations varies for all sorts of reasons. For one thing, because it is most common in first-time mothers, places where smaller families are the norm will seem to have more pre-eclampsia; for another, places where it is normal for obstetricians to induce delivery at 40 weeks – when signs of pre-eclampsia often appear for the first time – will seem to have less.

Eclampsia is much rarer than pre-eclampsia, affecting about one in every 2,500 pregnancies in the UK and a little more in some other countries. HELLP (**h**aemolysis, **e**levated **l**iver enzymes and **l**owered **p**latelets) syndrome is more common than eclampsia, affecting about 3-in-1,000 pregnancies.

Maternal deaths from pre-eclampsia

Although it is very rare for women to die of pre-eclampsia in developed countries, pre-eclampsia still ranks high among the possible causes of maternal death. However, in the UK the latest official figures show an encouraging decline in the rate of maternal deaths by comparison with other problems. This is associated with a nationwide implementation of guidelines, which are evidently working well.

Saving Lives, Improving Mothers' Care, the 2015 report of the Confidential Enquiries into Maternal Deaths and Morbidity, noted a fall in the incidence of deaths caused by pre-eclampsia/eclampsia from 0.42 per 100,000 in the period 2009-2011 to 0.25 in 2011-13 *(1)*. It may be that, at long last, the lessons of previous decades – particularly the need for vigilance in screening, diagnosis and management – are being acted upon.

Equally up-to-date information was not available from most other developed countries at the time of writing so it's not clear whether the UK experience is part of a global trend.

According to the World Health Organisation (WHO) the overwhelming majority of maternal deaths from all causes occur in developing countries, where the maternal mortality ratio is nearly 20 times higher than in developed countries.

Pre-eclampsia is one of five conditions which together account for nearly 75 per cent of all maternal deaths worldwide. The others are severe bleeding, infections, complications of delivery and unsafe abortion.

The impact of new definitions

The currently quoted incidence of pre-eclampsia is based on classical definitions including new hypertension and proteinuria. Extended definitions that allow for pre-eclampsia without one or both of these core signs are likely to increase the apparent incidence of the condition. One Australian study showed that taking account of 'atypical' presentations of pre-eclampsia increased the number of cases by more than 25 per cent – and this did not include 'normotensive' pre-eclampsia!

And while the incidence of classical pre-eclampsia is tricky to measure accurately, measurement of a more broadly defined condition would be almost impossible because its detection depends on more elaborate testing than is routinely available in even the best organised health care systems.

What we are learning, though, is that the health burden of pre-eclampsia is probably larger than expected and requires levels of competence in detection and management that have yet to be achieved.

The research challenge

Pre-eclampsia is notoriously difficult to research for the following reasons:

- It involves two distinct individuals – mother and baby.
- It can only be studied in pregnancy, which lasts a mere nine months.
- The clinical condition of pre-eclampsia lasts for about 10-15 days at most, after a diagnosis based on clear and sustained signs, before spontaneous or induced delivery.
- The placenta, where pre-eclampsia originates, is a highly complex organ – probably more so than any other organ of the body except the brain.
- Drug trials in pregnancy are difficult to justify in ethical terms.

Additionally, research on pregnancy complications attracts much less in the way of funding than the big diseases like cancer, heart disease and diabetes.

Nevertheless more research on pre-eclampsia is being carried out than ever before; more than 2,000 papers on the subject were published in 2014 compared with fewer than 400 in 1970.

Current research on pre-eclampsia focuses on the following aspects:

- **causes** – in the placenta, the mother's constitution, and genetics;
- **biological compatibility** between mother and baby (including the father's contribution);
- **maternal responses** to placental malperfusion, including inflammation and disturbances in the supply of nutrients to the unborn baby. These disturbances are particularly likely in mothers who are obese, suffer from diabetes or have inadequate diets;
- **long-term health issues** for mothers and babies, in terms of increased risk of conditions like obesity, diabetes and hypertension;

- **early prediction;**
- **better detection;**
- **prevention and treatment.**

What lies ahead

Future research will need to recognise the extraordinary complexity and variability of pre-eclampsia.

Given the growing evidence that pre-eclampsia is probably more than one disease, it is unlikely that there is one magic solution out there waiting to be discovered.

For the same reason, there will be no diagnostic or predictive tests, preventive measures or treatments that will apply universally to all women and all cases.

And no one gene will be found to be responsible – indeed pre-eclampsia is the only medical problem that depends on the genes of two individuals.

Pre-eclampsia will be controlled

We have no doubt that pre-eclampsia *will* be controlled eventually by measures that are firmly based on evidence.

Lifestyle and diet will probably prove to be as important for limiting the impact of the disease as many women have always believed.

New classes of drugs currently in development may offer safe ways of controlling or even preventing some forms of the condition. The era of personalised medicine, which takes account of important differences between individuals, is only just beginning and it promises to be perfectly suited to tackling the intricacies of pre-eclampsia.

No easy solutions

The road is long and the burden is heavy because pre-eclampsia is such a complicated condition. If there were easy solutions to be found they would have been identified many years ago.

It is important to recognise that good antenatal (or prenatal) care, developed by conscientious doctors and midwives who have learned better ways of detecting and managing pre-eclampsia, have already brought huge benefits to pregnant women over recent generations. In the developed world at least, the great majority of mothers and babies do well and suffer no long term complications from pre-eclampsia. But there is always room for improvement.

These days the level of research is more detailed, sophisticated and demanding. But progress is made each and every year, and the benefits will accumulate slowly but surely over the decades to come.

Reference

1. Knight M, Kenyon S, Brocklehurst P, Neilson J, Shakespeare J, Kurinczuk JJ (Eds.) on behalf of MBRRACEUK. Saving Lives, Improving Mothers' Care – Lessons learned to inform future maternity care from the UK and Ireland Confidential Enquiries into Maternal Deaths and Morbidity 2009–12. Oxford: National Perinatal Epidemiology Unit, University of Oxford 2014

CHAPTER 2: WHAT WE KNOW ABOUT PRE-ECLAMPSIA

The first chapter presented the 'big picture' about pre-eclampsia – what it is, how it has been recognised and defined through the ages, its global health impact and the various outstanding research challenges.

This chapter homes in on more specific features of pre-eclampsia – the risk factors, the signs and symptoms and the way the illness develops and progresses. It also explains the massive changes in a woman's body during pregnancy and how these relate to the development of pre-eclampsia.

We illustrate our points throughout with direct quotes from women affected by pre-eclampsia, drawn mostly from our international online survey about women's' experiences of pre-eclampsia.

The nature of the illness

Pre-eclampsia is an illness that happens only in pregnancy or shortly after birth. It starts with trouble in the placenta – the special pregnancy organ that supports the unborn baby and depends absolutely on a full blood supply from the mother. When this supply is inadequate, the placenta releases stress signals into the mother's circulation, leading to rising blood pressure and leakage of protein into the urine. At the same time, the baby's growth may be restricted, although other aspects of its development continue as normal.

Pre-eclampsia almost always gets worse once it has started. Mothers are at risk of serious complications, including *eclampsia* (fits, seizures or convulsions), stroke, kidney, liver and blood clotting problems. Babies can sometimes starve or suffocate in the uterus. The only known treatment for mothers and babies is delivery. Afterwards mothers usually recover, although this may take weeks rather than days, and most babies do well as long as they don't have be delivered too early.

Although there is much that the doctors and midwives of today still don't know about pre-eclampsia, they are much better informed than their predecessors.

An early case of eclampsia

Catherina Schrader, born in 1656, was a Dutch midwife who practised until the grand old age of 90 and recorded the details of the 3,072 cases she managed in nine notebooks. In 1701 she describes how she attended a woman who delivered twins. All seemed fine at first, but then on the day after the birth...

> *'... The woman was alone in the house; the people went milking. Then a strange man came in, who asked the woman in childbed whether he could light a tobacco pipe, which he did. After that the woman got such an attack of fits that three men could not hold her. She died the same day.'*

Catherina's patient died of eclampsia – the fits, seizures or convulsions that are familiar to modern doctors and midwives as a life-threatening endpoint of pre-eclampsia. In fact, as noted in the previous chapter, eclampsia was recognised by the ancient Greeks more than 2,000 years ago.

We now know that eclampsia is one possible crisis that can develop out of pre-eclampsia. But Catherina knew nothing of pre-eclampsia. In fact she almost certainly knew nothing about the blood circulatory system, which had only just been discovered.

The first step in our understanding of pre-eclampsia was taken nearly 150 years after Catherina's diary entry, when doctors discovered that women with eclampsia had abnormal amounts of protein in their urine.

What is protein – and how does it get into urine?

Most of us think of protein as an essential component of our diets. But actually there are thousands of different proteins, which make up the fabric of our bodies and help to control how they work.

Protein in the blood

There are hundreds of different proteins in our blood; these are contained in the colourless part of the blood, known as *plasma*. Our solid red and white blood cells are suspended in this plasma, which is basically water. It also contains many different molecules (chemicals), including proteins. Plasma also contains waste for disposal and this is filtered into the urine by our two kidneys.

Protein in the urine

Plasma proteins are so useful that they are normally retained in the blood rather than filtered out by the kidneys. In fact, the urine from healthy kidneys contains so little protein that it cannot be detected by tests used in clinics. When urine tests *do* detect protein in consistent amounts it means the kidney filters are not working properly. So the presence of protein in the urine (*proteinuria*) is a key sign of kidney damage. In pregnancy this damage is most likely to be caused by pre-eclampsia.

Once proteinuria was discovered in women with eclampsia in 1843, it was not long before doctors noticed that some pregnant women had it at an earlier stage, before the convulsions. And so, very slowly, the idea of an illness preceding eclampsia – *pre*-eclampsia – began to take shape.

How is proteinuria measured?

Protein in the urine can be detected by simple chemical dipsticks that change colour when dipped into a urine sample, according to how much protein is there. Dipsticks are cheap and give quick results – but they are not very reliable.

The concentration of protein in a pregnant woman's urine will depend on how much water and other fluids she has drunk in the few hours before the test. A little proteinuria looks like a lot if you are dehydrated and your urine is highly concentrated. Conversely, a significant amount of proteinuria can be undetectable if you have drunk a lot of water recently and your urine is diluted as a result.

That's why it is more accurate to test for proteinuria in a sample of urine collected over 24 hours. Another, quicker, way to achieve the same result is to carry out a 'protein:creatinine ratio' test on a single urine sample. This test measures the amount of protein per unit of creatinine, a waste product in the urine that is not affected by fluid intake.

Other causes of proteinuria

There are other possible causes of proteinuria, mainly kidney or urinary problems, that can occur in anybody, whether pregnant or not. One example is *cystitis*, a painful inflammation of the bladder. Other urine infections that cause no symptoms are unlikely to lead to proteinuria. There are also various kidney conditions that can cause proteinuria, although these mostly don't occur in pregnancy.

Blood pressure and hypertension

Blood pressure was first measured (inaccurately) in the 1870s. But it was not until 1903 that pregnant women with proteinuria were also found to have high blood pressure, known as *hypertension*.

What is blood pressure?

Our hearts normally beat about 60-70 times a minute, and a little faster in pregnancy. The heart is actually made up of two different pumps *(ventricles)* that work in tandem: the smaller right ventricle sends blood to the lungs to pick up oxygen, and the larger, more powerful, left ventricle circulates oxygen-rich blood all around the body, as shown in Figure 2.1 *(opposite)*.

Blood pressure measurements reflect what's going on in the left ventricle. Each time it contracts, or beats, it forces blood into the large blood vessels called *arteries* for distribution around the body. When this happens the pressure in the arteries rises to a peak, known as *systole* (pronounced sis-tilly). Once the ventricle is empty, the outlet valve that allows blood into the arteries shuts and an inlet valve opens to let in blood returning from the lungs. During this short time before the next beat, the pressure in the arteries drops to a low point, or trough, known as *diastole* (pronounced di –as –tilly).

Blood pressure is always measured as two numbers – for example 120/70. The first, higher, number is the peak pressure in the arteries during systole. It is known as *systolic pressure*. The second, lower, number is the trough pressure in the arteries during diastole, known as *diastolic pressure*. Blood pressure is measured in terms of millimetres of mercury because mercury manometers were the first accurate pressure gauges, although they are not generally used now. This is why the letters mmHg normally appear after the numbers, Hg being chemical shorthand for mercury.

Why blood pressure varies

The heart and its circulation are designed to adapt to all the various demands of our lives. If we run to catch a bus, or cycle energetically up a hill, our pulse (heart) rate and blood pressure go up to supply the hard-working muscles with the extra blood they need. When we go to sleep, blood pressure falls to the much lower levels needed during rest. Illness also leads to changes in pulse rate and blood pressure, which is why they are so regularly checked by doctors and nurses.

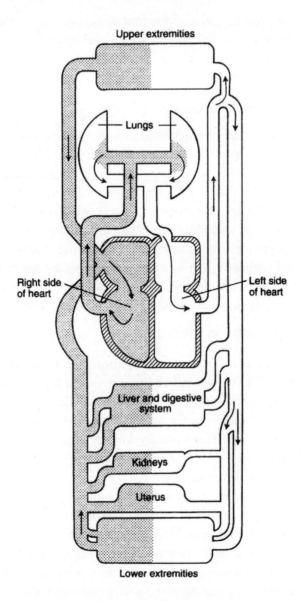

Figure 2.1 The heart and circulatory system

The left side of the heart receives oxygenated blood through the veins of the lungs and pumps it through the arteries to every part of the body, where the oxygen is removed to sustain the normal functions of all organs (including brain, muscles, liver and digestive system, kidneys and uterus). De-oxygenated blood then drains back to the right side of the heart, which pumps it into the lungs to get further supplies of oxygen.

So none of us has a regular, consistent blood pressure; rather, it varies according to what we are doing, how we are feeling and how well we are. This means that a single blood pressure measurement may not be enough to show whether or not we have a problem.

What do we mean by hypertension?

On average, though, some people tend to have low blood pressures, while others have higher pressures that can affect their health. Persistent high blood pressure is called hypertension. The word 'tension' is used here to refer to the physical pressure within the arteries. Confusingly, though, we also use this word to describe emotional stress, which can sometimes lead to physical symptoms, including raised blood pressure.

However, hypertension caused by emotional stress is normally temporary; and lasting high or low blood pressures are normally nothing to do with emotional states. There are plenty of calm people with very high blood pressures and many tense or anxious people with low pressures.

How blood pressure is measured

In clinics, blood pressure is measured by means of a cuff placed around an arm or wrist. The cuff is inflated to a pressure high enough to stop the blood flowing in the artery under the cuff. It is then deflated, and the way the blood flow returns to the artery allows the systolic and diastolic pressures to be measured. This is usually done by listening for special sounds through a stethoscope. It can also be done with a digital device that detects the relevant changes automatically.

Although blood pressure measurement looks precise, this is far from true. Many automatic devices don't work well in pregnancy. And even the old fashioned way of measuring blood pressure with a stethoscope calls for skill, care and patience. A hurried reading by a careless operator may be way off the mark. And some of these devices quickly lose their accuracy unless they are frequently maintained and recalibrated. For these reasons health professionals take good care of their equipment and are aware that their measurements should be taken slowly and carefully.

Signs and symptoms of pre-eclampsia

Definitions first: a symptom is a problem of which you are aware; a sign is a problem that a health professional detects and of which you are not necessarily aware. For example, lumps and rashes are both signs and symptoms, while high blood pressure is a sign, not a symptom, and a headache is a symptom, not a sign.

The concept of pre-eclampsia as an illness signalled by hypertension and proteinuria gradually took shape in the first half of the 20th century. In those days it was known as 'toxaemia' (literally 'poisoning of the blood') because it was thought to be caused by poisons (or toxins) coming from the placenta. As you will learn from this and later chapters, that idea is not entirely wrong-headed in the light of what we know now.

One of the biggest problems with pre-eclampsia was (and still is) that neither hypertension nor proteinuria makes people feel ill, so women are often blissfully unaware that trouble is brewing. Before 1950, when most pregnant women only saw a doctor if they felt ill, it was much more common for them to become seriously ill or even die because of pre-eclampsia. But this began to change when doctors came to realise that dangerous situations could be prevented by detecting pre-eclampsia *before* women got ill.

At about the same time, in the UK and many other countries antenatal clinics started to open up in every general practitioner's surgery, with no charge for attendance. The stage was set for modern antenatal (or prenatal) care, with its regular checks on blood pressure and urine.

How the illness progresses

Once regular antenatal checks were in place, doctors and midwives were able to see how pre-eclampsia developed from its earliest signs. Usually the first sign is newly raised blood pressure without proteinuria. This may be called *gestational hypertension, pregnancy-associated hypertension* (PAH) or *pregnancy-induced hypertension* (PIH). These all mean the same thing, but in this book we will use the term gestational hypertension. Not all women with gestational hypertension go on to develop pre-eclampsia, but the earlier in pregnancy it develops the more likely it is to cause trouble.

'At 24 weeks my BP was definitely on the rise and I was told to watch it. By 28 weeks it was consistently over 140/90, and a 24-hour urine sample showed proteinuria. I was placed on hospital bed rest at 33-and-a-half weeks and was diagnosed with HELLP syndrome [a dangerous complication of pre-eclampsia – see page 26] at 36 weeks, when I was induced.'

Stacy, US

Fluid retention and swelling

Some women with pre-eclampsia become swollen or 'puffy' because of fluid (water) retention, known as *oedema*. Oedema is easily recognised because it can be seen and felt. But it is unreliable as a sign of pre-eclampsia for two reasons:

- It doesn't affect *all* women with pre-eclampsia.
- It is common in normal pregnancy, particularly in the feet, ankles and fingers.

Swelling is most likely to mean pre-eclampsia if it comes on suddenly, affects the face and is linked with a sudden increase in weight.

> *'It started at about four months, first in my feet, then my hands. Then my face started swelling – even my eyes felt puffy. I gained 20lbs in the fifth month alone, even though I eat really healthily and hadn't changed my diet since the previous four months when I had gained a total of 20lbs.'*
>
> Allison, US

> *'I was swollen beyond belief – so badly that my eyes were shut.'*
>
> Sam, UK

Excessive weight gain in the second half of pregnancy is more likely to be caused by fluid retention than by eating too much. A steady gain of more than 1kg (or 2lb) per week over several weeks is a possible warning sign. Unfortunately, in the UK regular weighing in pregnancy was abandoned 20 years ago, so this cheap and easy check is no longer available, although it is still encouraged in some other parts of the world, including New Zealand and the USA.

Proteinuria usually sets in later than hypertension or swelling. From this point on, real illness can develop surprisingly quickly; and it doesn't get better until some time after delivery.

When women start to feel ill

Symptoms of illness mean the disease has reached a late and dangerous stage. The main ones are:

- severe headache;
- disturbances of vision, such as 'flashing lights';
- severe pain below the ribs, felt in the stomach, back or lower chest, usually on the right but sometimes the left. This 'epigastric' pain is caused by swelling in the liver;
- increasing difficulty with breathing, making it difficult to lie flat at night.

Some women suffer nausea and vomiting at this stage, but this is a less specific symptom.

> 'I went out grocery shopping and all of a sudden got the worst headache right in the front part of my head – it was HORRIBLE. I came home right away then lay down and started throwing up. I went to the ER and was admitted right away.'
>
> Sandra, US

> 'Eventually my headache wouldn't let up, my swelling was getting worse, my vision was blurred and I was seeing little bright white lights everywhere.'
>
> Brandi, US

> 'I had severe abdominal pain like I had never experienced before. It hurt to breathe, stand, lie, anything. I threw up a couple of times. I was in so much pain I wanted to die, except that would have taken my baby too.'
>
> Samantha, Australia

Women can help themselves by looking out for these symptoms and seeking prompt medical attention. If the symptoms are recognised for what they are, things start to happen really fast. Women need to be admitted to hospital and, in most cases, have their babies delivered as soon as possible. Afterwards they may need a period of intensive care before recovery sets in.

> 'After having my baby I spent three days in intensive care, with severely elevated blood pressure and liver and kidney problems.

I made a full recovery by three weeks postpartum but remain on antihypertensive meds to this day.'

Lynne, Australia

What causes pre-eclampsia?

The problem that leads to pre-eclampsia appears to start in the *placenta*, or afterbirth, the special organ that supplies all the unborn baby's needs during pregnancy. This extraordinary organ is like no other: it belongs to two people, exists for just nine months and has two circulatory systems – one for the mother and one for the baby. It is sometimes called 'nature's transplant' – a part of one person that lives within another. And, of course, it is the baby's lifeline.

We know that the placenta is involved in pre-eclampsia for these reasons:

- You can get pre-eclampsia without a baby but *not* without a placenta. Women are particularly at risk of pre-eclampsia if they develop a rare condition called *hydatidiform mole*, where the uterus contains an abnormal placenta but no baby.
- You can get pre-eclampsia without a uterus but *not* without a placenta. It can happen in a rare form of *ectopic pregnancy* known as *abdominal pregnancy,* where the baby and placenta grow outside the uterus in the mother's abdomen.
- Pre-eclampsia gets better after the birth (although not necessarily immediately), when the placenta follows the baby out of the uterus. But if the placenta is retained for some reason, recovery may be delayed. This can happen after abdominal pregnancy, when the placenta has to be left behind after the birth.

The wonders of the placenta

One of the most amazing things about the placenta is its ability to generate an enormous blood supply from the mother to meet the unborn baby's ever-growing needs. In the course of pregnancy, about 40 tiny *spiral arteries* (so-called because of their shape) in the lining of the uterus have to get big enough to carry *a hundred times* their normal volume of blood. By the end of pregnancy these arteries have to supply the placenta with nearly a litre of blood per minute.

No other part of the adult blood supply can pull off such a feat. It requires massive reconstruction of the spiral arteries, where special placental cells, called *trophoblast*, build foundations that anchor the placenta to the wall of the uterus *(see Figure 2.2 overleaf)*.

These cells belong to the baby but live in the lining of the uterus, which is the mother's territory. They are supported by a huge army of special maternal immune cells whose job is to help the placenta but make sure it doesn't overstep its boundaries. So cells from mother and baby mingle and work together to create a new person. And all of this happens in the first half of pregnancy, long before pre-eclampsia is an issue.

The placental tree

As illustrated in Figure 2.3 *(page 24)*, the placenta is built like an upside down tree, with the baby's umbilical cord as its trunk. Many branches from the trunk end in small twigs, called *villi* (pronounced vill-eye) and these are covered by leaves, known as *terminal villi*.

While the leaves of a tree float in air, the leaves of the placenta float in a vast pool of maternal blood. This pool, which is constantly being refilled, brings everything the baby needs, including oxygen, to be absorbed through the placental leaves. In turn the baby's waste products are discharged through the leaves to be removed by the mother's blood.

The blood that feeds the baby and removes its waste is all supplied by the spiral arteries mentioned above.

The four stages of pre-eclampsia

It is useful to think of pre-eclampsia as progressing through four stages, from its origins in the placenta, through the silent early signs of the illness to the severe symptoms and crises that signal danger for mothers and babies.

Stage 1: the imperfect placenta

There are two different patterns to this stage: one starts very early in pregnancy and leads to what is called *early-onset* pre-eclampsia, while the other, more common, pattern starts towards the end of pregnancy, leading to *late-onset* pre-eclampsia.

With early-onset pre-eclampsia, the vital reconstruction of the lining of the uterus in early pregnancy is incomplete. As a result, the spiral

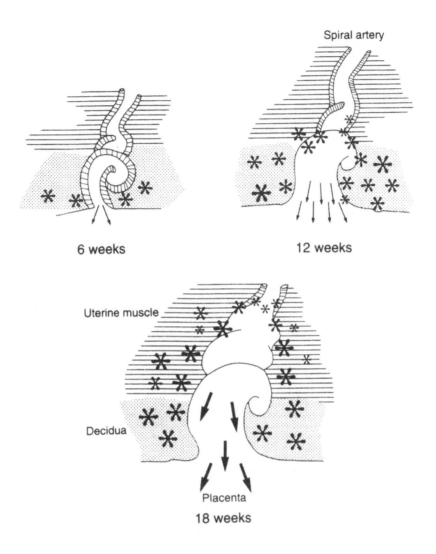

**Figure 2.2 Creation of the placenta's blood supply
in the first half of pregnancy**

*A highly magnified diagram showing how invading placental cells create the
placenta's blood supply from the small spiral arteries of the uterus. The cells
(black stars) infiltrate the walls of the arteries, which thin out, allowing the
vessels to enlarge progressively and carry much more blood. In pre-eclampsia
this process never seems to progress beyond the stage reached at 12 weeks. This
means the arteries end up too small for the task, causing the placenta to run
short of blood at some point in the second half of pregnancy.*

arteries don't get big enough to meet the needs of the placenta and baby as the pregnancy advances. So instead of supplying large amounts of blood continuously at low pressures, the too-narrow arteries deliver blood in spurts, at high speeds and pressures.

The placental 'tree' is pushed around by the tides of blood, which is distributed unequally so that some parts of the tree go short of oxygen while others get more than they need. In effect the placenta is thrown off balance, and over time it becomes damaged so that it can't function properly. This is known as 'poor placentation', and it is one important cause of the reduced maternal supply to the placenta that leads to pre-eclampsia.

With late-onset pre-eclampsia, the placenta is under-supplied because it outgrows what the maternal systems can provide. If you think of the placenta as a plant rooted in the wall of the uterus, it effectively becomes 'pot bound', unable to grow or flourish for lack of space and nourishment.

Stage 2: the stressed placenta

We are completely unaware of the tens of thousands of activities within the billions of cells that make up our bodies. This vast biological machinery maintains an overall balance that meets our needs. Balance is nature's overriding priority, and this is as true in the placenta as anywhere else.

When a biological system is thrown off balance it is said to be 'stressed'. This biological stress is quite different from the emotional stress we often complain about. Every day our systems are stressed in small ways and our clever bodies respond immediately to restore balance and normality. Meanwhile we continue to feel well and are completely unaware of what is going on inside.

When balance cannot be restored

But the abnormal blood flow, whether caused by poor placentation or limitations on placental growth, unbalances the placenta in ways it can't put right. This stops it achieving the best possible outcome for mother and baby. The placenta may not grow big enough; or its supply line to the baby may be restricted. In the worst cases, the baby may become starved and short of oxygen (see 'How the baby is affected', page 28).

The stressed placenta doesn't just affect the baby. As the master coordinator of pregnancy, it manages all aspects of the mother-baby partnership. So when the placenta is stressed, it can also harm the mother. This is not surprising: the extent to which the placenta changes a mother's

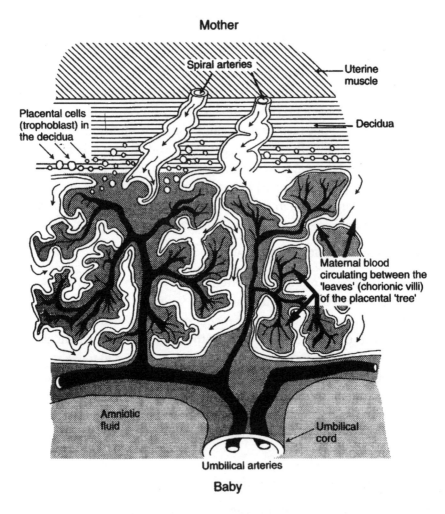

Figure 2.3 The placental 'tree'

Diagram (not to scale) of the branching structure of the placental tree, with the baby's cord as the trunk. For simplicity only the two arteries in the cord are shown, not the one large vein. The arteries bring de-oxygenated blood from the baby to be refreshed in the chorionic leaves (villi). They float in maternal blood, which provides new oxygen for the baby, carried back along the veins.

body, even in healthy pregnancy, is truly amazing. These changes are normally caused by the release of many different signals from the surface of the placenta into mother's blood. When the placenta is stressed, some of these signals are altered – and this particularly affects the way the mother's circulation works.

Endothelium – master controller of the circulation

Our organs and the billions of cells within them need oxygen and nutrients in order to function properly. Blood, pumped from the heart through arteries into a network of much smaller blood vessels called *capillaries,* brings the supplies the cells need and also picks up their waste for disposal. Capillary blood is then drained back into veins for recycling.

All our blood vessels – arteries, capillaries and veins – have an inner lining of cells called *endothelium.* The cells of the endothelium manage all the complex dealings between the blood inside the vessels and the cells outside them that need what the blood supplies. These clever, powerful cells also:

- control blood pressure in such a way that supply to the organs matches demand;
- manage the transfer of fluid out of the vessels, known as 'permeability';
- maintain the pipework, sealing leaks to stop bleeding and replacing worn-out vessels;
- detect and destroy local infections.

So crucial is the role of endothelium in maintaining a healthy circulation that when it is damaged we become sick very quickly.

The impact of pre-eclampsia on the mother was a mystery until it was found to target maternal endothelium. Now it is clear why it can affect every organ and system – liver, kidneys, clotting, brain, and so on. Everywhere the circulation goes, pre-eclampsia can follow.

What causes the damage?

But what substances are responsible for causing the damage in a pre-eclamptic pregnancy? We now know that they include 'angiogenic' and 'anti-angiogenic' factors, whose main job is to maintain endothelium and blood vessels. They have opposite actions in terms of encouraging or discouraging the growth of blood vessels and, as always in nature, it is the balance that matters. In pre-eclampsia they are out of balance, which causes trouble.

These substances (which have technical names, such as SFlt-1 and sEndoglin), are produced all the time, not just in pregnancy. But the key point is that they are also released by the placenta – and in particularly high amounts when it is under stress because of pre-eclampsia.

The impact of this excessive production of angiogenic and anti-angiogenic factors in pre-eclampsia is to disturb the normal functions of the endothelium, with the effect that:

- blood pressure rises for no good reason;
- the blood vessels become leakier than normal, allowing protein into the urine and fluid into the tissues;
- circulatory problems develop throughout the mother's body.

Stage 3: widespread damage

So we can see that pre-eclampsia is not just about hypertension and proteinuria. These are signs that doctors and midwives find it easy to search for, but they are not the only ones. As well as the rise in blood pressure, the blood itself changes so that it clots too easily. This can be very dangerous if clots form where they are not needed, leading to a complication called *disseminated intravascular coagulation* (DIC).

DIC removes all the blood's clotting 'firepower', so that the system becomes exhausted and unable to clot at all. This leads to uncontrollable bleeding. The combination of inappropriate clotting and uncontrollable bleeding is very dangerous indeed.

The red blood cells may become damaged so that their contents spill out into the plasma, causing mayhem. This dangerous development is called *haemolysis*. You could compare it to a road traffic accident in which a whole fleet of petrol tankers crash and spill their dangerous cargo over the road and other traffic.

HELLP syndrome

The liver may be damaged, too. In fact, these problems often come together in the so-called 'HELLP syndrome'. HELLP stands for a combination of changes that show up in a blood test: Haemolysis (as above), Elevated Liver enzymes, and Low Platelet count. Elevated liver enzymes are a sign of liver damage, while low platelets are a sign of overactive clotting.

Platelets are special blood cells that are vital for healthy blood clotting. When blood vessels are injured, such as from a minor cut, blood leaks out. At the point of injury, platelets become sticky and quickly plug the leak. A substance called *fibrin* is rapidly produced to cement the platelets firmly together and strengthen the plug. Finally, special repair cells swarm in and quickly rebuild the vessel wall. When the clotting system is overactive, as it is in pre-eclampsia, platelets are used up and their count in the blood starts to fall.

Stage 4: crisis

There are several dangerous – but thankfully rare – crises of pre-eclampsia. And these are signalled by severe symptoms of illness.

Eclampsia – fits or seizures – was the first crisis to be recognised. We don't know what exactly causes these fits. But we *do* know that it is not high blood pressure, since the fits can occur when a woman's blood pressure is normal or only slightly raised.

> 'I had "slightly high" blood pressure in the last few months of my pregnancy, but this was never flagged as a problem. I was working full time at this point and it was put down to my dashing about. I had an eclamptic fit during delivery and the pre-eclampsia was only diagnosed afterwards.'
>
> Heather, UK

The name pre-eclampsia suggests that eclampsia is the only possible crisis. But actually *HELLP syndrome* is more common, and the two often come together.

> 'At 30 weeks, after three days on the antenatal ward, I was taken to theatre for an emergency caesarean after blood tests showed I was suffering from HELLP syndrome. After my daughter was born, I was transferred to the high dependency unit, where I stayed for three days until my condition stabilised. Back on the ward, about five days after giving birth, I awoke in the night with a terrific headache and feeling sick. I remember pressing the bell for the nurses and am told they found me on the floor having an eclamptic fit. My husband and I were both traumatised by the whole experience and were put off any future pregnancies.'
>
> Janet, UK

Stroke and other complications

A *stroke*, caused by bleeding into the brain, is a very dangerous and often fatal crisis. In many countries it is the most important single cause of maternal death. It can come with both HELLP and eclampsia but is otherwise extremely rare.

Kidney failure is another possible crisis and can sometimes be permanent. *Liver failure* can happen with HELLP, and sometimes the liver can rupture (burst). Women usually recover quickly from liver failure, but liver rupture is an emergency that calls for highly specialised surgery, followed by intensive care.

> *'At 35 weeks I had terrible pains in my abdomen and was diagnosed*
> *with pre-eclampsia at the hospital. My daughter was delivered by*
> *C-section and was in NICU for two weeks. Afterwards I went into*
> *multi-organ failure and ended up needing a full liver transplant. I*
> *was in hospital for nearly six months.'*
>
> Kristen, US

The fluid retention that leads to oedema can become so severe that it affects the breathing, either by obstructing the airway or by filling the lungs with fluid. This latter complication is known as *pulmonary oedema*.

> *'I had been having trouble breathing for three days, to the extent that*
> *I could not lie down or sit back in a chair. And the swelling in my feet*
> *that normally went down every night had not gone down for three or*
> *four days. At the hospital they found my lungs were filled with fluid.*
> *A couple of hours after delivering my son, I went into respiratory*
> *arrest and was put on a ventilator for three days.'*
>
> Kristy, US

How the baby is affected

The unborn baby doesn't get hypertension or proteinuria; instead it suffers from a restricted supply of blood from the mother via the placenta. The baby cannot get enough food and its growth may suffer. This problem, known as *intrauterine* or *fetal growth restriction* (FGR), is especially likely with pre-eclampsia that starts before 34 weeks. It is rare with pre-eclampsia starting after 37 weeks.

*'I had very high blood pressure at around 30 weeks and was
immediately admitted to hospital, where they found I also had
proteinuria. I was kept in for three weeks as they tried to keep the
pregnancy going. However, the baby was found to have stopped
growing at 31 weeks, so he was delivered by caesarean at 33/34
weeks when it was felt to be too dangerous for both of us to continue.*

*'He was small but apparently healthy and had no real problems in
the special care baby unit. He was long and very thin and remained
small for his age for a few years. Now, 25 years later, he is nearly six
feet tall and well built.'*

Lesley, UK

Prematurity, stillbirth and placental abruption

Pre-eclampsia is the main reason for babies being induced prematurely. It
is also an important cause of stillbirths although, happily, these are less
common than they were a generation ago because we have much more
sophisticated techniques for monitoring unborn babies.

Bleeding into the placenta, known as *placental abruption,* is more common
in pre-eclampsia than in normal pregnancy. It can cause the baby to suffocate
as well as leading to serious blood loss for the mother.

*'I was diagnosed with pre-eclampsia at 33 weeks, when my BP was
160/110. I was put on bed rest and my BP came down slightly, but
at 34 weeks and five days I had a complete placental abruption and
my son was stillborn. I needed 14 units of blood and numerous other
blood products transfused, and spent five days in ICU.'*

Nicole, US

The disease of exceptions

The only consistent thing about pre-eclampsia is that it is *inconsistent,*
obeying no hard-and-fast rules. There are so many exceptions to what you
might call a 'classic' pattern that pre-eclampsia is sometimes called 'the
disease of exceptions'. Here are some examples:

- Hypertension usually appears before proteinuria, but it can
happen the other way round.

- Although the placenta is the cause of the problem, some of the worst crises come after the birth, when the placenta has gone.
- Although the name suggests that eclampsia follows pre-eclampsia, this is not always true. In 1-in-10 cases of eclampsia there are no warning signs, and the fits come at the same time as the hypertension and proteinuria. Sometimes they come with just hypertension *or* proteinuria. These exceptional situations are mostly likely to happen immediately after the birth.
- HELLP syndrome usually follows hypertension and proteinuria but, as with eclampsia, it can come after just one or the other.
- Pre-eclampsia is said not to happen before 20 weeks of pregnancy; but sometimes, very rarely, it does.
- We have said that pre-eclampsia is the result of poor placentation; but poor placentation can happen *without* leading to pre-eclampsia. In such cases the baby is smaller than it should be but the mother has no problems.

How do we know when it's pre-eclampsia?

It is increasingly clear from these examples that, as pointed out in Chapter 1, our definition of pre-eclampsia is too rigid and incomplete. What, for example, should we call hypertension or proteinuria alone combined with FGR? We have two features of pre-eclampsia (one maternal and one placental) but not all the signs that are needed to make a conventional diagnosis. Is this pre-eclampsia or not?

Just as you can have poor placentation without maternal signs of pre-eclampsia, it is also possible to have maternal signs without poor placentation. In this situation babies grow normally in the uterus, supported by apparently normal placentas. Does this mean the placenta isn't the cause of the problem?

Well, yes and no. There are two issues here: first, there is more to 'normal' pregnancy than meets the eye; secondly, pre-eclampsia is probably more complicated than we thought. We look at these two issues in more detail below.

Normal pregnancy is not what it seems

Not all women feel well when they are pregnant, especially at the beginning when tiredness, nausea or vomiting can be big problems. For some women the nausea particularly may continue right through the pregnancy, only to disappear like magic after the birth.

These features of normal pregnancy remind us that this natural process has major effects on women's health and wellbeing. Pregnant women tend to experience more severe effects from viral infections like 'flu, for example. On the other hand those suffering from conditions like rheumatoid arthritis, psoriasis and multiple sclerosis sometimes experience a temporary and very welcome 'cure' during pregnancy.

Temporary disorders caused by pregnancy

Temporary disorders that can be induced by pregnancy include diabetes, skin and liver problems. These and other problems show just how massively the placenta reorganises the way the mother's body works. In fact it is more remarkable that most pregnant women feel well than that some are unwell.

The nub of the issue is that even a healthy normal placenta unbalances or 'stresses' a mother's systems. In most women natural processes can cope and restore balance. But in others, stress lines begin to appear. Pre-eclampsia, with all the variations described above, is one of those stress lines.

Three main variants of pre-eclampsia

We can now see that there are three main variants of pre-eclampsia, which account for all the exceptions mentioned above:

- 'placental pre-eclampsia', where maternal illness is combined with poor placentation and some growth restriction (FGR) in the baby;
- 'maternal pre-eclampsia' without poor placentation or FGR;
- poor placentation and FGR without maternal illness.

In maternal pre-eclampsia it seems likely that the demands of a normal placenta place undue strain on some mothers with particular risk factors, including chronic hypertension and a tendency to diabetes. In these cases, the babies are usually well-grown.

Combinations are common

Combinations of the different types of pre-eclampsia are common; and combinations of maternal and placental pre-eclampsia tend to be particularly dangerous.

It is not clear why poor placentation doesn't always result in pre-eclampsia. But it may be that in these cases the signals from the stressed placenta don't get through to the mother in the expected way.

Pre-eclampsia is not caused by hypertension

One of the biggest fallacies about pre-eclampsia is that it is caused by hypertension. In fact, the hypertension of pre-eclampsia is a 'secondary' problem, caused by the primary problem within the placenta. If the hypertension is treated it can be normalised for a time, but the pre-eclampsia still marches on relentlessly; its other features continue to progress, and more and more antihypertensive medication is needed to maintain control.

The fact that eclampsia can appear without preceding hypertension is further proof that the hypertension is not the primary problem.

The one important problem of pre-eclampsia that *can* be caused by hypertension is stroke due to bleeding into the brain. This is known as *cerebral haemorrhage*. There is good evidence that control of blood pressure can prevent this kind of stroke; and for this reason alone it is vital.

Who is at risk?

No pregnant woman is immune from pre-eclampsia, as far as we know. But some are more at risk than others. Some factors that can increase a woman's risk of pre-eclampsia are listed in Table 2.1 (*opposite*). A simplified version of this table is included in Chapter 5 (*page 110*).

Maternal risk factors

Although first-time mothers make up less than half of all mothers, they account for most cases of pre-eclampsia. We look at the reasons for this in the next section. Most women don't get pre-eclampsia again; but most of those who do get pre-eclampsia in second or later pregnancies have had it before.

Having a change of partner makes it more likely that pre-eclampsia will happen again, especially if a woman gets pregnant within three months of starting sexual relations with her new partner. A very long interval between pregnancies – such as 10 years – with the same partner can also increase the risk of getting pre-eclampsia again.

Being a younger or older mother increases the risk of pre-eclampsia only slightly, but having a family history of pre-eclampsia is an important

Maternal risk factors	Placental/fetal risk factors

First pregnancy
First pregnancy by current partner
Short period of sexual relations (exposure to partner's semen) before pregnancy
Long interval between pregnancies
Being under 20 or over 35
Being obese
Pre-eclampsia in a previous pregnancy
A family history of pre-eclampsia
Needing treatment, such as IVF, to get pregnant
Having some other medical illnesses, such as:
  • chronic hypertension
  • long-term kidney problems
  • any type of diabetes
  • polycystic ovarian syndrome (a hormonal problem)
  • migraine
  • antiphospholipid antibody syndrome (a rare form of an autoimmune disorder called lupus)
	Increasing gestational age (the more advanced the pregnancy, the higher the risk)
	Multiple pregnancy (twins or more)
	Hydatidiform mole (a rare disorder where there is a placenta but no baby)
	Poor placentation

Table 2. Risk factors for pre-eclampsia

risk factor and obesity is becoming more prominent as a risk. The most significant risk factors, though, are the long-term medical conditions listed at the bottom of the table.

Placental risk factors

Not surprisingly, placental factors can also increase the risk of pre-eclampsia: the larger the placenta, the higher the risk. That's why pre-eclampsia is most common in late pregnancy, when the placenta is at its largest. It is also more common in twin or triplet pregnancies, where the placentas are larger than usual.

With poor placentation, though, the placenta is unusually small while the risk of pre-eclampsia is unusually high. This can be explained by the fact that the damaged placenta is inherently stressful for the mother, whereas a normal placenta is stressful only if it gets too big for the mother's system to supply its needs.

Why first-time mothers are most at risk

Why is pre-eclampsia mostly a problem for first-time mothers? What happens after a first pregnancy that makes pre-eclampsia much less likely in later pregnancies? The answers to these questions seem to lie within our immune systems.

How the immune system works in pregnancy

Part of the job of our immune systems is to remove and destroy anything entering the body that does not belong there. An infection is one obvious example; an organ transplant is another, unless it comes from an identical twin. A fetus, which inherits half of its genes from the father, is a kind of transplant, sometimes known as 'nature's transplant'; and just like an organ transplant it challenges the mother's immune system. So how does it survive?

The frontier between mother and baby

In fact, the mother's systems come into direct contact only with the placenta, not the baby. And the frontier between mother and baby is patrolled by specialised placental cells called *trophoblast*. Nature has various ways of protecting trophoblast cells from being recognised and destroyed by the maternal immune system. For one thing, they manage to hide most of the signals that trigger transplant rejection.

Some trophoblast cells continue to send out one of these signals, known as *HLA-C*. Remarkably, though, the specialised maternal immune cells packing the lining of the uterus in early pregnancy are primed to react positively to HLA-C. When this happens, the maternal immune system normally supports the trophoblast cells, guiding them to where they can do their work in remodelling the arteries supplying the placenta *(see Figure 2.2, page 22)*.

Learning to 'tolerate' the pregnancy

What we now know is that the maternal immune system has to 'learn' to be helpful rather than hostile to the biologically foreign cells. And this learning process, called 'tolerisation', may be only partly accomplished during a first pregnancy.

Tolerisation starts before conception, when a woman's immune system is exposed to the foreign cells in male semen. Continuing exposure to the semen stimulates the process; but if a baby is conceived quickly after first intercourse, tolerisation might be incomplete.

There are two possible consequences of this partial tolerisation. It could lead to such poor progress after conception that the pregnancy miscarries; or the pregnancy could continue but with poor placentation, leading to pre-eclampsia. This explains the increased risk of pre-eclampsia if conception occurs after a short partnership (see Table 2.1, page 33).

The importance of the partnership

This interaction between the part-foreign baby and the mother's immune system varies from couple to couple. Some combinations are naturally very helpful for a pregnancy, while others are not. And we now have good evidence that certain immune combinations between mother and baby are associated with an increased risk of pre-eclampsia.

When a woman gets pre-eclampsia, it is likely that the pregnancy itself completes the process of tolerisation so that she doesn't get pre-eclampsia in the next pregnancy.

The idea of tolerisation may explain many features of pre-eclampsia, including the fact that identical twin sisters do not usually have the same risk of pre-eclampsia, despite having exactly the same genes. The risk is not just to do with the woman but with the partnership.

Recovery and afterwards

The placenta, the prime cause of pre-eclampsia, is delivered shortly after the baby. Despite this, the illness may appear for the first time after the birth or get worse before it starts to get better.

'I had a natural birth with gas and air at 39 weeks. Almost immediately after giving birth I experienced agonising chest pain that went on all night. I kept being told it was heartburn but I was in too much pain for it to be that. I ended up in intensive care as pre-eclampsia developed into HELLP syndrome. My blood count dropped, my kidneys failed and my blood pressure rose so high that doctors thought I would have a stroke.'

Louise, UK

Worsening hypertension

Hypertension tends to get worse in the first week after the birth, with the highest readings often found 5-7 days later. After that it can persist at lower – but still abnormal – levels for weeks, even months, which is very frustrating for women who are told that their problems will disappear quickly once the baby is born. Sometimes it persists indefinitely as chronic hypertension.

> 'I had very high blood pressure from 30 weeks but wasn't diagnosed until 35 weeks and was induced at 37 weeks. Four days after having my son I was sent home. But that night I started to feel unwell. An ambulance was called and I was sent back to hospital, where it was found that my blood pressure had risen to 191/116. Six months later I am still on medication.'
>
> Emma, UK

When proteinuria becomes chronic

It can take three months or more for proteinuria to disappear, and in some women this becomes a chronic kidney problem. When hypertension or proteinuria become long-term it is often not clear whether they are caused by pre-eclampsia or whether the pregnancy simply uncovered an underlying problem.

When damage is permanent

The vast majority of mothers make a complete recovery from pre-eclampsia, but an unfortunate few are left with permanent health problems.

> 'I was in a coma for three days with severe brain swelling and I didn't get to see my child until she was seven days' old. My family were told I was going to be blind and paralysed. Eight years later I still have vision problems and memory loss.'
>
> Jody, US

Most babies also do well. When permanent damage occurs it is usually related to prematurity.

> 'At 27 weeks I delivered a 795g baby boy who suffered the most serious injury of prematurity, a grade lV intraventricular [brain] haemorrhage, and lived with multiple disabilities.'
>
> Christine, US

Will it happen again?

This is the most pressing question that women tend to ask after their immediate recovery from pre-eclampsia. The *good* news is that most women don't get pre-eclampsia again. A minority of women do, but in these cases it is usually less severe than it was the first time.

> *'In my first pregnancy I suffered from HELLP, pulmonary oedema and liver and kidney problems, and eventually had a seizure. In my second pregnancy I was expected to have a 34-week (or earlier) delivery. I did develop high BP and was borderline on proteinuria, but much to our surprise I went to term and was induced at 39 weeks and six days.'*
>
> Stacy, US

We can't predict with certainty who will get pre-eclampsia again. The earlier it appeared in the first pregnancy the more likely it is to recur, although usually at a later stage of pregnancy.

Only about one-in-20 women who get pre-eclampsia at the end of pregnancy will get it again. But it recurs in up to half of those whose babies are delivered at 30-32 weeks or earlier.

Long-term effects on the health of mother and child

In this chapter we have seen how even a normal pregnancy puts strain on a woman's health. Most women can cope, but in some women pregnancy shows up an underlying tendency to problems like high blood pressure or diabetes.

Pregnancy is a sort of 'stress test' for how a woman's body copes in exceptional circumstances. So it is not surprising that women who have had severe pre-eclampsia – particularly of the early kind – are more liable to face later health problems.

Long-term health problems for women

In their fifties and beyond these women have a higher-than-average risk of developing cardiovascular problems like chronic hypertension, stroke, and angina or heart attacks. Not everyone suffers in this way and, as mentioned, we don't know whether the pre-eclampsia creates the risk or simply gives early warning of what was going to happen anyway.

But some of these long-term problems can be prevented. And in future, women who have had pre-eclampsia may be followed up routinely with extra health checks, advice about diet and lifestyle and even medication, such as statins, to reduce their risk.

Long-term health problems for babies

Babies born prematurely, or with FGR, or both, have an increased chance of health problems in adulthood, including diabetes, obesity and cardiovascular problems. Again, it may prove possible to prevent some of these problems, although doctors haven't got very far in their thinking about this yet.

In the next chapter we look at the progress being made in predicting which women are most likely to get pre-eclampsia, various possibilities for reducing risk and ways to slow the progression of the disease once it has started. The good news is that progress is being made, albeit slowly.

CHAPTER 3: SCREENING, PREVENTION AND TREATMENT

The last chapter summarised what we know about pre-eclampsia, from its earliest beginnings in the placenta to the possible long-term effects on the health of mothers and babies. We looked at:

- how the condition progresses from 'silent' signs and symptoms like high blood pressure (*hypertension*) and protein in the urine (*proteinuria*) to serious complications like eclampsia and HELLP syndrome in mothers, and growth restriction in babies;
- possible causes and risk factors;
- huge variations in the way the illness can show itself in mothers and babies.

In this chapter we focus on what doctors and midwives can do to keep mothers and babies safe through careful screening and effective treatment. We also look at what can be done now – and might be done in future – to reduce women's risk of getting pre-eclampsia.

Where relevant we have referred to national guidelines on the management of pre-eclampsia. In most cases these are UK guidelines, but we are aware of international differences, which are mostly concerned with details, such as preferred medications. The biggest differences are between countries that do and do not involve midwives as autonomous practitioners. The UK, the Netherlands and New Zealand are examples of the former approach and the US of the latter, while Canada is moving towards midwife autonomy.

But we have to make it clear at the outset that there are no magic solutions and that progress in predicting, treating and preventing the illness remains painfully slow. That's because there is probably much more that we *don't* know about pre-eclampsia than we *do*. And that starts with the nature of the disease itself.

A 'syndrome', not an illness

Although we refer to pre-eclampsia throughout this book as an 'illness', that's not strictly accurate. In scientific terms an illness is a condition with a known cause, which can usually be diagnosed by means of a specific test, may be curable by a specific treatment and may even be preventable by vaccination.

Tuberculosis (TB) is a very good example: we know that it is caused by particular bacteria that attack the lungs; it can be diagnosed by means of x-rays, blood tests and detection of the bacterium in sputum or other samples; it can be cured with antibiotics and prevented by the BCG vaccine.

Before the bacteria that cause TB were identified, it was defined as a 'syndrome'. That means it was recognised by a collection of signs and symptoms that came together – mainly cough, fever, night sweats and weight loss. No one knew what caused the symptoms of what was known in those days as 'consumption', so they could not be effectively treated or reliably prevented.

That's where we are with pre-eclampsia right now. We recognise it not by its cause or causes, which remain unknown, but by a collection of signs and symptoms – including hypertension and proteinuria – that come together in the second half of pregnancy and may be followed by serious complications for mothers and babies.

This syndrome acts as an alarm signal to doctors and midwives, warning them of possible dangers ahead. But it tells us nothing about the *cause* of the signs and symptoms – or perhaps we should say *causes*. Although we assume we are dealing with one type of illness, we may be wrong. Pre-eclampsia may actually be an umbrella term for several different conditions that look alike.

More than one condition?

The idea that the term 'pre-eclampsia' may cover more than one condition is supported by significant differences between 'early-onset' pre-eclampsia – starting before 34 weeks – and 'late-onset' disease – starting after 37 weeks.

By comparison with late-onset pre-eclampsia, early-onset disease is:

- more likely to cause growth restriction and other problems in babies;

- linked with more placental damage and more severe placental bleeds (*abruptions*);
- more likely to happen again – or for the first time – in second or later pregnancies;
- more likely to lead to HELLP syndrome;
- more likely to affect women with long-term medical conditions such as chronic hypertension or kidney disease;
- easier to predict by testing early in pregnancy;
- linked with a higher risk of chronic hypertension and related problems for mothers in later life.

The period between 34 and 37 weeks appears to be an intermediate zone, where both types of disease can occur.

This concept of two types of pre-eclampsia is supported by our growing understanding of the crucial role of the placenta, as explained in the next section.

The role of the placenta

The fact that poor growth in babies is much more common with early-onset eclampsia is important. Poor growth is a sign of 'poor placentation' – the failure to develop a healthy placental circulation in early pregnancy (*see Chapter 2, pp 21-24*).

The later in pregnancy pre-eclampsia appears, the more likely the baby is to be well-grown. Indeed, babies delivered at full term (after 37 weeks) because of pre-eclampsia may even be *larger* than average. This does not seem to fit with the idea that all cases of pre-eclampsia start with a poor placental circulation.

With late-onset pre-eclampsia there is a different problem affecting the placenta, which seems to have reached its limits in providing for the growing baby. And we are now learning that this problem affects many pregnancies at and beyond full term.

When demand outstrips supply

The surface of the placenta that makes contact with maternal blood is lined by a remarkable cell structure known as *syncytiotrophoblast*. The 'trophoblast' part of the word describes the unique placental cell type (belonging to the baby) that is responsible for all communications with the mother; 'syncytio' refers to a specialised type of trophoblast, whose cells have merged to cover the whole surface of the placenta, where it is bathed in maternal blood. Its surface area is said to be as big as a tennis court, yet it is incredibly thin to allow for efficient transfer of nutrients, oxygen and waste products between mother and baby.

In late-onset pre-eclampsia there is evidence that the syncytiotrophoblast is increasingly stressed. And it now seems that many, if not all, placentas experience this stress sooner or later, especially beyond term at 40-42 weeks.

This is when many apparently well women begin to show what look like early signs of pre-eclampsia: blood pressure goes up slightly, output of protein in the urine increases a little and blood test results suggest mild pre-eclampsia.

What seems to be happening is that the demands of the baby via the placenta outstrip what the mother can supply. Levels of oxygen in the placenta decline, the organ itself runs out of space and the baby's growth slows or stops.

Time is running out

After pregnancies reach full term, there is a *six-fold* increase in the rate of eclampsia. Stillbirth is also more common at this stage. Contrary to popular belief, the period beyond full term is not a calm phase. Time is running out and, increasingly, delivery is the only option.

What we can conclude is that many women at this very late stage of pregnancy are drifting towards pre-eclampsia but will not get it, either because they go into labour naturally or because their doctors intervene to arrange delivery. It has even been suggested that *all* women would get pre-eclampsia eventually if their pregnancies could be sustained for long enough.

There are two key learning points here for all those concerned with the care of pregnant women:

- While early-onset pre-eclampsia is predictable in early pregnancy, late-onset disease is not, because there is nothing wrong with the placenta at that stage.
- Diagnosis of pre-eclampsia at term is particularly tricky because of the apparently normal drift towards the disease.

The differences between early-onset and late-onset placental stress are illustrated in Figure 3.1 (*opposite*).

Different types of pre-eclampsia

If pre-eclampsia is actually several conditions covered by one label, doctors and scientists are more likely to make progress in treating and preventing these conditions by separating them out.

This approach has already been adopted with other complex diseases, like obesity and adult-onset diabetes. We now think these problems can have many causes which differ from person to person, leading to different patterns of illness and pointing to different methods of prevention or treatment. This is what doctors mean when they talk about 'personalised' or 'precision' medicine.

Revised definitions of pre-eclampsia reflect this new way of thinking. And here the Australasians are leading the field: in their latest definition of pre-eclampsia, new high blood pressure *without* proteinuria but *with* an under-grown baby is recognised as a particular 'sub- type' of pre-eclampsia.

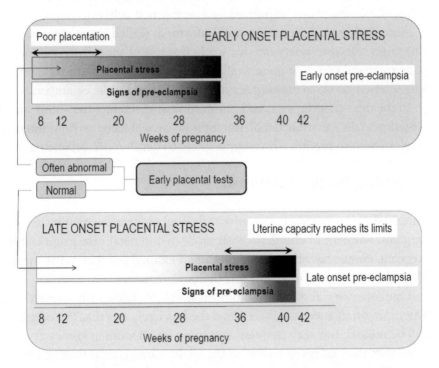

Figure 3.1 Differences between early- and late-onset pre-eclampsia

This figure illustrates how early- and late-onset pre-eclampsia arise from different placental problems. Only with early-onset disease can tests of placental function predict disease.

Bringing pre-eclampsia under control

So far in this chapter we have focused on what we *don't* know about pre-eclampsia. But, despite all this uncertainty, there has been enormous progress in making the illness less dangerous for mothers and babies.

How have we managed to make pre-eclampsia safer? We still don't understand the condition; we have no cure except delivery, which always resolves pre-eclampsia eventually even if it sometimes gets worse at first; we can't predict it accurately or prevent it reliably. So what did we start to do right?

The safety net of antenatal care

The answer is that we developed systematic antenatal (prenatal) care, which works by identifying women at risk, watching them carefully for the earliest signs of the illness and then referring them to specialist care, where the disorder can be limited by a well-timed delivery.

Antenatal care, delivered by well-informed, skilled professionals, is an amazingly effective 'safety net' for women at risk of pre-eclampsia. Indeed poor antenatal care – or none at all – is probably the biggest single reason why women go on to develop serious complications, like eclampsia.

In the next chapter we take a closer look at this safety net – and why it sometimes fails – in more detail. But for now we will focus on how antenatal care can help to predict who is most likely to develop pre-eclampsia.

Screening for pre-eclampsia

Antenatal care is based on a massive screening programme that includes all pregnant women. In countries with modern antenatal care programmes, pregnant women have their blood pressure measured and their urine checked for protein at regular intervals throughout pregnancy.

Opinions vary about how often these checks need to be carried out. The more often a woman is screened the less likely it is that pre-eclampsia will be missed. But very frequent screening for all women comes at a cost to women themselves as well as to the health care systems footing the bill.

Screening based on risk

For this reason, screening for pre-eclampsia is usually based on perceived levels of risk. Women thought to be at low risk can make do with minimal screening, while those at higher risk need more frequent checks. Of course, other potential complications of pregnancy also need to be considered as part of the 'big picture', and we discuss this further in Chapter 5.

The medical care of pregnant women is uniquely challenging for doctors and midwives. Pregnancy usually lasts for 42 weeks or less; and during this time the pace is hectic, with the condition of mothers and babies changing week by week and sometimes day by day. Good health today doesn't guarantee good health tomorrow, still less next week or next month.

Testing for placental health

Until quite recently, a woman's risk of developing pre-eclampsia was based on the factors listed in the last chapter *(see Table 2.1, page 33)*. These include first pregnancy, chronic hypertension and a history of pre-eclampsia. However, we now have some tests that allow doctors to assess risk more accurately. They all are based on measuring the function of the placenta, either in terms of its blood supply from the mother or signs of stress.

There is a lot of interest in testing for signs of placental health at around three months of pregnancy. The main tests used are:

- blood tests measuring substances in the circulation that may reflect early placental stress. These substances are often called *biomarkers*;
- ultrasound measurements of blood flow to the placenta through the two main maternal arteries that supply the uterus. This is known as *uterine artery Doppler scanning*.

Some of these tests can be repeated at 18-22 weeks, coinciding with routine scans to assess the baby's growth and development. The two types of test can be combined for more accurate prediction.

But they are far from foolproof, and in general they are better at predicting early-onset pre-eclampsia than later disease. As we have explained, blood tests that register placental stress can only predict the early-onset type of pre-eclampsia; at present there is no efficient way to predict late-onset disease – especially in first-time mothers – and we have to rely on risk factors.

The problem of misleading results

These new tests are more precise than a general assessment of risk factors. But they can suggest risk where there is none in some cases ('false positives') and give false reassurance in others ('false negatives').

Researchers from the UK recently found a significant proportion of false negatives and even more false positives in women screened for pre-eclampsia according to the current NICE guidelines. Screening picked up 93 per cent of early-onset cases and 85 per cent of late cases. In other words 85-93 per cent of cases of pre-eclampsia were accurately predicted by the tests, while 7-15 per cent went undetected (false negatives). At the same time the tests predicted pre-eclampsia wrongly in a huge proportion – 65 per cent – of 'normal' women (false positives) (1).

The problem with these misleading results is that more care is offered to many women who *don't* need it, while some women who *might* need it are led to believe they have nothing to worry about. And all this comes at considerable cost because the tests are far from cheap.

The need for a single test

What we need is a single test that produces no false negatives and a very small number of false positives. This is almost certainly impossible to achieve. Instead, we probably need to develop different tests for the various different types of pre-eclampsia. But even if we could do that, we would still face an even bigger challenge: how to prevent pre-eclampsia in those who seem most likely to get it.

The Holy Grail of prevention

Doctors would be much more enthusiastic about predictive tests if those who tested positive could be offered simple, safe and effective treatment to prevent the disease. So how close are we to reaching this Holy Grail?

It is helpful to divide methods of preventing a disease into three groups:

- 'primary' prevention that stops an illness before it starts;
- 'secondary' prevention that slows the development of the illness once it has started;
- 'tertiary' (third-stage) prevention that wards off serious complications.

The rest of this chapter looks at various potential methods of primary and secondary prevention. We consider the vital importance of tertiary prevention in Chapter 6.

Primary prevention of pre-eclampsia

One of the first problems with primary prevention is knowing when to start. As we saw in Chapter 2, the foundations of at least some types of pre-eclampsia are in place before the end of the third month, or even before conception. If prevention is to be successful it needs to start at these stages, when it is not at all clear who needs it.

Then we face questions of safety. Is any medication completely safe in the first few weeks of pregnancy, when the baby is at a very formative stage of development? Is a small benefit worth having? At what dose (medication) or intensity (dieting or exercise) should a treatment be offered?

For a long time preventive measures have adopted a 'shoot the messenger' approach, treating the symptoms rather than the cause. So doctors have used:

- diuretics to remove the excess fluid of oedema;
- dieting to restrict excessive weight gain;
- medication to reduce high blood pressure;
- low-dose aspirin to prevent overactive clotting.

In general, as you might expect, 'shoot the messenger' has not been a strikingly successful approach, as we will now show by looking at the various preventive methods that have been tried.

Low-dose aspirin

The only preventive measure that is generally accepted and has stood the test of time is aspirin, given in much lower doses than were once used when it was routinely used as a painkiller. But low-dose aspirin does not offer anything like a complete answer to the problem of pre-eclampsia. It reduces the risk by only about 10 per cent, meaning that it doesn't work in most cases.

How is it supposed to work? Platelets are very small cells in the circulation that play an important role in blood clotting (see Chapter 2, page xx). Low-dose aspirin makes platelets less active and so reduces clotting.

Since pre-eclampsia can be associated with excessive clotting activity, low-dose aspirin is an obvious candidate for preventing it.

Great results from early trials

When low-dose aspirin was first tested in small trials, as far back as 1985, there were excellent results which made it look very effective. However, as so often happens, larger, more rigorous trials showed less impressive benefits. Many large trials have now been completed, with another large European trial under way at the time of writing; and when all the results are combined they show a small but consistent benefit, with no important side effects (2).

What we can't tell from this research is whether aspirin offers minor preventive benefits for *all* women at risk of pre-eclampsia or major benefits for *some*. Since readers will now be aware that pre-eclampsia is a disease of exceptions, they should not be surprised to learn that not all women with pre-eclampsia – or even eclampsia – have major clotting problems and so would not be expected to benefit from aspirin.

Dosage and timing

Another thing we aren't yet clear about is the best dose of aspirin to prevent pre-eclampsia and the best time to start taking it. However, recent research suggests that aspirin is most protective when it is started before 16 weeks (3).

Regardless of its uncertain benefits, pregnant women have little to lose by taking low-dose aspirin: it is safe for them, while very little of it crosses the placenta to affect the baby. Low-dose aspirin is now recommended in UK, Australasian, US, Canadian and World Health Organisation guidelines for a wide range of women at increased risk of pre-eclampsia.

When aspirin was used routinely as a painkiller, it was usually given in doses of 600mg four times a day. The current recommended dose for preventing pre-eclampsia is 75mg a day, but there are some experts who think this could be doubled to 150mg.

Fish oils

Aspirin affects platelets by changing their balance of *prostaglandins* – powerful signals that cells use to communicate with each other. The activity of prostaglandins depends on the dietary fats from which they are derived. Prostaglandins derived from fat in dairy products make platelets more active, which would definitely *not* help to prevent pre-eclampsia. On the other hand, prostaglandins derived from fish oil make platelets *less* active, which should be beneficial.

For this reason fish oil supplements have been recommended in the past to prevent pre-eclampsia. But there is no evidence that they actually work. We know they extend the duration of pregnancy very slightly, particularly in women who don't get enough fish oil from their diets. But they don't appear to reduce the risk of pre-eclampsia.

Calcium supplements

What else is available to help prevent pre-eclampsia? Second on the list after low-dose aspirin is calcium supplementation. Some research studies have shown important benefits, but these have come mainly from areas with very low levels of calcium in the water supply, particularly some countries in South America.

How or why should calcium be involved in pre-eclampsia? We tend to think of calcium as important for healthy bones, but actually it is essential to the normal working of all our cells. Calcium also helps to activate blood clotting, which is why blood samples taken for testing are often placed in a preservative that removes all calcium, keeping the sample fluid and easier to handle.

Calcium and blood pressure

Calcium is known to reduce high blood pressure by small amounts in all people, including pregnant women. We know that the high blood pressure of pre-eclampsia is caused by disturbance of the endothelial cells that line the inner surface of all blood vessels and control their function (*see Chapter 2, page 25*). And calcium is thought to work by regulating the way these cells work.

But if calcium supplements really help to prevent pre-eclampsia, they should do more than just reduce blood pressure. Pregnancies should last longer and babies should be bigger and healthier. Some research studies show these benefits, but others do not. In fact no benefits were seen in the two largest and best conducted studies so far *(4)*.

It is now recommended that calcium supplements should be given to pregnant women in areas where supplies are low. And there is probably no harm in taking them if there is extra concern about getting pre-eclampsia.

Vitamin D supplements

Pre-eclampsia and poor growth in babies has been associated with low blood levels of vitamin D, usually from mid-pregnancy onwards. That's why it has been seen as a candidate for prevention.

Vitamin D has many important functions, including controlling the availability of calcium throughout our bodies. Many people are thought to be deficient in this vitamin to some extent, even in richer countries. This may reflect lack of sunshine as well as poor diet because we can't make enough vitamin D for our needs in our skin if we don't get enough sunlight.

In pregnancy the placenta conserves extra vitamin D to meet the mother's additional needs. And it may be that the low levels of vitamin D seen in pre-eclampsia reflect the placenta's failure to conserve it rather than a poor diet or inadequate exposure to sunshine.

In other words, although there is a problem with vitamin D in pre-eclampsia, it may not be possible to solve it through changes to diet or lifestyle. More research is needed and the subject is not yet closed, but vitamin D is not currently recommended to prevent pre-eclampsia.

The role of antioxidants

Whenever pre-eclampsia researchers get together, the discussion turns sooner or later to *oxidative stress* and *antioxidants*. What is this all about?

We normally use the terms 'stress' and 'distress' to describe emotional states; but in biology these terms have different and very precise meanings. Stress in our cells means they are working hard but at manageable levels; *distress* means the stress has become unmanageable, which could be dangerous. Fever is an example of stress, usually caused by an infection. It can be managed by our bodies, usually causing some damage that can be repaired once the fever is gone. But extreme fever is unmanageable and can be fatal.

Oxidative stress

Oxidative stress is another type of cell stress that can be very harmful. It is a consequence of any severe illness, when cells are forced to work hard in difficult circumstances. The stress may be limited to a particular organ, such as the heart or liver; or it may affect the many cells that circulate in our blood.

What do we mean by oxidative stress? Our lives are sustained by our ability to burn fuel from food to make energy. Another term for burning is 'oxidation', meaning that the process requires and consumes oxygen. Each of the trillions of cells in our bodies contains a tiny furnace, where useful energy is created by burning fuels derived from what we eat. If a cell is resting it needs little energy and its furnaces are turned down to low levels. If a cell is very busy, its furnaces are turned up and the cell may 'overheat' to dangerous levels. This is what we mean by oxidative stress.

Our bodies, being clever, can call on substances that reduce oxidation. These are known as *antioxidants*. In simple terms, what they do is cool overheated parts of cells and extinguish 'fires' *(see Figure 3.2 overleaf)*. This, of course, happens at the microscopic level of the cell and there are no actual fires involved. Most of the antioxidants we need are produced naturally in our bodies; but some come from our diet, and these include vitamins C and E.

In pre-eclampsia oxidative stress affects both the placenta and the mother's circulation. That's why dietary constituents with antioxidant effects have been considered for preventing pre-eclampsia.

Antioxidant vitamins

The first trial of vitamin C and E supplements for preventing pre-eclampsia was reported in 1999. It was a small study with extremely promising results. But several later larger trials did not confirm these benefits; worse, they suggested that taking such vitamins in the high doses chosen could cause problems for unborn babies. Nowadays these supplements are not recommended for preventing pre-eclampsia.

But the story doesn't end here because there are many other antioxidants to consider.

Selenium

One of these is the trace element selenium, which forms part of some powerful antioxidant substances within the body. It is absorbed from our food and is also available in some multivitamin preparations. In some parts of the world, including some developed countries, dietary intake of selenium is low. One study has shown that pregnant women who got pre-eclampsia had lower selenium stores than those who didn't. Another found that pregnant rats fed a low-selenium diet went on to develop symptoms of pre-eclampsia.

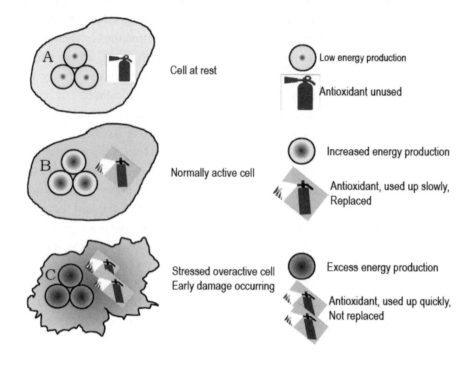

Figure 3.2 Oxidative stress and antioxidants

Cells need energy continuously. This comes from oxidising (literally burning) fuel from the food that we eat. Here's what this figure is showing:

A. Some cells are very quiet, use little energy and do not need protection from antioxidants.

B. Normally active cells burn and consume more energy and use their antioxidants to keep the burning limited and under control.

C. Very active cells (for example during infection, after damage or after intense exercise) burn so much fuel that they become overheated, with the risk of damage to parts of the cell. To prevent this damage, cells are full of antioxidants, which function like fire extinguishers to keep the oxidation under control. If the oxidation is too intense, the antioxidants get used up and the cell begins to suffer damage from the fires spreading beyond their normal limits. This is known as 'oxidative stress'.

It is possible, therefore, that selenium supplements could help to prevent pre-eclampsia. But since no trial results are available yet, they cannot be recommended at present.

Folic acid and multivitamins

Women at risk of pre-eclampsia might well benefit from taking folic acid and multivitamins. So far, the evidence is encouraging but not conclusive. There is good reason to take folic acid anyway, to prevent spina bifida developing in the baby; and many women choose to take it in the form of multivitamin preparations.

Since these preparations are made in different ways by different companies, it is hard to say what may be useful. The question deserves more detailed study, but while the jury's out there is probably no harm in taking one of these preparations before conception and for the first three months of pregnancy. As always, there is good reason not to take more than the recommended amount. Overdosing, even on vitamins, can be harmful.

Weight, work and lifestyle

Women who carry too much weight are known to be at increased risk of pre-eclampsia *(see Chapter 2, page 33)*. This is because the excess fat itself exerts a huge stress on their systems, whether or not they are pregnant. Pregnancy adds to this burden and may tip the balance enough to aggravate the processes that cause pre-eclampsia. So could losing weight either before or during pregnancy help to prevent the illness?

Several studies have considered the potential benefits of weight loss, although they have been small and often focused on other pregnancy-related problems, particularly diabetes. When the research is summarised, there is growing evidence that weight loss is effective in preventing pre-eclampsia. But it's early days yet and larger, more specific trials are needed to confirm this.

Weight gain and fluid retention

Excessive weight gain during pregnancy is one of the warning signs of pre-eclampsia. In the past this was put down to eating too much fatty food, and women with pre-eclampsia were put on strict diets. This no longer happens because we now know that this weight gain is caused by fluid retention rather than overeating.

Water is very heavy, so it's not surprising that the fluid retention of pre-eclampsia causes sudden and excessive weight gain. Happily, though, the weight is shed just as quickly after delivery, when the kidneys get back to normal and excrete the excess fluid as urine. This type of weight gain is not the issue here and should not be confused with weight problems linked with diet and lifestyle.

Achieving a healthy weight is a challenge for many women, and it is probably best attempted before rather than during pregnancy. A combination of a good diet (in terms of quality as well as quantity) and moderate exercise is probably the best approach for all but the most seriously overweight women, who may need highly specialised management.

The role of exercise

Can exercise itself help to prevent pre-eclampsia? There is not enough evidence to say one way or the other. The general health benefits of exercise are well known and there is no reason for women not to exercise normally during pregnancy, ideally avoiding extreme exertion.

Can smoking reduce the risk?

Strangely enough, cigarette smoking, which is discouraged on most health grounds, appears to *reduce* the risk of pre-eclampsia. This finding was first noted nearly 50 years ago and has been confirmed in many later studies.

So should women take up smoking in a bid to prevent pre-eclampsia? *Absolutely not*: while smoking appears to reduce the severity of the maternal illness, it increases the risk of pre-term birth and severe placental bleeding. At the same time, unborn babies clearly suffer from exposure to cigarette smoke: they grow less well, are less resilient and less likely to survive before or after birth.

How can something as obviously harmful as smoking be protective against pre-eclampsia? No one knows, but research is under way that suggests it could have something to do with the carbon monoxide in cigarette smoke. In very low doses this is not a poison but is produced naturally inside our cells where it has a number of important functions, some of which may be helpful in pre-eclampsia. Nevertheless cigarette smoke also contains hundreds of other poisons, such as nicotine and tobacco tars, which are bad news for mothers and babies.

Tea and coffee

Little or nothing is known about the influence of drinking tea or coffee on the risk of pre-eclampsia, although one small study has suggested that drinking tea might increase the risk slightly.

Working

Much more is known about working during pregnancy, and here the evidence is reassuring. At the moment there is no reason to believe that stopping or limiting work plays any part in preventing pre-eclampsia. So women who have had pre-eclampsia need not torment themselves with thoughts that working may have caused or added to their problems.

Secondary prevention

So far we have looked at candidates for primary prevention – things that might stop pre-eclampsia before it starts. This section focuses on secondary prevention – things that might slow the progression of the illness once the first sign – or signs – have appeared.

Usually the first warning sign of pre-eclampsia is rising blood pressure, known as *gestational hypertension*. Here it is the 'messenger' that warns of coming pre-eclampsia; and the standard 'shoot the messenger' approach is to bring down the blood pressure with 'antihypertensive' medication. However, as we will see, this does nothing to halt the progress or reduce the severity of the disease for mothers or babies.

The role of antihypertensive drugs

In Chapter 2 we explained that the raised blood pressure of pre-eclampsia is just one outward sign of the underlying problem in the placenta. So antihypertensive drugs can't be expected to cure the disease. But if the raised blood pressure makes the pre-eclampsia worse, might these drugs be able to slow its progression?

For many years researchers have been investigating this possibility, with disappointing results. There is no evidence that lowering the blood pressure slows the relentless advance of pre-eclampsia. In other words, it doesn't seem to play a role in secondary prevention.

However, when blood pressure is very high there is an increased risk of a brain haemorrhage (stroke). And, indeed, stroke is the major cause of maternal death from pre-eclampsia in many countries (*see Chapter 2, page 28).* For this reason, women with very high blood pressure need urgent treatment with antihypertensive drugs. And if, as sometimes happen, the drugs don't work, the pregnancy may need to be ended to protect the mother.

What we are less sure about is the level of blood pressure at which treatment needs to be started. In recent years the threshold for treatment has tended to come down. And UK guidelines now advise treatment if the systolic pressure – the higher of the two blood pressure readings – goes above 150 or the diastolic (lower) reading above 100. In Australasia and the USA, higher limits (160 and 110) are used.

Treating lower pressures

Is there any point in treating lower pressures with antihypertensive drugs? Different doctors have different views. Some believe that even moderate and short-lived increases in blood pressure can be dangerous. Others argue that tight control of blood pressure might reduce blood flow to the placenta, with damaging consequences for the unborn baby.

Trials are in progress that should clarify who is right. A recent trial (the CHIPS trial) showed no benefit from tighter control, although the thresholds where conventional treatment would be started were less often reached in women under tight control. Meanwhile, our view is that, while high blood pressure has to be well enough controlled to prevent maternal strokes, there is little evidence to justify treating lower pressures that do not increase the risk of stroke and are simply external signs of a problem in the placenta.

The problem of 'white coat hypertension'

It is well known that some people, particularly women, have higher-than-usual blood pressure when it is measured in a clinic or hospital. For some the effect is dramatic, with very high readings that simply disappear when blood pressure is checked at home.

This so-called 'white coat hypertension' sounds like a harmless response to a stressful situation. But actually it is linked with a higher risk of chronic hypertension and diabetes in later life. And in pregnancy it seems to carry a slightly increased risk of pre-eclampsia. For this reason, pregnant women with white coat hypertension need to be carefully monitored, although it is important not to overreact to the apparently high readings.

Chronic hypertension – a special situation

Some women are already under medical supervision for permanently raised blood pressure, or 'chronic hypertension' when they start pregnancy. Others are found to have chronic hypertension when their blood pressure is first checked in early pregnancy. This is important because chronic hypertension carries an increased risk of pre-eclampsia. In these cases pre-eclampsia is not normally diagnosed until protein appears in the urine. It is then known as 'superimposed pre-eclampsia', in that the illness comes on top of an existing blood pressure problem.

Doctors used to believe that women with chronic hypertension tended to get pre-eclampsia because the high blood pressure itself damaged the placenta. If this were the case then treating the blood pressure should reduce the risk of pre-eclampsia, which it doesn't. There may be good reasons to treat chronic hypertension in pregnancy, but preventing pre-eclampsia is not one of them.

Treatment of fluid retention

Abnormal fluid retention and swelling is a feature of some, but not all, cases of pre-eclampsia. The 'shoot the messenger' approach led earlier generations of doctors to use diuretic drugs to get rid of the excess fluid and (so they believed) slow down the progression of pre-eclampsia.

Diuretics were also used in the past to control blood pressure. They work by encouraging the kidneys to excrete more salt with the urine. Salt helps to raise blood pressure through its effects on the endothelial cells lining the blood vessels and the muscles, which cause arteries to constrict.

Various trials of diuretics for the secondary prevention of pre-eclampsia have not shown any benefits and they are no longer recommended, except for emergency treatment of the rare problem of excess fluid in the lungs (pulmonary oedema). The effects of these drugs are similar to those that can be achieved by reducing salt consumption. For this reason, salt restriction used to be recommended to either prevent or treat pre-eclampsia. This was despite clear research evidence that salt restriction tended to *increase* rather than reduce the risk of pre-eclampsia. Fortunately, salt restriction is never recommended now for women with – or at risk of – pre-eclampsia.

In Chapter 5 we look at the role of antenatal care in screening for and detecting pre-eclampsia and in Chapter 6 we consider what happens after diagnosis, including the vital importance of tertiary prevention to ward off complications.

But in the next chapter we focus on the woman's experience of pre-eclampsia, drawing on a wide range of case history reports submitted in response to our worldwide online survey.

References

1. Poon LC, Kametas NA, Chelemen T, Leal A, Nicolaides KH. Maternal risk factors for hypertensive disorders in pregnancy: a multivariate approach. J Hum Hypertens. 2010 Feb;24(2):104-10

2. Henderson JT, Whitlock EP, O'Conner E, Senger CA, Thompson JH, Rowland MG. Low-Dose Aspirin for the Prevention of Morbidity and Mortality From Pre-eclampsia: A Systematic Evidence Review for the U.S. Preventive Services Task Force [Internet]. Rockville (MD): Agency for Healthcare Research and Quality (US); 2014 Apr

3. Roberge S, Nicolaides KH, Demers S, Villa P, Bujold E. Prevention of perinatal death and adverse perinatal outcome using low-dose aspirin: a meta-analysis. Ultrasound Obstet Gynecol. 2013 May;41(5):491-9

4. Hofmeyr GJ, Lawrie TA, Atallah AN, Duley L, Torloni MR. Calcium supplementation during pregnancy for preventing hypertensive disorders and related problems. Cochrane Database Syst Rev. 2014 Jun 24;(6):CD001059

CHAPTER 4: PRE-ECLAMPSIA – THE WOMAN'S EXPERIENCE

Pregnancy and childbirth are major events in a woman's life, and the memories are likely to stay with her for a long time, if not forever.

The truth of this perception is strikingly demonstrated by US research showing that birth stories written by women as long as 15-20 years after the event were remarkably similar to those they wrote soon after their babies were born *(1)*.

A woman who is pregnant for the first time enters completely unknown territory. And it is normal to have mixed emotions, whether or not the baby is planned. Pregnancy marks the beginning of huge and uncontrollable physical changes. It also starts the emotionally challenging journey to parenthood.

A healthy pregnancy can be stressful enough. But for a woman who experiences pre-eclampsia – particularly the severe kind – it can assume nightmare proportions.

- Her apparently normal pregnancy suddenly turns into a mysterious and frightening illness.
- She may be kept in hospital for days – or even weeks – without understanding what is going on.
- She might need to cope with a premature baby – maybe one too small and sick to survive.
- The trauma may stay with her for a long time after the birth.
- She will probably be very fearful about the next pregnancy.

In this chapter we look at how women experience pre-eclampsia, from the earliest signs to the baby's birth and beyond.

We consider not just the physical effects of the illness but its emotional impact on women, their partners and their families.

Since we hope that midwives and other birth attendants and healthcare providers as well as those affected by pre-eclampsia will read this book, we also look at what they can do to help women and families cope with the burden of pre-eclampsia. The sections headed 'What midwives can do' should be taken as applying also to other non-doctor health providers.

We illustrate our narrative with first-hand accounts from women affected by pre-eclampsia. These come from a number of sources, including our own online survey, which drew responses from many parts of the world.

To make it easier for readers to dip in and out of this chapter and focus on the aspects of most interest to them, the various section headings and the pages they begin on are summarised below:

What women expect when they're expecting

Many women have some worries during pregnancy – particularly about the changes to their bodies, the birth process and the health of their babies. How confident they feel will depend on many things, including their health, their family histories, their education, the influence of doctors and midwives and, of course, what they learn from the media and their peers.

But these days most women in the developed world expect to enjoy a normal pregnancy and a safe birth. And while they may accept that health professionals have a role to play, they also, quite naturally, expect some degree of control over what happens. This means having all the information they need, having access to the right care and being able to make decisions about treatment.

Some women have much higher expectations, wanting almost total control over the place, the timing and the manner of their babies' births.

Some are lucky enough to get most, if not all, of what they want. Others have to make compromises. But those who get pre-eclampsia may be left with no control at all.

Women are not prepared for pre-eclampsia

Although pre-eclampsia is far from rare *(see Chapter 1, page 6)*, it still seems to come as a big surprise to most women who get it.

A recent survey of members of Australian Action on Pre-eclampsia (AAPEC) found that more than three quarters had no knowledge of pre-eclampsia before they were diagnosed. The same was true of many of the respondents to our own online survey *(2)*.

'I had never heard the word in my life. I was even in a nursing program and when we went over [obstetrics] it was never discussed.'

Sandra, US

'I knew absolutely nothing. Everyone told me to be careful of gestational diabetes and I received literature on that condition from my doctor and the hospital. I am still appalled to this day at how little I knew about pre-eclampsia and its symptoms – and I hold a graduate law degree! Most of the women I worked with had never heard of it before either – until it happened to me.'

Mary, US

Others had received limited, often misleading information.

'I had been led to believe that it was more likely to be suffered by women who were overweight, over 35 or very young. I was not in any of those categories so didn't worry about it.'

Lesley, UK

'I had been told things I later learned were not very accurate; such as that mostly women of African descent were at risk and if you weren't part of that group you were virtually free of worry about pre-eclampsia. Also, it could only happen to overweight women. That was all I "knew" about it, so it's like saying I knew absolutely nothing.'

Jo, Canada

Are pregnancy handbooks to blame?

Some of our respondents complained of a dearth of information about pre-eclampsia in pregnancy handbooks.

> 'The only thing I knew about it was what I read in What to Expect When You're Expecting [Murkoff & Mazell, Workman Publishing] and that wasn't much. It wasn't until I saw an episode of the TV medical drama ER that I realized it was a serious, complicated and sometimes fatal disease.'
>
> Joyce, US

> 'All the pregnancy books led me to believe that only people with pre-existing problems like obesity and high blood pressure or smokers had problems like pre-eclampsia. You never think it can happen to you. They need to tell you it can be anyone. It can be you with no warning.'
>
> Corina, US

Is it fair to blame the pregnancy handbooks? It is true that they tend to focus more on the normal and positive aspects of pregnancy than on complications like pre-eclampsia.

But it is also true that some people turn a blind eye to risk, while others make assumptions about what they need to worry about and filter out any conflicting information.

As Corina, quoted earlier, explained:

> 'We are healthy, middle class young professionals with no reason to suspect "high-risk" would ever be part of our lives.'

Other respondents to our survey expressed similar sentiments.

> 'It was in the last chapter of What to Expect When You're Expecting and I chose not to read that chapter. Why drive myself crazy with worry since everything was going well.'
>
> Anon, US

> 'I pretty much just skimmed that section in baby books because I assumed it would never apply to me.'
>
> Christina, US

*'I knew what the symptoms were and that it was related to high
blood pressure and, if left untreated, could become eclampsia. But
I am a runner and an organic vegetarian so I just never thought it
would happen to me.'*

Rene, US

The role of antenatal classes

In theory antenatal classes (sometimes called parentcraft classes) offer
another opportunity for women to learn about pre-eclampsia and its risks,
but the evidence suggests that this doesn't normally happen.

A recent study of antenatal education in Sydney, Australia, concluded
that women attending classes are largely focused on coping with labour
and birth and may not be receptive to education on other issues, including
parenting.

Should health professionals focus more on risk?

Of rather more concern to our respondents – and to us as authors – is
the apparent reluctance of many health professionals to inform pregnant
women about the existence and risks of pre-eclampsia and the signs and
symptoms to look out for.

*'I had never heard of it when I was filling out the forms about pre-
existing conditions when I first found out I was pregnant. I remember
having to ask the nurse what it was. I believe she said if I didn't
know then I hadn't had it, but it is when you deliver early. That was
all I was told! I can't believe I wasn't more informed about it.'*

Allison, US

It may well be the case that health professionals don't want to alarm the
large majority of pregnant women who are *not* destined to get pre-eclampsia.

*'I was told by one nurse we don't talk about it as we don't want to
frighten pregnant women.'*

Louise, UK

But the risks of making pregnant women anxious are surely outweighed
by the perils of ignorance, as our respondents were quick to point out, and
as confirmed by research studies.

'Although it might worry some women, telling them about the importance of antenatal checks, why they are done and the consequences of missing them would be valuable. I nearly didn't go to my last check because all the others had been fine, I felt well and it was an effort to travel the 25 miles to the hospital. I only realised later that it could have been so serious if I hadn't gone as my husband was away and possibly no one would have known if I'd fallen ill.'

Lesley, UK

'Pre-eclampsia and HELLP syndrome should be discussed during prenatal visits, at hospital baby care classes and information should go home post-delivery since PE or HELLP could still hit at that stage. You can't scare people to death – and being better informed is key to a quicker diagnosis.'

Johanna, US

'Education is so important. It can be done in a non-alarmist way. I fell through the gaps and nearly died. So the traditional prenatal appointment structure can fail to detect pre-eclampsia, with disastrous consequences. I hold no grudges; I just think if I'd known about pre-eclampsia I'd have picked up the symptoms earlier rather than ignoring them.'

Katharine, Australia

A tendency to play down risk

Heather (UK) made a more general point about the prevailing trend to emphasise normality rather than risk in pregnancy.

'I feel there is too much window-dressing in pregnancy. We are told how "natural" it is and that it is not an illness. There is a tendency to play down the complications and risks. I also wonder if the "natural childbirth" message is also reflected in midwifery training and whether warning signs of complications are not highlighted sufficiently.'

What midwives can do

- Carefully assess risk factors for pre-eclampsia – including health status, personal and family history – at the first antenatal visit.

- Refer women with risk factors to a specialist as early as possible. It is important to make sure that those who might benefit from preventive treatment with aspirin and/or calcium are reviewed early, ideally in the first trimester.
- Be sure to document care plans at the time of the obstetric review and make sure women understand the various roles and responsibilities involved.
- Use blood pressure and urine tests as an opportunity to educate women about the existence, risks, signs and symptoms of pre-eclampsia. Some women may feel able to test their own urine, but you retain responsibility for teaching them how to do it properly and for checking the results. The colour difference between a trace and a plus on the stick may be slight but the significance is considerable! Women who detect positive results need rapid access to competent advice.
- Document all findings and discussions you have with women.
- Hand out literature about pre-eclampsia if it is available, but always back this up with spoken explanations, and check that you have been understood. There is so much information to take in during pregnancy that it is a good idea to revisit this topic more than once. Patient organisations almost invariably have materials available for healthcare providers to use with their patients.
- Encourage women to report possible signs and symptoms of pre-eclampsia, however vague, and make sure they have clear instructions about how – and with whom – to make contact if they have any concerns between antenatal visits. Make it clear that contact is acceptable *at any time*, however seemingly inconvenient.
- When women do report signs and symptoms, always follow up with a visit rather than trying to make an assessment over the phone. Always complete blood pressure and urine checks and act on abnormal results.
- If there are real grounds for concern, be honest. False reassurance helps nobody, and there is no point trying to normalise the abnormal to avoid worrying women and their families.

The lead-up to diagnosis

As explained in chapter 2 *(pp 21-25)*, poor development of the placenta is a factor in many cases of severe pre-eclampsia, particularly those starting before 34 weeks. The typical signs of pre-eclampsia – hypertension and proteinuria – appear at a later stage. And symptoms of illness come later still.

But pre-eclampsia is a highly variable, unpredictable disease and each woman experiences it in her own unique way.

The disease can 'show' itself in various ways, some obvious but others confusing. The 'classic' warning signs of hypertension and proteinuria may appear in an unusual order or at the same time as symptoms of illness.

The symptoms themselves may get steadily worse; or they may come and go; or they may arrive suddenly with frightening severity.

A 'classic' case

Evelyn (New Zealand) showed fairly typical warning signs, which were detected at a routine antenatal appointment.

> *'It was around my 28th week when my midwife picked up that my blood pressure had risen slightly and referred me to an obstetrician. He explained about pre-eclampsia but didn't say I would necessarily get it. So they just kept an eye on me and then a month later I was referred back to him when my blood pressure had gone up further and I also had 1+ of protein in my urine.'*

Evelyn was lucky. Because the first warning sign was detected by a midwife before she was really unwell, she had time to adjust to the possibility of pre-eclampsia; and her caregivers had time to watch and wait, knowing they would probably need to intervene at some later stage.

But other cases unfold in less predictable ways and at less convenient times. This can confuse women, midwives and doctors, leading to potentially dangerous delays in diagnosis.

The dangers of ignorance

As the respondents to our survey suggested earlier in this chapter, the greatest risk posed by ignorance of pre-eclampsia is that women will fail to spot warning signs and symptoms that appear between antenatal visits.

This is a particular problem for first-time mothers-to-be, who may find it very difficult to tell the difference between normal discomforts of pregnancy and those that warn of pre-eclampsia.

'I had started to look bloated. I hadn't picked up on it, but other people did. My sister passed me in her car the day before I was diagnosed. I was so puffed up she hadn't recognised me. I had noticed that my ankles were very swollen, but thought nothing of it. Who would? Swollen ankles are one of the big pregnancy clichés! I felt well otherwise.'

Fiona, UK

'I did feel the baby wasn't moving as much as it should. Of course, it being a first pregnancy, I had no way of knowing what normal movement was like.'

Jo, Canada

'At exactly 37 weeks I started having some pain in my chest. I thought it was the baby pushing on my ribs. There were 2-3 episodes of dizziness and "seeing stars" that I had blamed on dehydration, but I now wonder if those might also have been signs of pre-eclampsia.'

Katherine, US

When warning signs are vague

Swelling, reduced fetal movements, chest or 'epigastric' pain, vomiting, visual disturbances – these are all established signs and symptoms of pre-eclampsia that well-informed women might be able to recognise. But some women just feel generally unwell.

'I felt horrible – as if I was catching a cold or 'flu. My body ached, I couldn't sleep at all or get comfortable. My neck hurt and I looked puffy. I had no appetite and it was difficult for me to eat or drink anything.'

Sally, Germany

'I had a bunch of weird stuff that is not on the official symptoms list. I had tingly extremities that became worse and worse. I just never felt great. I gained more weight than someone with my age, fitness level and diet should have but the swelling and water weight didn't really show as obvious.'

Amy, US

'All of a sudden I became impossibly, inconceivably tired. That's not even the right word. After waking up, it would take me half an hour to get up the energy to swing my legs over the side of the bed.'

Michelle, US

In such cases it is all too easy for women to slip through the antenatal safety net – with potentially dangerous consequences.

Symptoms before signs

In the textbook version of pre-eclampsia, women experience *signs,* like hypertension, proteinuria and oedema, before they start to feel unwell with *symptoms* like epigastric pain and headache.

But sometimes things happen the other way around, and this can obscure the correct diagnosis.

Sarah (New Zealand) had a high risk of developing pre-eclampsia in her first pregnancy, with twins. Her mother had a history of the illness, and she herself had already developed pregnancy diabetes, which is known to increase the risk of pre-eclampsia.

At 32 weeks she was investigated for abdominal pains and vague feelings of illness; but she was sent home when all the tests results were normal.

'Everything was perfectly normal until about 32 weeks, when I developed some right upper abdominal pain. It was so bad at one stage that I rang the on-call obstetrician and went into the assessment unit. I had also had some vomiting and diarrhoea and felt generally unwell and hot. They did tests for listeria and some liver function blood tests but the results came back normal. They suggested the pain could have been caused by one of the babies kicking me, or maybe a gallstone. They said I should have my liver scanned during the next ultrasound examination.

'Over the next two weeks the pain got worse and definitely felt like liver pain. It was right under my ribs, almost like my ribs were being squashed in, and it was quite uncomfortable especially at night. I didn't have any swelling except a little in my fingers, but I did have a slight headache at times.'

Two weeks later Sarah was diagnosed with HELLP syndrome, the combined liver and blood clotting disorder that is a serious complication of pre-eclampsia *(see Chapter 2, page 26)*. She had continued to feel unwell after her first assessment; but she had no idea that she was developing pre-eclampsia since her blood pressure was normal and there was no protein in her urine. Luckily, Sarah was already in hospital for assessment of fetal growth when her condition became serious.

> 'At 34 weeks I was admitted to hospital so that a series of Doppler studies could be done for one of my babies, who seemed not to be growing as well as the other. But while I was waiting for my scan, one of the doctors came rushing down with my blood test result and said I would have to be delivered immediately!'

Normal blood pressure can conceal pre-eclampsia

Sarah was admitted because of suspected poor growth in one of her babies – a common sign of pre-eclampsia. Although she had neither of the classic maternal signs of pre-eclampsia, the underlying disease was getting steadily worse.

Because high blood pressure, in particular, is closely linked with pre-eclampsia, a normal blood pressure may conceal the illness and give women and their caregivers false reassurance.

The fact is, though, that blood pressure may not rise until quite a late stage in the disease; and supposedly 'late' symptoms like abdominal or 'epigastric' pain can come first.

The varying nature of 'epigastric' pain

The upper abdominal or 'epigastric' pain that signals liver problems in pre-eclampsia *(see Chapter 2, page 19)* can take a variety of forms. Because the liver is large, lying just under the abdomen and extending through to the back of it, pain from the liver can be felt in the back, or on breathing (as the diaphragm moves), or even in the neck or shoulder, as well as in the front (typical epigastric pain). The pain experienced by Nadia (New Zealand) was far from typical.

> 'I just had a bit of pain in my chest, but only when I breathed in. It kept going during the day, while I was at work, so that evening

I rang the midwife who thought it was probably the baby kicking my ribs. That evening the pain just disappeared, but I took the next day off work because I was feeling tired. Then in the middle of the night I got this back pain between my shoulder blades, which didn't go away. In the morning I rang the midwife again and she had me admitted. Up to then I'd had a little swelling in my ankles and hands but nothing major, and my blood pressure was pretty OK.'

Nadia's was not the classic epigastric pain of severe pre-eclampsia and she was reassured when it went away the next day. In fact, Nadia was starting to feel that she didn't need to be in hospital at all when she was diagnosed with HELLP syndrome.

'They did the blood tests and everything was fine! I remember the consultant said it was probably gallstones or something like that. By early afternoon the pain had gone and I thought, "What am I doing here?" I had more blood tests just to double-check before going home. The results showed my platelet levels were incredibly low. They had been low earlier but nothing to be really concerned about – that was how fast things developed. I was feeling better than I had in the morning. I was saying, "Are you sure this is right"?'

Nadia's story shows just how rapidly the underlying disease, as shown in blood test results, can deteriorate in pre-eclampsia – even in the absence of pain or other symptoms.

Liver pain in the back

As explained above, some women feel liver pain in the back rather than the upper abdomen. Lynda (New Zealand) first felt the pain between her shoulder blades, but later in hospital it became more severe and moved up to her head.

'The pain was between my shoulders and up to my head. It was just like a force, like something was pushing really hard. I tried to stay as still as I could but it was very uncomfortable. If I took Panadol it took the edge off it, but I felt restless because I couldn't get comfortable.'

Pain on breathing

When women do not have the classic epigastric pain, their pre-eclampsia may remain hidden, particularly if they don't have hypertension. Like Nadia, Kate (New Zealand) also experienced pain on breathing, which she didn't recognize as epigastric.

> 'I started getting some epigastric pain but I didn't realize that was what it was. It just hurt to breathe. I found it really uncomfortable and was really quite worried about dying in my sleep or not being able to breathe. I wouldn't have buzzed the nurse about that, but I would have been silently scared about it.'

One reason Kate was reluctant to call for further help was that she had already mentioned her chest pain to a nurse, who hadn't realised it was significant.

Like many women, Kate was torn between worry about her symptoms and fear of being thought 'paranoid' by staff. In this case the problem was compounded by ignorance about the various forms of epigastric pain.

Since pain does not come with a label to help with diagnosis, women have to rely on their own interpretations, but may have very little experience to base them on. Experiencing epigastric pain and recognising it for what it is are two very different things.

A late and unexpected case

Pre-eclampsia and even eclampsia can develop without the classical warning signs of either hypertension or proteinuria. This most often happens after delivery. Leigh (New Zealand) became seriously ill after giving birth to her second baby, having shown none of the classic antenatal signs of pre-eclampsia.

> 'After a seemingly normal second pregnancy my daughter Lexi was delivered in the early hours of the morning, in perfect health. A few hours later I was able to walk out of the hospital into the postnatal unit, feeling pretty good considering I had just given birth.'

But this feeling of wellbeing was to be short-lived.

*'In the late afternoon, as I got off the bed to take some photos of
daddy and his two wee girls I was struck by an incredibly intense and
persistent headache. I remember thinking, for some reason, "Is this the
only photo I'm going to get to take of my two wee girls?"'*

By this point Leigh's blood pressure had risen to 169/96 from the normal
reading of 110/72 recorded after the birth. Leigh told the staff she had
seen 'flashing lights' before her eyes and they explained she could have
pre-eclampsia.

In fact tests showed that she had HELLP syndrome. Her blood pressure
rose still further and she had distressing chest pain, breathing difficulty and
vomiting. She needed medication to bring down her blood pressure and a
magnesium sulphate infusion to ward off fits (seizures). In all, she needed
four days of intensive care, when she couldn't take care of her baby.

Yet her pregnancy had seemed normal, with no blood pressure problems
and only a trace of proteinuria found at 38 weeks.

However, Leigh did have risk factors for pre-eclampsia. Her mother
had had pre-eclampsia in both her pregnancies; Leigh's first baby had been
small for her gestational age; and baby Lexi's birth weight was very much
lower than expected.

The link between slow growth in babies – fetal growth restriction *(FGR)*
– and pre-eclampsia is well known. Growth restriction in pregnancy can be
a sign that pre-eclampsia is developing. Equally, a low weight at birth may,
rarely, mean that a woman is about to get postnatal pre-eclampsia, even if
the pregnancy has appeared to be normal.

When health professionals get it wrong

As we have seen, the variable, unpredictable nature of pre-eclampsia can
make it difficult for doctors and midwives, let alone pregnant women, to
recognise the signs and symptoms. Additionally the severe manifestations
of the disease are now so rare that many health professionals have little or
no experience of them.

Nevertheless some health professionals manage to overlook signs and
symptoms that are staring them in the face.

Lynda (New Zealand), mentioned earlier, had experienced pre-eclampsia
in her first two pregnancies, and telephoned her midwife when she had
'flu-like symptoms and backache in her third.

'She said it was just a virus, so I went back to bed, and the next day I felt OK.'

When the pain returned, Lynda consulted her GP.

'I went to the doctor crying, thinking it must be a kidney infection after looking through my books. The doctor took my blood pressure and told me it was high.'

Lynda also had three plusses of protein on dipstick urine test, but was treated with antibiotics for a presumed urinary infection. The GP asked Lynda to see her midwife in three days to have her blood pressure checked, by which time she was becoming seriously unwell with HELLP syndrome and was admitted to hospital urgently.

Sadly, she grew rapidly worse and needed an emergency caesarean. Nine days later, her baby died from complications of prematurity.

Lynda's story shows up three key pitfalls in detecting and diagnosing pre-eclampsia:

- It is risky to make a diagnosis over the phone, as the midwife did in this case.
- Pre-eclampsia can be confused with other conditions, in this case a urinary infection.
- The illness can progress very rapidly, and leaving someone unsupervised for a few days can be extremely dangerous.

Delayed diagnosis

A number of respondents to our survey complained of delays in diagnosis that had left them vulnerable to dangerous complications.

Andrea (UK) told a horrific story of failure to diagnose pre-eclampsia despite raised blood pressure, headaches, oedema and blurred vision.

'My midwife was concerned about me from 34 weeks and had sent me to the antenatal clinic at the hospital on a couple of occasions, but each time they sent me home. She then came to see me over the bank holiday as she was so worried, and immediately insisted I went into hospital. Once I arrived at hospital it all happened very quickly.

My blood pressure was very high. They tried to induce me and then I had an eclamptic fit and the baby had to be delivered by emergency caesarean.

'I had intensive care treatment after the birth. The doctors thought I was going to go into cardiac arrest that first night: I had too much potassium in my blood and my kidneys were not functioning properly. After being moved to the ward after four days, I was still not very well and ended up back in the delivery suite. Even after I left hospital they were concerned that my kidneys might be damaged, and I had to attend the liver unit as an outpatient and was on medication for my blood pressure for six months.

'I will always remember that the doctor I saw on one of the occasions that I was sent to the antenatal unit actually wrote on my notes "no sign of pre-eclampsia"! Perhaps if they had done further checks and not just sent me home to take a couple of paracetamol, I might not have got so poorly. It is only thanks to my midwife that I'm here today to tell the story.'

Others responded to our survey with similarly distressing stories.

'I was diagnosed just hours before our daughter was born after several wrong diagnoses from GP/midwives, even though I had most symptoms, including swelling in the face, hands and feet, abdominal pain and headaches. When I went to my GP with all my symptoms, including very high blood pressure and protein in the urine, I got sent home with a bottle of [antacid medicine for heartburn].'

Melissa, UK

'I was swollen in my second and third trimester and had high blood pressure on a couple of visits. I was told by my doctors that this was normal because it was summer and hot. Being young and in my first pregnancy I trusted what doctors told me. By the time I found out it was pre-eclampsia it was too late and my son was stillborn.'

Heather, US

'I was diagnosed at 24-25 weeks' gestation. I had visited triage at

around 23 weeks with intense migraine. BP was taken and was
220/100 but the machine was blamed as faulty and I was sent home.'

Gail, UK

Kerry (UK), who had an eclamptic fit during labour, blamed her very late diagnosis on poor continuity of care.

'*I had all the classic symptoms of pre-eclampsia from about 28 weeks.*
There was no continuity of care and so each time the symptoms
got worse they were missed. At 39 weeks I could no longer bend my
fingers, I had protein in my urine, my blood pressure was high and I
was having visual disturbances. It was then that pre-eclampsia was
diagnosed.'

Failure to listen

Many respondents to our survey, who were convinced something was wrong, complained that doctors and other health professionals had failed to listen to them.

Meghan (US) found her concerns overlooked and her symptoms ignored, with terrible consequences. This was despite the fact that, as a paediatric nurse practitioner working in the family birthing and neonatal intensive care units, she knew quite a lot about pre-eclampsia.

'*I knew about sudden weight gain, hypertension, proteinuria,*
visual changes, headache and the risk to the life of the mother and
child, but it did no good because reports of my signs and symptoms
were ignored or just not recognised when I told my providers about
them.

'*I was officially diagnosed at 35.5 weeks after I took my complaints*
to the nurse practitioner in an urgent visit. However, I should have
been diagnosed at 26 weeks, when I was hypertensive, had overnight
weight gains of four pounds, had a headache and visual changes and
a 24-hour urine protein level that was 533mg (diagnostic being more
than 300mg/24hours).

"*My daughter was born at 36.5 weeks after a 51-hour induction.*
She has a gross motor and expressive language delay. From delivery

complications (I ruptured my whole cervix and into my lower uterine segment) I am unable to confidently and safely have another child. I continued with hypertension for a year afterwards and I have memory loss (both of the delivery and other events throughout my life). Emotionally the complications will continue the rest of my life.'

The consequences of failure to listen were also highlighted by a number of other respondents to our survey.

'I had terrible swelling in my hands, feet and face, my BP was extremely high and I had ++++ protein in my urine. But doctors kept shrugging me off and it took what felt like weeks to actually diagnose the condition. It had turned into eclampsia before the doctors did anything. I had two fits on the ward of the hospital and I and my unborn child nearly died. Afterwards they found my placenta completely covered in blood clots. They should have listened to me from the start. I was not crying wolf and something was clearly wrong.'

Michaela, UK

'I was found to have high BP at 33 weeks during a routine visit. After that I had off-and-on pain in the abdomen, nausea and vomiting, but my [obstetrician] dismissed these symptoms as related to the position of the baby and the stress of being on my feet too long during the day. Pre-eclampsia was eventually diagnosed at 35 weeks after I insisted they see me at labour and delivery ER. I ended up with Class 1 HELLP.

'Afterwards I was mad that no one at my [obstetrician's] office listened to me when I was clearly having worsening symptoms and had already been diagnosed with high BP. The only symptoms they were looking out for were headache or vision changes and I had neither of those.'

Anon, US

'I was told by my consultant that I had "white coat syndrome". This made me feel that I was to blame for my blood pressure being so high.

The consultant told me this two days before my baby was delivered at 34 weeks, when my mother was pleading with her to admit me to hospital.'

Mhairi, UK

Sometimes health professionals fail to listen to each other. Mignon (Ireland) described how her GP diagnosed pre-eclampsia at 32 weeks but her specialist was 'in denial'.

'I had severe swelling in my face, hands, legs – everywhere. I was breathless with a feeling like fluid on the lungs. I was absolutely exhausted all the time; I had blurred vision in the mornings and I had pressure and discomfort like heartburn under my ribs.

'My GP referred me to the hospital on two occasions but [the obstetric department] kept discharging me. I admitted myself a few times too but was sent home. Our baby boy was stillborn at 37 weeks. A postmortem showed he was perfect. He died because of pre-eclampsia.'

Even a history of pre-eclampsia is no guarantee of better care second time around, as Emma (UK), whose baby was stillborn, discovered to her cost.

'I was diagnosed at 26+ weeks but I had been complaining of various symptoms for at least three weeks. My baby had suffered from severe [growth restriction], which wasn't picked up on my growth scan or was ignored. I wasn't listened to when I told of my symptoms and was told I was over-anxious because I had had a previous loss at 22 weeks. Even when I told them my baby never moved they didn't listen. If someone had listened to me then my baby could at least have had a chance at life.'

What midwives can do

The hope is that a predictive test for pre-eclampsia will eventually be available, giving advance warning to women and their caregivers and ensuring closer monitoring for those at risk.

In the meantime, though, midwives and other health professionals need a better understanding of the full range of signs and symptoms that can warn of pre-eclampsia. And they need to keep at-risk women under close surveillance, even when symptoms come and go.

- Remember that pre-eclampsia is the 'disease of exceptions' and that signs and symptoms can come in any order. Waiting for the blood pressure to reach 140/90, or for proteinuria to appear, can introduce a dangerous delay.
- Vague symptoms like nausea and vomiting can be as significant as headache and epigastric pain; always listen to women – they usually know when 'something's not right'.
- Carry out prompt assessment when contacted by women with potential signs and symptoms, and refer them according to local guidelines.
- Follow up on laboratory test results and ultrasound scans on the day they are ordered. Make sure you discuss abnormal results with an expert on pre-eclampsia, and refer the woman to hospital for urgent review if indicated. Waiting until the next day can sometimes be too late!
- Don't drop your guard if laboratory results appear normal, particularly if there are symptoms. Things can change rapidly and supposedly 'mild' pre-eclampsia can explode within hours into severe disease. Request a repeat test if your clinical judgment suggests the woman really is unwell.
- Don't be falsely reassured when symptoms appear to go away.
- Keep up to date with clinical research on pre-eclampsia, and always err on the side of caution.
- Remember that fetal growth restriction can be an early sign of pre-eclampsia.

Monitoring, birth and after

Some women with early signs of pre-eclampsia, such as slightly raised blood pressure or a small amount of proteinuria, can be monitored on an outpatient basis, for example at home, in the community or in day assessment units.

However, pre-eclampsia is an illness that almost *always* gets worse, and admission is inevitable at some point. Some women are in and out of hospital before delivery but others need to stay in hospital until their babies are born. And women with severe disease usually need that to happen sooner rather than later.

The main reason for admission before the birth is to closely monitor the condition of mother and baby, as described in more detail in Chapter 6 (*page 127*), and make sure the baby is delivered before either gets into serious difficulty.

The problem is that most women feel perfectly well at the time pre-eclampsia is diagnosed and don't understand why they need to go to hospital at all, let alone stay there.

> '*I had no idea my son or I were in any kind of danger. I couldn't understand why everyone was so concerned and stressed out and I kept telling everyone, "My baby and I are going to be OK".*'
>
> Michelle, US

The shock of diagnosis

In the last few weeks of pregnancy, women tend to focus on preparing for birth and meeting the new baby. A diagnosis of pre-eclampsia cuts right across their hopes and dreams of motherhood, and there may be little time to adjust to the new reality. Most women find this very challenging and frightening, particularly if the diagnosis comes many weeks before the due date.

Katie (UK), who was admitted at 33 weeks, and delivered a week later, had this to say:

> '*I felt completely overwhelmed by the whole situation of being ill in hospital with a condition I didn't really understand. I unfortunately had a pretty traumatic birth (failed epidural and forceps delivery), which didn't help, and had nightmares about it afterwards. For the first few days after birth I was really worried that my BP was not under control and that I was still at risk of fitting or stroke.*'
>
> '*I was moved between the [high dependency unit] and postnatal ward a few times and found it really difficult to fit in with the routine of being in hospital and managing my worry about my health; but also worrying about our son in the neonatal unit and finding time (in amongst the routine of seeing doctors, being given medication, having set meal times, enforced rest) to be with him whilst he was ill.*'

Looking back it was only a few months after it all that I realised just how stressful, worrying and overwhelming the whole situation was.'

The need for information and support

In this kind of situation, women need realistic information, support and, where possible, reassurance from the health professionals looking after them.

'It is hard to describe the feeling of helplessness during hospital bed rest. Providing women with more information about pre-eclampsia could go a long way towards combatting the feeling of being powerless. Our culture builds up this picture of a perfect pregnancy, and I think there is a mourning period from not having had that experience, but with pre-eclampsia it goes beyond that. I was terrified knowing that my body was causing danger to my son, and I feel I would have benefitted from more communication and information about the disease during my time in hospital.'

Emily, US

A few respondents to our survey felt they had received excellent information and support, combined with the best care.

'I had some amazing doctors at the larger hospital I was in for two weeks. They kept me very informed about what was going on with me and what the plan of attack would be if anything were to change. So I was very prepared that my baby was going to more than likely be delivered early. They were concerned about both me and my baby and knew where the fine line was between letting her stay in longer and judging when it was too dangerous for me.'

Lindsay, US

But for many of our respondents, poor communication about their illness was the most distressing aspect of their time in hospital.

'It disgusted me that the nurses didn't even know what pre-eclampsia was – and they were [obstetric] nurses! My doctors gave me very very minimal information about what was going on with my body. Nobody told me about pre-eclampsia or HELLP syndrome. I was totally in the dark.'

Kayla, US

*'The doctors and nurses seemed too busy to explain and didn't care
that I was bewildered – they just wanted me to do as I was told,
submit to unexplained tests and not to question anything; but I
needed more information in order to understand what was happening
and to feel that I was a participant in the fight against this disease –
not just a victim.'*

Laura, Canada

*'I was in hospital for four weeks before delivery and was given no
information about pre-eclampsia – I did all my own research via the
internet. I never once was able to see a consultant, always fobbed off
with [junior doctors].'*

Julia, UK

Side effects of treatment

Others were distressed by the side effects of treatment, particularly the
magnesium sulphate given to prevent eclamptic fits.

*'Magnesium sulphate was the worst part of the whole experience.
That drug does not make you feel very good at all. I was on it for
a total of 11 days and I was bedridden for at least eight of those.
Let me put it this way: there are seven and a half years between my
pregnancies, and the traumatic experience of my first pregnancy is
the reason I waited so long.'*

Allison, US

The stress of waiting

In hospital there is nothing much for women to do but wait and worry; and
this can be very stressful. Research on the experiences of women admitted
to hospital for pregnancy complications has shown that fear, anxiety, anger,
frustration, loneliness and uncertainty are very common.

*'Emotionally I was affected by the fact that I was in hospital for
such a long time – nearly a month – and there wasn't anyone else
there who had been in my position, and no one to counsel me. It was
horrible being on a ward where all the other women had either had a
perfect birth or had just lost their babies. I was stuck in a limbo, not
knowing whether my baby would be okay or not but aware that she*

*would be pre-term. It gets very lonely and worrying spending that
much time in hospital.'*

Jade, UK

Fears for the baby

Women diagnosed with pre-eclampsia are often more concerned for their
babies than themselves, as Kate (New Zealand) made clear:

> *'I was terrified about how Lilly was doing. I can remember lying
> there counting the kicks, especially the night before I had her. I was
> probably a lot more worried about her than me, because you don't
> realise how sick you are.'*

Checking on the baby's condition is part of the monitoring process,
but watching it can be stressful in itself, as Evelyn (New Zealand) found.

> *'I found it very stressful watching Grace's heartbeat on the monitor.
> They would have me on the monitor for 45-50 minutes and I would
> just lie there worrying.'*

Just as hard for Evelyn was being asked to monitor her baby's movements:

> *'They would ask me questions about her movements, but I didn't know
> what was normal – in your first pregnancy everything is so new. I
> started feeling movements at 18 weeks and so I sort of measured
> everything against that. To me that seemed normal, but I kept being told
> there should be a bigger range of movements and that was really hard.'*

When things happen really fast

For some women, though, things move so fast that there is no time to grasp
what is happening, let alone worry about it. For Victoria (New Zealand)
who, at 31 weeks, had just 24 hours from diagnosis to emergency delivery,
there was no time to make sense of the new reality:

> *'Everything just kind of happened; there was no build-up, no time to
> think how I was going to deal with this premature baby, no time even
> to worry about my own health.'*

The problem of denial

Some women underestimate how serious things are and even go into denial, as Lynda (New Zealand), admitted at 24 weeks, made clear:

> 'When I was admitted I felt all right, quite relaxed actually. I was worried about my baby because I knew how small he was, but because the other pregnancies had gone on further I thought I might be in there for a few weeks. Also the specialist had said to me on Friday morning that it looked like it was going OK, so she'd probably send me home for the weekend.

> 'I didn't have the flashing lights; they asked me that a million times. I got dizzy, but I think that was because of some of the medication. I didn't want to tell them. I just answered questions. If I didn't have the symptoms they mentioned I didn't have the pre-eclampsia did I?'

Tragically, though, Lynda needed an emergency delivery of a baby too premature to survive only hours after she had been told she might be able to go home for the weekend.

Loss of the dream pregnancy

Women and their partners may feel a strong sense of loss as they contemplate a caesarean delivery or induction instead of the spontaneous natural birth they were expecting. Nadia (New Zealand), who had a caesarean because of HELLP syndrome, felt this very keenly:

> 'All my dreams about a full term natural birth and a lovely healthy baby went out of the window. A woman is supposed to be able to carry a baby for 40 weeks with no problems and then go into labour. But I never got to know what a labour pain was and I guess I felt robbed.'

Kate (New Zealand), who gave birth at 29 weeks, also felt she had missed something vitally important.

> 'I was quite resentful of women having the whole pregnancy. My friends were all pregnant at the same time so I was really aware of

the fact that I never really got big like them. It was really upsetting for me not to have a big tummy or to feel really pregnant.'

Andriana (US) expressed her resentment in even stronger terms:

'I felt cheated that I didn't get to fully experience the joys of being pregnant. I would hear mothers-to-be complaining about being "huge" and I would get jealous and angry. At least you ARE huge – that's a great thing. I am hoping that when I have another pregnancy I will be able to get the chance to be huge.'

Feelings of guilt and failure

Many struggle with feelings of guilt and failure. Evelyn (New Zealand) felt her body had let her baby down.

'I felt like a failure because my body hadn't been able to perform as it should and give my baby the best start in life.'

This reaction was echoed by many respondents to our survey.

'You feel useless. Your job being pregnant is to keep your baby healthy and growing inside you. When you are diagnosed with pre-eclampsia you fail both jobs.'

Brenda, Spain

'Not having the energy to see my baby in [the neonatal intensive care unit] was crushing. I felt so guilty for putting my baby through so much, guilty for not being able to visit as much as I wanted to because I felt so ill, guilty for not being able to produce enough milk due to the meds I was on.'

Siofra, Ireland

'I knew it wasn't my fault but I still felt like it was since I couldn't carry her to full term. She was fine in the uterus, it was me having the health problems, so it's kind of hard not to blame yourself. I think I told her "I'm sorry" a million times.'

Kerri, US

For some women the sense of failure was exacerbated by insensitive and ill-informed comments from health professionals.

'Whenever the techs came by to take my blood pressure, a few of
them kept telling me I "need to relax" as it if were my fault; this
really added to my guilt over having my daughter early. The doctors
and nurses were excellent, but it would have helped if others involved
in care were a little more informed so as not to add insult to injury.'

Monika, US

The long road to recovery

Severe pre-eclampsia can lead to life-threatening problems with various
organs, including the liver, kidneys, lungs and blood clotting system. These
problems are normally reversed after the birth, but women still need time
to recover; and recovery can be a long and complicated business if you've
also had a caesarean section and a premature baby, as Kate (New Zealand)
describes:

'I remember going in to see Lilly in a wheelchair and the nurse
telling me off because I shouldn't need a wheelchair two days after a
caesarean. At the time I thought maybe I should have recovered faster.
But when I think back and look at the photos, I was obviously feeling
awful and had so much fluid on me. I was obviously not well, but you
don't think about that; you just think you've had the baby, they've
taken the problem away, and you should be fine. And anyway I was
so worried about Lilly that my own health didn't really feature.'

Women are usually encouraged to walk as soon as possible after surgery,
but the needs of women like Kate are clearly different from those of
women who have been well before a caesarean section. The difficulties of
establishing lactation can add to the trauma, as she points out:

'During that time I was expressing milk, and I think this must be
hell for a lot of women who have early babies. Your baby is critically
ill, you're not feeling 100 per cent, but you have to express milk every
three hours for at least half an hour, so you have this unbelievably
broken sleep.

'By the time I'd lived with that for 5-6 weeks, I was losing it big time.
I saw one of the mental health workers and got assessed for postnatal

depression. In fact I didn't have it: she just said that I was behaving completely normally, given the circumstances.'

Melissa (US), who had pre-eclampsia in both her pregnancies, told a similar story.

'After my second baby was delivered I was better emotionally but was exhausted and had severely high BP. Caring for a newborn and caring for my own medical problems was exhausting, confusing and stressful.'

The need for extra support

It seems reasonable to assume that women who have been through a serious illness and may also be coping with a sick or premature baby would be offered additional support.

Fiona (UK), whose baby was delivered by emergency caesarean at 32 weeks, was well satisfied in this respect.

'The care I received was absolutely first class. I was so well looked after and treated with such care and compassion. The neonatal staff were just lovely – I was welcome down there any time of the day or night.'

But others were less fortunate.

'Once I went onto the postnatal ward, care was appalling. I was surrounded by other people's babies and felt thoroughly ignored as my baby was in the [neonatal unit]. After I had been on the ward several days a midwife came and told me that they were discharging me as I had reached my quota of days on the ward. When I got home the health visitor was useless and thoroughly unsupportive – she virtually had me in tears every visit.'

Claire, UK

'I feel like my health professionals really dropped the ball post-delivery. I was sent home like nothing ever happened. I had a premature baby and a history of pre-eclampsia and was just told to "get enough sleep".'

Jodi, US

Longer-term problems

While blood pressure and blood test results usually return to normal within a month or two of the birth, full recovery may take a lot longer. One research study found that after severe pre-eclampsia women were much more likely to complain of ill health in the weeks and months after their babies were born than those who had enjoyed normal pregnancies. The problems they reported included headache, upper abdominal pain, visual disturbances, tiredness, loss of concentration and mental health problems; and these symptoms generally lasted substantially longer than six months.

What midwives can do

Midwives and other birth attendants, such as doulas, are very well placed to help women come to terms with the impact of pre-eclampsia both before and after the birth.

- Before delivery, take time to listen to women's concerns, hopes and fears. Try to help them come to terms with the diagnosis and fill in the gaps in their knowledge and understanding.
- Be sensitive to the impact of pre-eclampsia on postnatal recovery, particularly if it was compounded by surgery. Most women find the postnatal period very tiring after a normal pregnancy, but the exhaustion caused by the physical and emotional stress of pre-eclampsia can be overwhelming.
- When you feel the time is right, provide information about support groups and assess the need for professional counselling. The real impact of pre-eclampsia may not be apparent until some time after discharge from midwifery care, so it is important for women to know how to access later support if they need it.
- Discuss diet and lifestyle strategies to aid recovery and safeguard future health. At first women need extra rest and should be encouraged to seek extra support from family and friends.
- Make sure the GP (or other health professional responsible for ongoing care) is aware of the extent of the woman's illness and the need for additional support and follow-up. Also be sure to highlight her added long-term risk for diabetes and arterial disease and the consequent need for appropriate regular expert supervision.

- Make women aware of the availability and importance of specialist assessment before the next pregnancy and the need to 'book' early for antenatal care.

The emotional legacy of pre-eclampsia

For most women affected by pre-eclampsia, the emotional and psychological scars persist much longer than the physical ones; indeed for some women they never heal at all.

There are many potential reasons for these serious effects:

- shattered expectations about the hoped-for perfect pregnancy;
- the shock, fear and uncertainty associated with the illness itself;
- having to cope with prematurity, stillbirth or neonatal death;
- poor care and lack of support during the illness or afterwards;
- fears about future pregnancies.

Our respondents were most eloquent when answering the question 'How were you affected emotionally?' Some experienced a confusing jumble of emotions.

> *'I felt incredibly guilty for failing my son and not keeping him safe until term. I also felt robbed of my pregnancy for a very long time, with a still-present craving to have a normal pregnancy (and a bump!) I was frightened for the health of my child and I worry that the experience means I should not go on to have more children.'*
>
> *Anna, UK*

> *'Sometimes I just feel lucky that my daughter is perfectly healthy despite it all. Sometimes I feel very sad that I didn't get to have a full pregnancy and that this traumatic event happened to me. Sometimes I feel angry that more isn't known or being done to find the cause and offer a treatment. I am also very scared for future pregnancies and for when my daughter someday has her own children.'*
>
> *Nicole, US*

Others, like Kerry (UK), mentioned earlier, went on to develop clinical depression.

'I suffered with severe depression, which also included psychotic episodes. I was treated for depression for 18 months, and two years on had to see a psychologist to help with issues surrounding the birth and lack of bonding. I only started to feel "normal" after two-and-a-half years.'

Post-traumatic stress disorder

One recent online survey found that women recovering from a pregnancy complicated by pre-eclampsia were more than four times more likely to suffer a severe condition known as post-traumatic stress disorder (PTSD) than women who had had normal blood pressure in pregnancy. Symptoms of PTSD, most famously associated with wartime horrors (it used to be known as shell shock), include:

- flashbacks and bad dreams;
- feeling emotionally numb and avoiding places and people associated with the bad experience;
- feeling tense and anxious and having trouble sleeping.

A significant minority of our respondents gave eloquent description of their experiences of PTSD.

'I still have nightmares and flashbacks to this day', said Kayla (US), who had HELLP syndrome in 2009. *'I had anxiety before but now it's gotten worse. I am so afraid that it will happen again that I don't know whether or not I ever want another child.'*

'I have been severely traumatised', said Kristen (US), who suffered multi-organ failure and ended up needing a full liver transplant. *'I've suffered extreme depression and PTSD. I still feel the effects emotionally three years later. For a long time I'd break down sobbing when I saw a pregnant woman, fearing she could end up like me.'*

'For many years after the birth I would have bad dreams and thoughts of the whole experience', said Lynne (Australia), who spent three days in intensive care and was separated from her

premature baby, who was moved to another hospital. *'I found Alex's birthday a very hard time as I would often say to myself "this time three years ago...". I became very upset and cried on his birthday for about the first five years. When Alex was eight or nine I actually had some counselling to help me through the emotional turmoil that was still affecting me.'*

Some women never seem to get over the emotional effects of pre-eclampsia.

'I was devastated that my daughter had to be delivered at 26 weeks. I've never looked for sympathy, but I felt during the whole experience that no one understood the serious psychological effects for me as a mother. Actually, 21 years later, I am crying as I write this. The attitudes then were "get over it and move on". So I moved on but never got over it.'

Janet, US

'I was quite calm at the time, but later discovered that I cried at any programme, book or film which featured birth, premature babies or maternal illness. This is still the case 25 years later despite the fact that I did not lose my baby and he is now a strapping healthy lad of 25.'

Lesley, UK

Bonding difficulties

For some women, struggling to bond with their babies adds to the emotional burden of pre-eclampsia.

'Because I was so ill after the birth, I struggled to bond with my daughter straight away, as I couldn't care for her the way I wanted.'

Angela, UK

'I did not bond with my daughter until after 15 months. The psychological effects of this were long term.'

Janet, US

Jayne (UK), whose first baby was stillborn after she developed very early pre-eclampsia, found it difficult to bond with her next baby, delivered at 32 weeks.

'During my second pregnancy I was scared I would lose the baby and when I developed pre-eclampsia again it was very difficult to think I would actually have a baby that would survive; when my daughter was born I found it hard to bond with her.'

The need for explanations

It was clear from responses to our survey that women need to 'debrief' about their experiences and be fully informed about what had happened to them in order to come to terms with their experiences of pre-eclampsia.

Claire (UK), who only found out she had suffered HELLP syndrome when looking through her medical notes several years later, had this to say:

'I think one of the important things that would help women post-PE is a good debrief shortly afterwards and definitely before leaving hospital. I think they should be offered this because you are in such a state at the time that you do not think to ask. Not all the gory details at that point, as you are not necessarily ready for it, but at least a full explanation of what happened and of the diagnosis.

'I'm not sure anyone actually told me at the time that I had pre-eclampsia; I worked it out from the symptoms; and they certainly never told me I had HELLP syndrome.'

A number of other respondents complained of an almost total absence of information or explanations after their experience of pre-eclampsia.

'I was in hospital for seven days following the birth and was discharged with no information about what had happened and what I could expect in the following months. I later found out that it was not policy to advise patients on eclampsia.'

Kerry, UK

'[My doctors] were kind, gentle and diagnosed me quickly. But they missed the mark on providing material to help educate me when leaving hospital. I was upset/angry later on when I had processed what had happened and had done some research and found out about the Pre-eclampsia Foundation.'

'I felt the hospital and/or my [specialist] could have been more proactive and provided information about where I could find out more about what had happened. Later, I found out the hospital had 15-20 pre-eclamptic patients a month. That's a lot of people leaving hospital without any helpful information!'

Johanna, US

The need to talk

Some women find they need to replay their experiences over and over again in their heads and talk endlessly about what happened in order to come to terms with it.

'When I got home I realised we both could have died. That was pretty frightening and all I wanted to do was talk about it. But no one in my family has been through what I did and it was hard for people to understand.'

Lorena, New Zealand

'For several months after my son's birth I was haunted by the knowledge that I had been very, very sick. The pre-eclampsia struck without warning and it took me a while to process what had happened. I obsessed about learning more about pre-eclampsia, about replaying my son's birth in my head and trying to remember the details through the fog the magnesium sulphate had created.'

Gina, US

The role of patient advocacy groups

Other women echoed Johanna's view that patient groups provided more helpful information and support after pre-eclampsia than health professionals (for a comprehensive list of these groups see Chapter 8, pp 173-174).

'No one gave me any support or information. I went back some months later to try to get some answers and information from my original consultant but was told to be grateful that I had survived. I later found Action on Pre-eclampsia and all my questions were answered. I can never express enough how grateful I was to APEC in those dark days and how finding them changed everything for me.'

Yvonne, UK

'I have joined several PE support groups online as well as support groups for mothers of premmies, and both have let me connect with other women with similar experiences and those who are far worse off than me, so I can put my own into perspective. Medical care can only do so much to support women and their families in such an emotional time.'

Rhian, Australia

'I had little information and no support until I found the Pre-eclampsia Foundation through my own research. I became a volunteer for them as a way to heal my emotional wounds and be able to bring more awareness to PE so that others may not have to go through what I did.'

Anon, US

The impact on partners

When women are confined to hospital with pre-eclampsia, their partners may have to shoulder a lonely burden of worry, fear and responsibility.

'He had to deal with his wife in [intensive care], then a week in a hospital bed, and he also had to register our baby and then get a death certificate issued and organise a funeral. After that he had to take care of a physically and emotionally broken wife.'

Anon, Mozambique

'At the start he felt guilty because he left me at the hospital on my own on strong advice from a midwife. He missed the birth and, as I was still unconscious, this was a real problem. He was torn between looking after me and his new baby. He had to care for me physically and mentally after the birth, which was extremely tough.'

Kerry, UK

But with caregivers' attention focused on mother and baby, there may be little support available for the father.

'No support was offered to my husband, who was never informed of anything going on by any medical staff. They failed to recognise that, *although the condition was obviously physical for me, there was an emotional side for the family.'*

Sarah, UK

'No one seemed to tell him much so he was left feeling ill-prepared for an event that nearly killed me and our son.'

Guinevere, UK

Some fathers put their own emotions on one side, or even deny them altogether, because they feel it is their duty to be 'strong' in support of their partners.

'My husband occupied himself with telephoning our friends and family, organising our son's funeral and arranging support for me. He went straight back to work when I came out of hospital, and when we were offered counselling he said he was "fine". A few weeks later, when I was starting to recover from my intense grief, he suddenly collapsed and was signed off work for a fortnight.'

Ruth, UK

Sometimes they may even be encouraged to behave as if nothing has happened to them.

'When he went back to work after our baby's death, none of his colleagues said a word, whereas all mine visited me, wrote lovely letters or sent me flowers.'

Anon, UK

Some men are too traumatised to face another pregnancy.

'My partner was told as they were taking me into theatre that there was a good chance he could lose us both. He will not go through another pregnancy.'

Trudy, Australia

Sadly, this can impact on the relationship, as Laura (Canada) related:

'Ruairi's father was so traumatised by his death and watching me

near death that he refused to have any other children and, since I wanted another child, we had to break up.'

When a baby dies

Some women have to face the cruellest outcome of pre-eclampsia – the agonising loss of a longed-for baby.

'I had a natural water birth planned. To go from that to a two-week stay at a major hospital and having my son die in my arms and to not bring him home – it's been an absolute nightmare. The pain, the worry, the physical and emotional stress of having pre-eclampsia was horrifying; but I would do it all over and over and over again if it somehow magically meant that I could bring my son home, alive and well.'

Laura, US

'Losing a child is something no one should experience. It has been a tough road to travel and I was very sad for a long time. I think about our son daily and feel like a piece of me is missing. It is so hard to be at that stage in life with friends pregnant, having baby showers and healthy babies. I hate hearing women complain about being pregnant or about their children. They are so blessed to have a healthy pregnancy and baby.'

Elizabeth, US

'I was emotionally distraught. I was devastated, angry that this had happened to me, my fiancé and our baby girl. It was the hardest and worst time of my life.'

Amanda, UK

Too premature to survive

Such a loss can be particularly painful when a baby has to be delivered very prematurely to ensure its mother's safety.

'I was diagnosed with severe pre-eclampsia and HELLP syndrome at 23 weeks and one day, with an emergency [caesarean] performed shortly after diagnosis. We didn't have the option of gestating longer.

Either he would die or both of us would die. We had to learn to be OK with what happened.

'We ultimately chose that no life-saving measures be taken for our 23-week little guy. I was scared to death that that he would start breathing or something and then the decision we made not to take any action would make his little life even more profoundly painful and full of suffering. He lived four hours. I don't remember much except that I got to hold him briefly. I got to feel his heart beat in my hands; I'll never forget that.'

Danielle, US

The death of a baby can impose an enormous strain on a relationship, particularly if the partners grieve in different ways, as Danielle goes on to explain:

'Our relationship was negatively impacted for a time. We had been together eight years before trying to get pregnant, so we had a great relationship to rely upon as well as communication skills. But no one can prepare you for this kind of loss. Our coping skills fell apart. We always seemed to be at different stages of the grieving process. We saw a perinatal loss counsellor, who helped. The goal was not to get us back to the "old us" but the new version who had lost a child.'

Saying the right thing

At this difficult time, women are often acutely sensitive to other people's responses, however helpfully intended.

'After my baby died, having been delivered prematurely to save my life, a nurse told me God must have wanted him for an angel. As an atheist, that made me furious. Then my sister said he didn't look like a real baby and my brother said "couldn't you pretend it was a miscarriage?" Nearly 30 years later these remarks still hurt.'

Ruth, UK

'Teaching all medical students how best to deal with parents whose children have died would perhaps result in fewer ignorant comments in general. A few I heard (from medical staff!) were: "Well it's best

*as he was really sick"; "Everything happens for a reason"; "You're
young – you can have more babies"; and "It was better that he
died as a baby instead of when he was older and you were more
attached". What would have been more helpful would be simply: "I
am sorry about your son's death".'*

Laura, Canada

What midwives can do

Midwives who have supported women through their pregnancy, their
experience of pre-eclampsia and, where relevant, their sad bereavement
are in the best position to offer extra support at what can be a very difficult
time. This may involve calling in extra professional or social support.

- Always try to maintain some continuity of care, if possible,
  even when you have handed over responsibility to another
  professional team.
- Acknowledge the grief, disappointment and other negative
  emotions your patients may feel in the aftermath of pre-
  eclampsia; encourage questions and be on the lookout for signs
  of clinical depression and/or PTSD. Listening can be time-
  consuming for you, but very healing for the woman sharing
  her grief with you.
- Consult and refer on to other professionals as appropriate.
- When a baby dies, facilitate the involvement of bereavement
  support, which is available in most hospitals.
- Acknowledge your own natural grief after a baby has died.
  Being emotionally detached from grieving parents can add to
  their distress.

The next pregnancy

After an experience of severe pre-eclampsia most women are very worried
– even terrified – about the prospect of another pregnancy. Will it happen
again? is the question to which no one can give a completely reassuring
answer *(see Chapter 2, page 37)*.

For some women the fear of recurrence is so overwhelming that they
can't even contemplate another pregnancy.

'I am so terrified of having such severe pre-eclampsia at such an early stage again that I will never have another pregnancy, despite the fact we intended to.'

Gail, UK

Others make the same decision on the basis of perceived risk...

'My [specialist] advised me that there was a high chance of HELLP syndrome in a subsequent pregnancy, so I didn't have another child.'

Janet, US

... or for the sake of their surviving child(ren).

'After having eclampsia with my first child, which resulted in me being in a coma, it took six years for us to think about another child. When I got pre-eclampsia with that child we decided to count our blessings. My tubes are tied and we will not be having any more children.'

Tina, US

The influence of health professionals

For many women, the advice, support and encouragement of expert doctors plays a crucial role in their decision whether to go ahead with another pregnancy.

'I was scared beyond belief and never thought I would be able to have another pregnancy. This caused great emotional distress, especially after burying my much longed-for son. I just could not see any light at the end of the tunnel. I felt emotionally tortured until I spoke to a lovely haematologist who said she would look after me if and when I chose to try for another baby. She gave me the little chink of hope when I was feeling hopeless.'

Sam, UK

'First advice was that I needed to go under the high-risk team at the hospital and could never go private again. I was advised I had an almost certain risk of future PE but that they were confident they could get a pregnancy to 28 weeks; that gave me hope. Perhaps the most valuable piece of advice for my mental health was that it would

be a scary journey, but they'd hold my hand and keep a very close eye on me.'

Susie, New Zealand

When doctors rule out further pregnancies

Kristen (US), who suffered multi-organ failure, needed a full liver transplant and was in hospital for nearly six months after her daughter was delivered at 35 weeks, was told not to consider another pregnancy.

Jody (US), who lay in a coma for three days after suffering eclamptic fits, was given the same advice.

But some doctors actively discourage further attempts at pregnancy in less extreme circumstances.

> *'I was diagnosed at 36 weeks six days at a routine check-up and my baby was delivered the next day. My blood pressure remained high for a month or so afterwards and I now have to take aspirin to thin my blood. I was told not to risk another pregnancy.'*
>
>
>
> *Jo, Canada*
>
>

Where medical advice conflicts with women's own instincts and wishes, there is always an option to seek a second opinion – ideally from an acknowledged expert on pre-eclampsia.

Taking the plunge

After an experience of pre-eclampsia, the next pregnancy is inevitably fraught with tension, anxiety and a desperate fear of recurrence.

> *'As there was only a year between losing my son and my daughter being born, my whole pregnancy was incredibly stressful. Even after my daughter arrived I suffered with terrible feelings of anxiety, and still do to some extent four years later.'*
>
>
>
> *Caroline, UK*
>
>

> *'Obviously I was extremely worried. Everything had turned out all right first time round, but at the time I thought I was going to die. I did not want a repeat performance where the outcome could be the same or worse.'*
>
>
>
> *Karen, UK*
>
>

The need for expert care and support

In a time of such uncertainty, women and their partners benefit hugely from the care, support and encouragement of expert teams, committed to a regime of precautionary measures, intensive monitoring and early intervention if necessary.

Sadly, some of the respondents to our survey received complacent, inadequate care despite their history of pre-eclampsia:

Linda (UK), whose first baby was stillborn and whose second baby was eight weeks premature, had to fight for attention in her third pregnancy:

> 'I felt very let down by my consultant for the final pregnancy. I was only offered appointments every four weeks at her clinic and never actually met her, which was really upsetting as she'd been recommended to me.

> 'My midwife was excellent and agreed to see me weekly, but only because I asked and pushed for it. Basically I had to sort my own care plan out to meet my expectations and for my own reassurance which, given my history of a [neonatal death] and a premmie, I found very poor.'

But Susie (New Zealand), whose first baby failed to survive a premature delivery at 25 weeks and who suffered long-term kidney and blood pressure problems herself, had had nothing but praise for the care she received in subsequent pregnancies.

> 'It took eight years before I plucked up the courage to try for another baby: to be brutally honest, I had low expectations of a good outcome but still wanted to give it a damn good shot.

> 'Since then I have had two successful pregnancies – in 2009 and 2012. Both pregnancies were managed with military precision by a [maternal-fetal medicine] consultant and an extensive medication regime. I was allowed to work in the early stages of both pregnancies and then was put on "lady of leisure" rest.

> 'I had the same medical team for both these pregnancies and developed an enormous trust in them. I appreciated their brutal

honesty in monitoring the babies' progress and what the "game plan"
for the next day/week would be. I felt a power shift from being the
passive patient to being a part of the "team".

'*My blood pressure was rather difficult with both pregnancies and*
both babies were delivered early via emergency C-sections at 34 and
32 weeks, but neither pregnancy was pre-eclamptic, neither baby
suffered [growth restriction] and both came home!'

What midwives can do

- When women are contemplating another pregnancy after pre-eclampsia, emphasise the importance of pre-pregnancy counselling and early booking.
- Facilitate early access to an appropriately skilled and equipped high-risk pregnancy team.
- Acknowledge the anxiety women feel in the next pregnancy – particularly around the time pre-eclampsia was diagnosed the last time.
- Respond promptly and sensitively to any concerns about the current pregnancy.
- Schedule extra visits if you feel it would help to give a woman more peace of mind.
- Without giving false reassurance, try to help women celebrate the normal 'magic' of pregnancy. Remember that they are first and foremost mothers-to-be.

Another Susie, also from New Zealand, described how a special midwife helped her to experience this magic – and we leave her to end this chapter on a positive note:

'*My experience has been that my high-risk pregnancies missed the*
magic of pregnancy that my "normal" friends have had because the
focus is (quite rightly) so intent on getting baby here safely. But I
was too apprehensive to have a baby shower or tell most people that
I was pregnant until my bump was too visible to ignore; and I didn't
decorate the nursery.

'*There is a midwife attached to the high-risk team who has the happiest, most positive attitude you could ever encounter. She was the cheerleader who used to ask me the "normal" baby questions like what names we were considering. I also remember her telling me with one of the pregnancies that it was "okay to get excited now". Those words were magic to my ears.'*

References

1. Simkin P. *Just another day in a woman's life? Part II: Nature and consistency of women's long-term memories of their first birth experience. Birth.* 2002;19(2), 64- 81
2. East C, Conway K, Pollock W, Frawley N, Brennecke S. *Women's experiences of Pre-eclampsia: Australian Action on Pre-eclampsia Survey of Women and their Confidants.* J Pregnancy. 2011; Article ID 375653, 6 pages doi:10.1155/2011/375653

Further reading

Roes EM, Raijmakers MTM, Schoonenberg M, Wanner M,Peters WFM, Steegers EAP. Physical well-being in women with a history of severe pre-eclampsia, J Matern Fetal Neonatal Med.2005; 18:(1), 39-45, doi: 10.1080/14767050500127740

Porcel J, Feigal, C, Poye L, Postma IR,Zeeman GG,Olowoyeye A et al. Hypertensive disorders of pregnancy and risk of screening positive for Posttraumatic Stress Disorder: A cross sectional study. Pregnancy Hypertension: Int J Womens Health. 2013; Vol 3 (4). 254-260

White G. You cope by breaking down in private: Fathers and PTSD following childbirth. Br J Midwifery.2007; 15(1): 35-45.

CHAPTER 5: THE ANTENATAL SAFETY NET AND WHY IT SOMETIMES FAILS

This chapter focuses on the main form of protection against pre-eclampsia available to mothers and babies: the systematic programme of antenatal (or prenatal) care that is provided for pregnant women throughout the developed world.

Antenatal care is not just about pre-eclampsia, of course. There are many other pregnancy and birth-related problems it is designed to screen for and detect. But pre-eclampsia is by far the biggest problem that develops before birth in terms of its combined threat to mother and baby; indeed, if pre-eclampsia didn't exist the number of antenatal clinic visits could probably be halved at a stroke. No other antenatal problem is so common and so dangerous for both mothers and babies.

The key goals of modern antenatal care programmes in relation to pre-eclampsia are to identify women at risk then monitor them for signs and symptoms of the condition.

This chapter examines the rationale for antenatal care and its role in reducing suffering and deaths from pre-eclampsia.

It looks at the principles of good care and the impact of poor care. And it considers ways in which antenatal care might get even better in future.

Why all pregnant women need antenatal care

It is often argued – with good reason – that most women don't need antenatal care because most pregnancies are normal, leading to the delivery of healthy babies.

But that misses the main justification for antenatal care: it is needed much like insurance is needed – to protect people against events that are rare but potentially disastrous.

Is your house insured? It is? When was the last time it burned to the ground? Never? And yet you still pay the premiums?

We all do if we're sensible, not because we expect our houses to burn down but because we want the peace of mind that comes with knowing we are protected – at least financially – against losing our homes and all our possessions.

The same principle holds true of antenatal care. Most pregnant women don't get pre-eclampsia. But those who do can suffer terrible consequences. Antenatal care is there as a form of insurance, to alert people to any increased risk, then to step in at the first signs of trouble and protect them against the worst that can happen.

It has often been suggested that women at low risk of pregnancy complications could make do with a reduced schedule of visits. But, quite apart from the difficulty of determining who is at low risk of pre-eclampsia, research has shown that any potential financial savings are offset by poorer outcomes *(1)*.

It's not a perfect safety net – and women regularly fall through some of its larger holes; but it's the best we've got. And it is the main reason why maternal death from pre-eclampsia, which used to be commonplace, is now incredibly rare – at least in developed countries.

The myth of 'natural childbirth'

Pregnancy and childbirth are natural events. Any sort of systematic care inevitably 'medicalises' the process to some extent. And some women who are lucky enough to enjoy problem-free pregnancies resent this apparent interference.

But the vision of 'natural childbirth' as a beautiful ideal that is spoiled and trampled over by doctors and their technology is a flawed one. In reality, nature doesn't care whether babies or mothers die; and they *did* die in much greater numbers before antenatal care existed.

The pregnancy care women in the developed world enjoy today has evolved from traditional care by birth attendants and midwives. Obstetricians are fairly recent additions to the list of caregivers. Their role has developed in response to the need to protect mothers and babies from the worst that nature can throw at them.

Antenatal care in general

There is much more to antenatal care than pre-eclampsia. As knowledge grows and technology improves, there is a corresponding increase in the range of antenatal care procedures available to women.

At the same time, a powerful new vision of the role of antenatal care is emerging from the discovery of so-called 'intrauterine programming'. It seems self-evident that good health starts at the very beginning of life, in the uterus, and that the strongest unborn babies will develop into the healthiest children and adults. What's new is the idea that many diseases of later life, including diabetes, obesity and chronic hypertension, are caused to some extent by poor conditions in the uterus.

Moreover, we now know from the science of molecular biology that the genes of the unborn baby are 'tuned' to suit its environment. If that environment is unfavourable, the baby will be born with genes set to work in ways that may have bad effects on its long term health. So antenatal care can also be regarded as an investment in the future.

The range of antenatal care

The potential range of antenatal care is enormous – from checking for Down's syndrome and spina bifida to anticipating and coping with preterm labour, infection and even postnatal depression. In time, antenatal care is highly likely to extend to predicting and avoiding health problems that can set in decades later. As far as pre-eclampsia is concerned, it represents important and effective insurance against disaster.

Most of current antenatal care is about screening, which means checking people who have no problems now for preventable problems that may arise later. For example, a blood count is a routine part of antenatal care that screens for anaemia (shortage of red blood cells). If this problem is discovered it can be remedied well before the birth, when heavy bleeding could deplete the red blood cell reserve still further.

Some screening tests need to be carried out only once because the problem (such as Down's syndrome) is not going to change. Other tests need to be repeated at intervals to allow for changing or evolving situations, of which pre-eclampsia is the classic example.

No screening tests are perfect and all of them sometimes produce 'false-negative' results (failing to detect a problem that is actually there) or 'false-positives' (raising the alarm when there is nothing wrong).

The screening challenge

In previous chapters we have shown what a tricky condition pre-eclampsia can be. It is unpredictable and changeable; it probably consists of more than one disease; and, worse, it cannot be reliably prevented, nor resolved except by delivery. It should come as no surprise, then, to learn that screening for pre-eclampsia is far from straightforward.

In some cases the seeds of pre-eclampsia may be sown even before conception. Yet it remains silent and hidden almost to the very end of pregnancy, causing symptoms only in the last few days or even hours. Figure 5.1 (*below*) illustrates the various stages of this 'journey'.

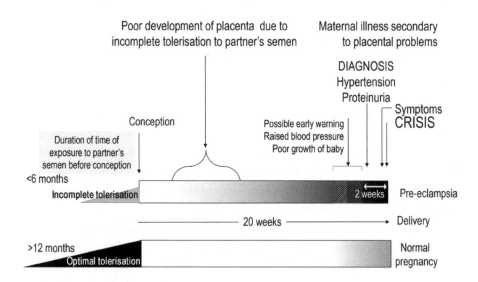

Figure 5.1: The long journey to pre-eclampsia

The wheels of pre-eclampsia may be set in motion well before pregnancy starts. Normally a woman's immune system becomes 'tolerant' to her partner's child because of exposure to his semen. Poor 'tolerisation', which is more likely if the couple have been together for less than six months, increases the risk of pre-eclampsia. It affects early development of the placenta in such a way that it cannot sustain a normal pregnancy. Instead, the damaged placenta pours out stress signals into the mother's circulation, which itself becomes damaged. The shading in the diagram shows the increasing severity of the problem after 20 weeks of pregnancy. There may be early warning signs (cross-hatched areas) but by the time of diagnosis the pregnancy usually has a 'life' of about two weeks or less. The mother only begins to feel seriously ill shortly before a crisis, such as eclampsia or HELLP syndrome. Pre-eclampsia is a 'silent' condition, not easy to detect until it is already very dangerous.

How antenatal care evolved

Antenatal care began to develop into the pattern we know today largely because of pre-eclampsia. In the 1930s pre-eclampsia and eclampsia were of such concern to the UK Department of Health that they commissioned two reports on the problem. The first, published in 1932, concluded:

> 'There is too little ante-natal supervision by general practitioners and midwives and what there is is often too perfunctory to deserve the name... it is necessary to emphasise that if the heavy annual toll of life and health incident to the toxaemias of pregnancy is to be diminished, more attention must be given to early diagnosis and adequate treatment.'

The second report, published five years later, investigated 100 deaths from pre-eclampsia or eclampsia that had occurred in selected parts of the country in just one year (1934). Reading this report reveals a world far removed from our own, with vastly different expectations. Only one-in-five of the women who died had enjoyed reasonable or adequate care, even by the much lower standards of the time. The rest had received inadequate care or no care at all. For example, more than two out of three had no records of blood pressure tests and less than 10 per cent had had more than one blood pressure reading.

Remember that this survey sample of 100 women represented only a fraction of national deaths from this condition *in that one year*. Nowadays, fewer than 10 women per year die of pre-eclampsia/eclampsia in the UK.

So, much has changed and improved since the 1930s, but those improvements have not been distributed equally and have not yet reached the poorest countries in the world. In South Africa, for example, the death toll from 'hypertensive disorders' is nearly 30 times higher than in the UK. The story in other poor countries is similar or worse.

Post-war changes

One of the reasons why antenatal care was so poor in those days was that, with no universal health service, many women simply could not afford it. It took a world war to change all that. In the UK, the introduction of the National Health Service in 1948 gave all women access to proper, systematic antenatal care, regardless of their means.

An influential paper published in *The Lancet* in 1952 described the implementation of systematic screening for pre-eclampsia in Sydney, Australia. The author noted that women who felt well often failed to attend their scheduled visits. He was not prepared to accept this and sent them letters and telegrams telling them they had to come.

> 'Those who did not respond were visited. [For] those who lived in the distant suburbs and did not reply to letters or telegrams, the nearest police were asked to deliver the message that an immediate visit to the hospital was expected. Excellent results followed in most instances.'

A dramatic decline in eclampsia

The programme went further: those who showed signs of pre-eclampsia were admitted to hospital and had their babies delivered early when necessary. As a result, the incidence of eclampsia declined dramatically; and similar methods were adopted throughout the UK, other European countries and the US.

Figure 5.2 (*opposite*) shows the dramatic decline in maternal deaths from pre-eclampsia in the UK after the Second World War. This was a direct result of an antenatal care programme, heavily influenced by the Sydney experience, which succeeded in neutralising the worst dangers of pre-eclampsia.

Screening tools for pre-eclampsia

The screening tools currently available – blood pressure and urine tests – are very simple, cheap and painless. They are also fairly imprecise. But they are a thousand times better than nothing.

Women begin to enter the jungle territory of pre-eclampsia any time after 20 weeks – although some rare cases have been documented as early as 16 weeks.

But testing has to start earlier than this – ideally at 8-14 weeks – in order to get reliable 'baseline' readings. There is no way for doctors and midwives to know whether a woman is developing protein in the urine or hypertension unless they are sure those abnormalities weren't there before.

The screening interval

After that, expectant mothers usually have their blood pressure measured and their urine tested for protein at every antenatal visit. Checks for

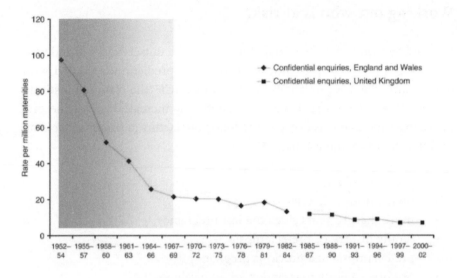

Figure 5.2: The impact of systematic antenatal care on maternal deaths in the UK from 1952

The most dramatic decline in maternal deaths occurred at the beginning of this period as antenatal care became systematic and available to all. The figures are derived from reports on maternal deaths, known as 'Confidential enquiries', carried out every three years from 1952. Initially these covered just England and Wales but were extended to the UK as a whole from 1985.

proteinuria are not routine in all developed countries, but they are important because proteinuria can precede raised blood pressure as the first sign of pre-eclampsia.

The length of the intervals between checks determines how fine the mesh of the screening net will be. Very frequent checks are likely to catch most cases, but at a cost for 'normal' mothers-to-be, caregivers and health systems. Infrequent checks are less intrusive but will miss more cases.

A compromise is needed in which the screening interval is dictated by individual risk. Women judged to be at low risk of getting pre-eclampsia can be screened less often than those at higher risk. Most antenatal care programmes reflect this principle. A minimum programme of care is enough for women at lowest risk, but this can be stepped up incrementally so that those with the highest risk have very frequent screening. Of course, other potential complications of pregnancy also need to be taken into account as part of the 'big picture'.

Working out who is at risk?

It would be wonderful if we could know from the outset who will and who will not get pre-eclampsia. But the process of prediction is riddled with uncertainty. The UK guidelines produced by NICE (the National Institute for Health and Care Excellence) for identifying increased risk at the first ('booking') antenatal visit specify the following factors (a simplified version of Table 2.1 in Chapter 2, page 3):

- age 40 or older;
- no previous deliveries;
- more than 10 years since the last pregnancy;
- family history of pre-eclampsia;
- pre-eclampsia in a previous pregnancy;
- obesity – a body mass index of 30 or above;
- long term arterial disorders, such as hypertension;
- long term kidney problems;
- multiple pregnancy (twins, triplets or more).

These criteria were derived from an earlier guideline (PRECOG) produced by the UK charity Action on Pre-eclampsia (APEC). But whereas PRECOG used the criteria to indicate the need for referral to a specialist and to trigger an increase in the frequency of antenatal visits above the low-risk baseline, NICE also used them to identify women who should be offered low-dose aspirin from 12 weeks onwards, to try to reduce the risk of pre-eclampsia.

Prediction is imprecise

The predictive value of these criteria is far from precise: many women labelled high-risk will go on to enjoy uncomplicated pregnancies, while some of those considered low-risk will still get pre-eclampsia. But they are the best we have for working out whether individual women need enhanced antenatal care or can cope with the basic level of provision.

With both basic and enhanced care programmes there are usually longer screening intervals between 20 and 32 weeks, when pre-eclampsia is less common, and shorter intervals (1-2 weeks) after 32 weeks, when it is *more* common. This is not ideal because, as described in Chapter 3 *(see page 40)*, the worst cases are often seen before 32 weeks, when they might well be missed, with very serious consequences.

When screening doesn't work

If women fall through the antenatal safety net it is usually for one of three reasons:

- They fail to turn up for one or more checks, so lengthening the screening interval.
- Their caregivers fail to carry out careful checks on blood pressure and urine at each visit.
- Warning signs are noticed but not taken seriously.

Why women refuse care

Some women find it hard to believe in pre-eclampsia as a real threat. It has no visible shape or form, it isn't very common and it doesn't make you feel ill – at least not until an advanced stage. Moreover, there is plenty of unreliable information out there suggesting that you can ward it off through healthy living or diet changes. People tend to think of it like a road accident – as something that happens to somebody else, through bad luck.

The whole business of checking blood pressures and urine is boring and seems pointless. It is hard to think of it as high priority – a crucial defence against real danger. So missing an appointment doesn't seem too risky.

In fact, though, missed appointments rip holes in the fine gauge of the antenatal safety net. Does that matter? Only if you are the one who falls through the gap and are suddenly exposed to the dangers of pre-eclampsia. To go back to our previous comparison with insurance, it's all about keeping up with your premiums.

A victim of its own success

The real problem is that antenatal care has become a victim of its own success. The dangers of pre-eclampsia have been reduced to the point where they are scarcely visible to women – and even to some health professionals. As with all good safety precautions the original reasons for introducing them have been eliminated and so forgotten. But remembering is vital because, in the words of the philosopher George Santayana, 'Those who cannot remember the past are condemned to repeat it'.

When professionals miss the signs

As mentioned, caregivers can also damage the safety net if they don't respond appropriately to clear warning signs. One of the commonest mistakes is to discount a raised blood pressure because it appears to have settled on a second reading; it is assumed, for no good reason, that the second reading is more reliable than the first, or that the high blood pressure seen in the first reading was caused by anxiety.

Explaining away an important sign of pre-eclampsia is in nobody's interest. If the sign is there, the correct action is to respond to it.

The appropriate response is simple – to shorten the time to the next screening visit. Instead of sticking to the next appointment as set out on the schedule, the woman should be seen again in a day or two. If the sign is still there the schedule should be changed, with screening intervals reduced to no more than 2-3 days. If the woman is receiving midwifery-based care she should be referred to an appropriate specialist without delay.

Eventually, because pre-eclampsia is a progressive illness, the time will come when screening has to be carried out more than once a day. That's when a woman needs to move out of the antenatal clinic and into an environment that can provide higher-level care.

Day care and hospital units

Day assessment units and other types of drop-in clinics have been a major step forward for women who need very frequent screening for pre-eclampsia, although these are not universally available.

In the UK 40 years ago, women with high blood pressure were immediately admitted to hospital; what's worse, if their hypertension persisted they stayed there, even if they had no other complications. And they stayed for weeks and weeks. Antenatal wards had to be huge to accommodate all these unfortunate women.

Day assessment clinics put a stop to all that. They allow women to be screened on a daily basis without being confined to hospital.

But they have their limits; and once pre-eclampsia is finally diagnosed, or related problems emerge, women need to be monitored day and night, and hospital admission is inevitable.

Screening in hospital

As the illness evolves, pre-eclampsia becomes more and more unstable so the screening interval needs to be reduced to 3-4 hours. At this stage the risks are high, so women need to stay in hospital for their own safety, with facilities for immediate delivery or other emergency care close at hand in case of crises.

The main criteria for admission to hospital are:

- a diagnosis of pre-eclampsia (with confirmed new hypertension and proteinuria);
- very high blood pressure that needs treatment, even if there is no proteinuria;
- symptoms that suggest severe pre-eclampsia even without very high blood pressure, such as upper abdominal ('epigastric') pain or severe headache;
- concerns about the growth or health of the baby, including uterine pain or vaginal bleeding.

What about 'mild' pre-eclampsia?

It is not clear whether pre-eclampsia can ever be described as mild. As it evolves, the earlier stages usually seem comparatively mild. But this is 'the disease of exceptions' and some cases become severe with alarming speed.

So experts tend to err on the side of safety and consider all confirmed cases of pre-eclampsia potentially unstable. This is consistent with the policy of the International Society for the Study of Hypertension in Pregnancy (ISSHP) that 'all cases of pre-eclampsia should be treated in the knowledge that the condition can change rapidly' (2).

Planned delivery

The entire antenatal care programme comes to a climax with delivery. A well-judged delivery today can avoid a pre-eclamptic crisis tomorrow or next week. That is the whole point of planned delivery. Fortunately, it is now safe to deliver early through either induction of labour or caesarean section, and this has made a major contribution to better outcomes for mothers and babies in pre-eclampsia.

Is screening effective?

We have seen in this chapter that there are four stages to antenatal care for women at risk of pre-eclampsia:

- assess risk in early pregnancy and plan the screening programme accordingly;
- screen repetitively, without omissions, according to the schedule and make sure women are informed about signs and symptoms to look out for;
- admit to hospital when pre-eclampsia begins;
- use planned delivery to ward off dangerous complications for mother or baby.

Does this programme work? The answer has to be yes. The proof lies in what happens when antenatal care is inadequate or even non-existent. And here, reports from the UK, USA, Middle East, Far East, Africa, and Caribbean all tell the same sad story: maternal deaths and crises like eclampsia are overwhelmingly associated with no care, poor care or insufficient care.

When antenatal care fails

In the developing world, poverty and ignorance are the main factors in the failure of antenatal care. Developed countries like the UK don't have these excuses: here the problem tends to be inadequate care in maternity hospitals. In the government enquiry into all maternal deaths in the UK in the period 2006–2008, a staggering nine out of 10 deaths from pre-eclampsia / eclampsia were linked with 'substandard care', with nearly two-thirds of those who died having experienced a 'major deficiency' of care. Similar statistics were quoted in the Netherlands.

Appalling as these deficiencies are, they are probably the exceptions that prove the rule. And, indeed, more recent reports from the UK show a gratifying fall in maternal deaths from pre-eclampsia, with no reference to substandard care. The evidence is that current methods of controlling the dangers of pre-eclampsia are outstandingly successful. What's more, they have been achieved without a full understanding of the disease, without a specific diagnostic test, without reliable preventive measures and with no resolution except by ending the pregnancy.

There has been no fancy molecular medicine involved, no stunning breakthroughs – simply a slow, step-by-step approach that has progressively reduced the dangers of pre-eclampsia.

What could make antenatal care even better?

Still, it's far from perfect, so before we end this chapter we should consider what improvements might be expected in future.

The current 'Holy Grail' for researchers is a predictive test – one that could be used at the first antenatal visit to reliably discriminate between women who will and won't get pre-eclampsia.

Some possible tests

There are four types of tests that might be useful.

- a blood test to detect biological 'markers' of early problems in the placenta. We know that poor development of the placenta is a factor, particularly in early-onset pre-eclampsia;
- a more sophisticated urine test, checking for more than protein;
- better tests of a woman's circulatory system, measuring more than blood pressure;
- Doppler ultrasound tests that can detect disturbances in blood flow from the mother to the placenta.

The list of possibilities is growing all the time as new knowledge becomes available. During pregnancy the placenta secretes tens if not hundreds of 'signals' that can be found circulating in maternal blood. Some of these changes occur before pre-eclampsia develops and could potentially serve as the basis for predictive tests.

A predictive system that seems to work

One of the best predictive systems so far combines known risk factors with various measurements taken at 11-13 weeks. These include Doppler measurement of placental blood flow, blood pressure, and tests for no fewer than eight markers in the blood; of these markers, three relate to the mother's circulation and the other five to the placenta (3).

This combination of tests, while producing a large number of 'false positives', appears to predict nine out of 10 cases of early-onset pre-eclampsia and six out of 10 late cases. These are impressive results but we have yet to see whether they will be upheld in further research. Even if they were, the number of tests involved would make this system very expensive for widespread use.

At present it is still not possible to rule pre-eclampsia in or out with certainty. Until this can be done, antenatal care programmes must continue to screen women who are apparently at low risk of pre-eclampsia. It would be a false economy to do otherwise.

How could better prediction help women and caregivers?

At present, coping with pre-eclampsia means living with uncertainty. At every stage of pregnancy, and even for a short time after the birth, we have to allow for the sudden appearance of this elusive threat.

Prediction is a bit like weather forecasting. Without it how could we know whether to expect sun or rain? These days we have information available through weather satellites that give us very reliable information, at least for the short term. Similarly, with pre-eclampsia prediction we can now get short-term forecasts (over a week or two) that are pretty good.

Weather forecasts are particularly important for those at sea; and a mother is a bit like the captain of a boat: she needs to know which way to go and whether to take precautions now or to steam ahead through what seem to be the calm waters of life.

As far as doctors and midwives are concerned, better prediction or forecasting, would allow them to focus care on the women who are destined to get pre-eclampsia. But it is extremely unlikely that we will ever know this for certain.

How prediction might aid prevention

Testing possible ways of preventing pre-eclampsia can be very difficult and expensive. You need thousands of women to take part in research trials that can take many years to complete.

There have been a number of large trials of potential preventive treatments in recent years – and nearly all of them have produced negative results. In other words, huge expense has led to no major progress.

The trials have probably failed for one of two reasons: either the treatment itself didn't work or it worked only for *some* women and *some* types of pre-eclampsia.

Better prediction could improve the chances of finding a preventive treatment that works. If, for example, a test became available that could routinely predict early-onset pre-eclampsia, research could be restricted to those who tested positively. The trials could be smaller and more focused, and if benefits were found they would apply to the most severe form of pre-eclampsia.

This would be a huge step forwards. And, while there is still a long way to go, it no longer looks like a hopeless dream.

References

1. Henderson J, Roberts T, Sikorski J, Wilson J, Clement S. An economic evaluation comparing two schedules of antenatal visits. J Health Serv Res Policy. Vol 5 No 2 April 2000.

2. Tranquilli AL, Dekker G, Magee L, Roberts J, Sibai BM, Steyn W, Zeeman GG, Brown MA. The classification, diagnosis and management of the hypertensive disorders of pregnancy: A revised statement from the ISSHP. Pregnancy Hypertens. 2014 Apr;4(2):97-104.

3. Akolekar R, Syngelaki A, Sarquis R, Zvanca M, Nicolaides KH. Prediction of early, intermediate and late pre-eclampsia from maternal factors, biophysical and biochemical markers at 11-13 weeks. Prenat Diagn. 2011 Jan;31(1):66-74.

CHAPTER 6: DIAGNOSIS AND AFTERWARDS

Why pre-eclampsia is difficult to diagnose

Pre-eclampsia appears to be simply defined in terms of signs that are easy to detect. So why is it so often difficult to diagnose?

As suggested in previous chapters, there are three problems here:

- Existing definitions are over-simplified and don't cover all forms of the disease.
- Pre-eclampsia may, in fact, be several different diseases sheltering under one umbrella.
- Pre-eclampsia is essentially a placental problem and it is not easy to know what is going on inside this mysterious and largely hidden organ.

Figure 6.1 (*page 120*) shows three different levels at which the diagnosis can be made. The traditional signs (*level 3*) represent the mother's response to the problems in her placenta. But diagnosis at this level can never be totally reliable because all these signs and symptoms – even convulsions – could potentially have other causes unrelated to pregnancy.

The role of biomarkers

One important 21st century advance has been the ability to detect specific signals coming from the placenta that reflect its unhealthy state and could predict pre-eclampsia (*level 2 in the diagram*). Several of these so-called *biomarkers* have already been identified and many others will probably be discovered in future.

In order to be useful, biomarkers of pre-eclampsia need to have two key features:

- They must be produced by the *syncytiotrophoblast* – the surface of the placenta that is bathed by maternal blood.
- Their production levels have to be changed by the problems in the placenta that eventually cause pre-eclampsia.

Among the biomarkers identified so far are the 'angiogenic' and 'antiangiogenic' factors that affect the health of blood vessels *(See Chapter 2, page 25)*.

It would be naïve to imagine that the unhealthy maternal condition we call pre-eclampsia is caused by over-production or under-production of any one biomarker. It is more likely to be caused by a combination of changes.

At the time of writing we are in a state of transition, but we can expect further knowledge about the value of biomarkers to change the way pre-eclampsia is diagnosed. Traditional screening of blood pressure and proteinuria will continue; but when pre-eclampsia is suspected blood tests for placental biomarkers will be used to confirm the diagnosis and – crucially – to judge the severity of the condition.

With these more sophisticated tests at our disposal we will probably find that some apparently mild cases are actually severe, and *vice versa*.

Limitations of Doppler scans

Figure 6.1 *(overleaf)* suggests that uterine artery ultrasound Doppler measurements *(level 1)* should be able to diagnose or even predict early-onset pre-eclampsia. But in fact these measurements are far from reliable because they produce many false positive and false negative results. There are many possible reasons for this: most importantly, these scans measure the *speed* of blood flow through the arteries rather than the *volume* of blood flow, which is what we really need to know. Newer techniques with greater power and resolution may eventually resolve some of these issues.

Having looked at the various problems associated with diagnosis, let's now take a look at the traditional methods.

Making the diagnosis

Diagnosing pre-eclampsia can be easy when signs of severe disease suddenly appear after a steady period of normality, as shown by the real life example in Figure 6.2 *(page 121)*. Here a woman who had totally normal blood pressure and urine results between 12 and 28 weeks suddenly developed

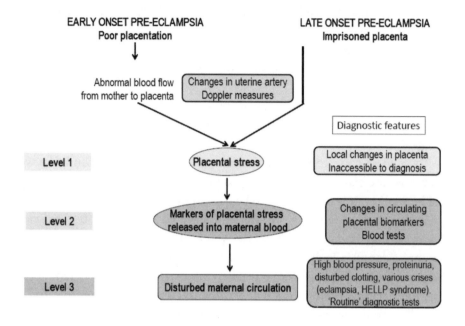

Figure 6.1 Diagnosis of pre-eclampsia

Typically, diagnosis of pre-eclampsia depends on detecting the features caused by problems in the placenta at level 3. Every one of these features is non-specific in that each (even convulsions) could be caused by another illness coinciding with pregnancy. Our ability to measure markers of placental stress in the maternal blood (level 2) should make the diagnosis more accurate. Doppler ultrasound measurements should, in theory, detect the immediate consequences of poor placentation, but in practice they do not.

raging hypertension and proteinuria at 30 weeks. Regular checks on this apparently well woman triggered a timely and well-managed 'rescue' of her pregnancy. This is effective antenatal care in action. But not all cases are so straightforward. A typical sequence is shown in Figure 6.3 (*opposite*).

Here the build-up is slow, with possible signs of pre-eclampsia coming and going.

As these two very different cases demonstrate, pre-eclampsia can progress slowly and gradually or erupt like a sudden storm. Usually the first detectable sign is gestational hypertension; but only the second of these two cases presented with gestational hypertension, while the first exploded into the full-blown disease with no warning.

It is important to understand that not all women with gestational

Age 27, First pregnancy, Good health
No unfavourable features at booking

	Blood pressure (mm/Hg)	Urine Protein
12 weeks	120/80	Not tested
16 weeks	110/70	Neg
20 weeks	124/70	Neg
24 weeks	120/70	Neg
28 weeks	110/70	Neg
30 weeks	170/120	++++ Feeling well

Admitted immediately;
Caesarean section 2 days later for maternal problems of pre-eclampsia.
Mother and son both did well.
Note how quickly and silently the problem develops.

Figure 6.2: Sudden appearance of pre-eclampsia

Age 31, First pregnancy, mildly overweight

	Blood pressure (mm/Hg)	Urine Protein
12 weeks	120/75	Neg
16-32 weeks	Normal	Neg
34 weeks	140/80 rechecked to normal	
36 weeks	130/90	Trace
36 weeks-39 weeks	Sometimes elevated	Intermittently neg or trace or +
39 weeks, 3days	130/90	++, confirmed

Induced, mother and well grown daughter did well.
Slow development of pre-eclampsia over more than 4 weeks.

Figure 6.3: A less clear-cut case

121

hypertension go on to develop pre-eclampsia. However, the earlier in pregnancy it is detected the more likely it is to predict pre-eclampsia. At 28 weeks almost half of women with gestational hypertension will go on to get pre-eclampsia, compared with just 1-in-14 who develop gestational hypertension at full term.

When signs come in the 'wrong' order

Although gestational hypertension is usually the first sign of pre-eclampsia, proteinuria comes first in up to 1-in-10 cases. When this happens, it is often mistaken as a sign of a urine infection. It is true that proteinuria can be a feature of urinary infections that have reached the bladder, but this is usually accompanied by pain. Proteinuria without pain is very unlikely to be caused by infection.

There are other possible variations too. In the British Eclampsia Survey of 1992, which analysed 383 cases of eclampsia, about 1-in-5 cases were preceded by gestational hypertension alone, 1-in-10 by proteinuria alone and a further 1-in-10 by absolutely no features of pre-eclampsia at all. In these cases signs of pre-eclampsia appeared *at the same time* as the convulsions.

In other words, as many as 2-in-5 of these critical cases could not have been predicted by traditional screening; and 1-in-10 women appeared totally normal before they convulsed.

Just to make the picture even *more* complicated, sometimes a problem with the unborn baby can be the first sign of pre-eclampsia; in other cases the first maternal sign is abdominal pain from the liver – a sign of the serious complication known as HELLP syndrome.

After the diagnosis

A confirmed diagnosis of pre-eclampsia is one of the most important landmarks of a pregnancy. Even if the mother feels well, she has entered a time of uncertainty, change and danger. The stakes are high, and much depends on how she and her carers work together to keep her and her baby safe.

The pregnancy is likely to continue for about 14 days more before either she or her baby are in such danger that delivery is essential. This is an average, though, and some women last as long as 20 days, while others need delivery within hours.

The questions now facing the mother and her caregivers are: where will she and her baby be safest? And when should delivery take place?

The harsh reality is that pre-eclampsia does not get better until after the birth; and until then it gets progressively worse. The deterioration may be slow and gradual or fast and sudden. The worst cases can evolve from apparent stability to crisis in a few hours.

We should acknowledge here that for some women pre-eclampsia gets worse – or even appears for the first time -*after* the birth. We look at such situations in more details later in this chapter (*see 'Serious problems after delivery', page 138*).

Disease stages	Disease features	Occurrence
Stage 0: unestablished pre-eclampsia Longest duration: weeks or months	Hypertension only Proteinuria only Fetal growth retardation (FGR) only Symptoms	Sometimes Sometimes Sometimes Never
Stage 1: established pre-eclampsia Medium duration: 2 days - 3 weeks	Hypertension Proteinuria FGR Symptoms	Always Always Sometimes Never
Stage 2: severe pre-eclampsia Short duration: 2 hours - 3 days)	Hypertension Proteinuria FGR Symptoms	Always Always Sometimes Always
Stage 3: CRISIS Instantaneous	Stroke Eclampsia HELLP syndrome	Sometimes Sometimes Sometimes

Table 6.1: Staging pre-eclampsia

This table sets out three stages of pre-eclampsia, which end in a 'crisis', and the features that may or may not be present at each stage. There are many potential crises that can occur at Stage 3. These are just a sample few – see Table 6.2 (overleaf) for a comprehensive list

Stages of pre-eclampsia

Pre-eclampsia comes in varying stages of severity. At one extreme are women who suffer a crisis – like an eclamptic fit or HELLP syndrome – without warning at home. At the other are those who seem to have a low-grade and fairly static problem. The features of the different stages are shown in Table 6.1 (*page 123*).

We should point out here that staging is most useful when a pregnancy is at or near term when it should determine the immediate response in terms of management. It is not recommended at earlier stages because *all* cases of pre-eclampsia are potentially severe.

The crises of pre-eclampsia

The various potential crises of pre-eclampsia are listed in table 6.2 (*see below*). Between them they affect many organs of the body, and it is not uncommon for them to come in combination – eclampsia and HELLP being a particularly important pairing, to the extent that HELLP is probably the most significant risk factor for eclampsia.

The most dreaded crisis is *cerebral haemorrhage* – a stroke caused by bleeding in the brain. When women with pre-eclampsia die, which is thankfully very rare, this is the most common reason.

Pulmonary oedema, the build-up of fluid in the lungs, is another crisis that can be fatal. Women with pre-eclampsia are prone to swelling (oedema) caused by leakage of fluid from damaged blood vessels into the surrounding tissues. This leakage presents particular risks in the lungs, where the fluid starts to fill the air spaces needed for breathing, causing the sufferer to start drowning in her own fluids.

Build-up of fluid in the lungs can be detected with ease by modern devices that measure the oxygen content of blood and are widely available in maternity units. A fall in the oxygen content of arterial blood should always be regarded as a danger sign in women with pre-eclampsia.

Table 6.2 Crises of pre-eclampsia

- HELLP syndrome
- Eclampsia
- Cerebral haemorrhage – stroke due to bleeding in the brain
- Cortical blindness – temporary blindness originating in the brain rather than the eyes

- Retinal disturbances, including accumulation of fluid and small haemorrhages
- Acute renal cortical necrosis – permanent kidney failure
- Acute renal tubular necrosis – temporary kidney failure
- Pulmonary oedema (waterlogged lungs) and adult respiratory distress syndrome
- Laryngeal oedema – swelling of the vocal chords due to fluid retention, causing breathing difficulties
- Disseminated intravascular coagulation (DIC) – abnormal activation of the clotting system leading to widespread bleeding
- Hepatic infarction – massive liver damage
- Liver rupture.

Features of severe pre-eclampsia

With early pre-eclampsia *(stages 0 and 1 in Table 6.1 on page 123)* women often feel completely well. But severe pre-eclampsia is marked by symptoms warning of a crisis that could be just around the corner.

For the first time the mother feels ill – often ill enough to seek urgent medical help. The problem is, though, that these symptoms – headache, visual disturbances and upper abdominal ('epigastric') pain – are quite vague and easily mistaken for signs of other health problems.

Headaches

The headaches of severe pre-eclampsia are typically very bad, often described as the 'worst ever'. They are *vascular* headaches, which throb with each heartbeat and are often accompanied by visual disturbances. In this they are similar to migraines, and it is interesting that women who get migraines have a slightly increased risk of pre-eclampsia.

Migraines can also occur throughout pregnancy, so this type of headache can be classified as pre-eclampsia only if other features of the condition are present.

Visual disturbances

On their own, visual disturbances, such as the dark, random floating objects known as 'floaters', are very common in pregnancy and at other times.

The ones that can signal an impending crisis in pre-eclampsia are bright flashing lights and partial or complete loss of vision.

Epigastric pain

The term 'epigastric' refers to the upper area of the stomach, just below the ribs. This pain, which comes from the liver, tends to be felt on the right hand side of the stomach or lower chest; more rarely it can be felt on the left side or in the back, as explained in Chapter 4 *(see page 69)*. It is a sign of HELLP syndrome, described in more detail in Chapter 2 *(see page 26)*. The pain varies in severity, and inexperienced staff may mistake it for the more common epigastric discomfort of heartburn. But, in contrast to heartburn, the pain of HELLP syndrome:

- may be sudden and *very* severe;
- almost always makes the woman restless, not wanting to lie still;
- does *not* spread up into the throat;
- is *not* burning in quality;
- may radiate through to the back on the right side;
- causes tenderness. Typically women wince with pain when pressed on the abdomen;
- is most common at night, often settling during the day.

HELLP syndrome itself has varying grades of severity. The acronym stands for **H**aemolysis, **E**levated **L**iver enzymes and **L**ow **P**latelet count; and the diagnosis depends on detection of these three features in laboratory tests. Without haemolysis, which is not always present, it is known as ELLP syndrome, which is less dangerous.

What do we mean by mild pre-eclampsia?

Pre-eclampsia is often graded according to the level of blood pressure or the amount of protein in the urine. However, feeling ill is a more reliable indicator of severe disease. Pre-eclamptic women without symptoms, who wouldn't know they had a problem without screening, are usually less severely affected. But their unborn babies may still be severely affected and in need of urgent delivery.

Pre-eclampsia is like an unexploded bomb: the fact that it is inactive doesn't mean it is safe. This is because the transition from the first sign to severe illness can, in rare cases, take place over less than an hour. So to classify someone as having mild pre-eclampsia may, as US guidelines have recognised, be misleading and potentially risky because it promotes a false sense of security. Once the diagnosis is confirmed there is always uncertainty, unpredictability and danger; and caregivers need to maintain their vigilance.

It is true that many women show a clear progression from mild to more severe disease over several days. This progression is marked by increases in blood pressure and proteinuria, laboratory results suggesting worsening disease and, often, signs of problems with the baby's wellbeing. But to track this progress calls for close monitoring, which is hard to achieve out of hospital.

This raises the very important question of when a woman with pre-eclampsia should be admitted to hospital, which we consider below. Once admitted with diagnosed pre-eclampsia, a woman should not leave hospital until her baby is delivered – usually within about two weeks. This is a logical – and vital – extension of the antenatal safety net.

When to admit

There are considerable variations between countries over the criteria for admission. The UK NICE guidelines, however, are clear: if pre-eclampsia has been diagnosed, the mother needs to be admitted to hospital. But admission comes at a cost, not just to health systems but to women themselves, especially if they already have one child or more at home. (In practice this is not an issue for the two thirds of women with pre-eclampsia who are first-time mothers.)

Women with pre-eclampsia often find it difficult to understand the point of being in hospital. Unless the pregnancy is sufficiently advanced to justify prompt delivery, it seems that nothing happens – at least nothing important. The mother's blood pressure and urine samples are checked from time to time, medication may be given to control her blood pressure, her baby is checked every day, and occasional blood tests are taken.

This apparent inaction may be tedious and frustrating for the mother, but from her baby's perspective it is a way to gain valuable extra time in the uterus.

More importantly, emergency rescue services remain close at hand, ready to swing into action at a moment's notice to offer urgent delivery and access to high-dependency or intensive care.

In some developed countries – Denmark, for example – women with so-called 'mild' pre-eclampsia may be monitored as outpatients. But in these circumstances women need the highest level of attention if complications are to be avoided.

'Z events': a question of insurance

One of us (CR), used to refer to sudden dangerous deteriorations of pre-eclampsia as 'Z events' if they happened after admission to hospital. They were rare events – occurring once or twice a year in a busy high-risk practice – but life-threatening for mother and/or baby. By definition they were serious enough to need emergency delivery, which could not have been achieved safely had the mother been at home.

Such events might include massive bleeding from the placenta, sudden severe HELLP syndrome, threatened or actual eclampsia, or a severe decline in the baby's condition, threatening his or her survival.

To return to the insurance metaphor used in the last chapter, mothers who agree to stay in hospital are effectively paying a premium to protect themselves and their babies against Z events. If we own a house or drive a car we regularly pay insurance premiums without questioning the need. If, over many years, we manage to avoid accidents, burglaries or house fires, we count ourselves lucky rather than resenting the payments.

For a woman with pre-eclampsia, a week in hospital should not seem too high a price to pay to assure her safety and that of her baby. But some mothers resist admission because they don't understand the rare but terrible risks they are facing. Unfortunately, this is also the case with many caregivers, with no experience of what can happen in the worst cases.

The gathering storm

One important thing to understand about pre-eclampsia is how the features can change very rapidly – from hour to hour in fact. Blood pressure, for example, may be stable for hours, even days, then suddenly spike to a very high level.

The amount of protein lost in the urine can also fluctuate dramatically. In other medical conditions where there is abnormal protein in the urine, protein loss is fairly constant. And pregnant women who have long-term kidney disease but *don't* have pre-eclampsia also lose protein steadily. But women with pre-eclampsia show remarkable variation in protein loss.

We can compare this situation to a gathering storm, with sudden gusts of wind, short squalls of rain and the occasional rumble of thunder. No one knows why this happens in pre-eclampsia. It seems that the combined forces of the placenta, the baby and the enlarged uterus affect the mother's body in powerful ways that sway her systems unpredictably under changing pressures.

Controlling high blood pressure

We have already covered this topic in Chapter 3 *(see page 55)*, but controlling high blood pressure is more critical with established pre-eclampsia, when it could lead to a stroke caused by a bleed in the brain – a rare but very dangerous crisis of pre-eclampsia.

When should treatment start? The threshold has been a little too high in the past and in the UK current guidance (from the National Institute of Health and Care Excellence – NICE) is to start using antihypertensive drugs once the systolic pressure has reached 150 and/or the diastolic level has reached 100. Thresholds for treatment vary between countries. In Australia, for example, it is a little lower.

Why stress is not to blame

It is common – and misleading – to link the high blood pressure of pre-eclampsia with stress. A woman confined to hospital with pre-eclampsia is bound to feel stressed – by lack of sleep and privacy and loss of family support, among other things. As mentioned earlier, blood pressure in pre-eclampsia can often 'spike' dramatically, which can only add to her anxiety. If further readings are as high or higher, the poor mother often comes to believe that she is actually *causing* the problem by her inability to relax.

It is important for women and their caregivers to understand that this is simply not true. Although there is a general connection between anxiety and high blood pressure, this is not the main problem in pre-eclampsia. Here the mother's circulation is irritable because it is affected by disruptive signals coming from the stressed placenta *(see Chapter 2, page 24)*.

Which drugs to use

There are various different drugs that can be used to treat high blood pressure. Because we have to assume that all treatment taken by mouth will cross the placenta, the possible effect on the baby is a crucial factor in the choice of drug.

The modern class of blood pressure drugs known as *ACE inhibitors* and the related group called *angiotensin receptor antagonists* are very effective for men and non-pregnant women but are *not* safe for babies and so can't be given in pregnancy. In the UK, the drugs most commonly prescribed for pregnant women are labetalol, methyl dopa and nifedipine. Others may be preferred in the United States or Australasia; and the evidence is that they are all safe enough.

Treatment may need to be adjusted day by day in response to rapid rises in blood pressure; and sometimes two or more drugs may be given together. However, there may come a point where the blood pressure can no longer be controlled by drugs and the only safe course for the mother is to deliver her baby, however premature.

Treating and preventing eclampsia

Eclampsia is rare with good antenatal care. But when it *does* occur, urgent treatment is needed. In the UK and the former British Commonwealth, eclampsia used to be treated with the drugs used for epilepsy. But they didn't work and could be unpleasant – even dangerous.

The role of magnesium sulphate

Doctors in the United States took a very different approach as early as the 1930s, treating eclampsia with infusions of a simple salt called magnesium sulphate. There was no scientific basis for this treatment, but those who used it believed it worked based on the results they achieved.

They were finally proved right 20 years ago, when two randomised controlled trials – the highest grade of scientific evidence – showed beyond doubt that magnesium sulphate worked better than anti-epileptic drugs for women with eclampsia.

These days magnesium sulphate is the treatment of choice, not just to treat eclampsia and stop further fits but to prevent them happening in the first place. It is given in high doses, either by injection into a muscle or infusion into a vein. And women have to be treated in hospital under close supervision to make sure they get enough of the drug but not too much. Overdoses can be dangerous – even fatal. So magnesium sulphate should be used only when there is good evidence that it is needed.

This is not a long-term treatment. It is used to create a window of safety – usually lasting no more than 24 hours – during which the baby can be delivered and the mother set on the road to recovery. If the first fit happens after the birth, treatment for 24 hours will control the situation in all but the most severe cases.

Preventing eclampsia

Prescribing magnesium sulphate for women who have already had a fit is a straightforward decision. Most eclamptic fits stop spontaneously and the point of treatment is to prevent further fits. But prescribing magnesium sulphate to prevent a first convulsion is a much trickier business. You would think doctors could see the fits coming, but in many cases they can't, particularly if, as sometimes happens, the fits come before pre-eclampsia is diagnosed *(see 'unheralded eclampsia', below)*.

If a woman with pre-eclampsia gets a sudden and severe headache, with extremely high blood pressure, few doctors would argue about the increased risk of eclampsia and the need for magnesium sulphate. The same is true of women with HELLP syndrome. But often the decision is less clear-cut.

How should doctors treat a woman whose only signs are very high blood pressure and proteinuria? The UK NICE guidelines suggest she needs magnesium sulphate, but it is probably more important to treat her with antihypertensive drugs to prevent stroke.

The problem of 'unheralded' eclampsia

As pointed out earlier in this chapter, UK research on women with eclampsia found that only 3-in-5 cases of eclampsia were preceded by the classic signs of pre-eclampsia – hypertension and proteinuria. What this suggests is that the remaining 2-in-5 cases are hard or even impossible to predict, with no justification for using magnesium sulphate.

The good news is that the vast majority of women with pre-eclampsia will not go on to suffer eclampsia even if they are *not* treated with magnesium sulphate. The large MAGPIE trial of magnesium sulphate to prevent eclampsia showed that in developed countries as many as 400 women with severe pre-eclampsia had to be treated to prevent just one case of eclampsia.

For a medication that is potentially dangerous and causes side effects like vomiting, muscular weakness and breathing problems, this is an unsatisfactory situation.

So who should have magnesium sulphate?

If we don't give magnesium sulphate to *all* women with pre-eclampsia, how do we decide who needs it?

131

Women are considered at high risk of eclampsia in the following situations:

- after a first seizure;
- with HELLP syndrome;
- when symptoms are severe.

In pre-eclampsia problems tend to come in clusters; and it is quite common for eclampsia and HELLP syndrome to occur together. One study has suggested that women with pre-eclampsia who develop HELLP are as much as 100 times more at risk of eclampsia than those who don't.

Other symptoms that may warn of eclampsia are not very precise. The main ones doctors and midwives worry about are headaches and visual disturbances, as mentioned earlier in this chapter.

Some doctors worry about eclampsia when blood pressure is very high. But there is no reason to believe that high blood pressure causes eclampsia, particularly as we know that up to 1-in-5 women who have fits had no documented high blood pressure immediately beforehand. So the level of blood pressure may not be the best guide to the need for magnesium sulphate.

Overall the regular use of magnesium sulphate has been a major step forward. But, as you can see, it takes thought and skill to make sure it is reserved for women who really need it.

Treating and preventing HELLP syndrome

The term HELLP is used to describe three complications that tend to come together, as explained earlier in this chapter, namely haemolysis (rupture of red blood cells) and damage to the liver and blood clotting systems.

The main symptom is very severe pain in the upper right part of the abdomen. This pain, which comes from the liver, can come on so suddenly that it is sometimes mistaken for a problem needing emergency surgery.

Affected mothers sometimes feel the pain in their back and may have other signs and symptoms such as severe headache, jaundice, nausea or vomiting. Women with partial HELLP – with only two out of the three complications (ELLP syndrome) – may have milder symptoms.

Later in this chapter we describe how mothers facing preterm delivery are treated with high-dose corticosteroids to improve their babies' breathing after birth. At one time it looked like this medication also improved the condition of women with HELLP. But further research has failed to confirm this apparent benefit, and high-dose corticosteroids are not recommended as a treatment for HELLP syndrome, at least in the UK.

The need for urgent delivery

Women who develop HELLP syndrome before delivery need to have their babies delivered in whatever way is considered safest – not necessarily by caesarean section – as soon as their condition can be stabilised.

In the worst cases there is a rapid and sudden deterioration, with several organs and systems – liver, kidneys and blood clotting system – failing all at once. As explained earlier in this chapter, there is also a risk of fluid in the lungs (pulmonary oedema) and stroke caused by cerebral haemorrhage.

These crises need to be managed in intensive care units, where most women can recover even from apparently disastrous crises.

Caring for the unborn baby

As explained in Chapter 2, the placenta, the baby's lifeline, is often faulty in pre-eclampsia. And this problem is fundamental to the disorder.

Until the 1970s, when ultrasound scanning was introduced, it was practically impossible to know anything about the health of an unborn baby. Doctors and midwives couldn't even assess its growth accurately. All they could do was feel the size of the uterus and guess – often wrongly. If the baby was considered small-for-dates, another regular mistake was to tell the mother her dates were wrong and give her a later expected delivery date.

It is hard to believe how hidden and inaccessible unborn babies were in those days, given the type of assessment that is now taken for granted.

This was bad news for babies affected by early-onset pre-eclampsia. Neonatal care was very basic in those days: ventilation to support breathing was quite a new practice and corticosteroids to strengthen babies' lungs before birth were not yet available. So there was every incentive to delay delivery for the baby's sake without any ability to assess whether it could cope with life in the uterus. Tragically this delay led to many stillbirths.

The magic of ultrasound

Today life in the uterus is so much clearer. Pregnancies can be precisely dated at 12 weeks, and any apparent growth problems can be clarified at a later date. When pre-eclampsia rears its head, doctors and midwives can accurately assess its impact on the baby.

This has all been made possible by the use of ultrasound, which also allows health professionals to monitor the baby's heartbeat and gives accurate information about its size and shape.

A special type of ultrasound scanning, known as 'Doppler scanning', gives important information about the blood supply from mother to baby and blood flow within the baby's body.

Monitoring the baby's heartbeat

Techniques to check on the baby's heartbeat were first used during labour. As this kind of monitoring became routine, it was logical to extend it to the antenatal period when babies were considered at risk, as in pre-eclampsia.

It soon became obvious that this monitoring, known as *cardiotocography* (in Europe) or the *non-stress test* (in North America), was a major breakthrough. It could distinguish between patterns of stress that the baby could cope with and patterns of *dis*tress, called terminal traces, which called for immediate rescue by caesarean section.

Over a relatively short period, the outlook for babies in distress improved enormously. And nowadays the technique is in daily use. It is cheap to perform and surprisingly effective, particularly with new computerised systems to help interpret the patterns.

CTG has one major limitation, though: it can tell you how the baby is *now*, but not how it will be in the future – even one hour later. It is an excellent diagnostic tool but a poor predictive test.

That's why the frequency of this kind of monitoring needs to increase as the illness gets worse. In uncomplicated pre-eclampsia it might be used once or twice a week. In severe pre-eclampsia, complicated by vaginal bleeding and uterine pain, it might need to be used several times a day to start with and then at least once daily to give assurance about the baby's safety.

Doppler measurement of blood flow

Doppler tests of blood flow in the placenta and umbilical cord are better than CTG tests for predicting the baby's future. At first these examined the baby's blood flow down one of the two arteries of the cord, into the placenta. This has a characteristic ebb and flow with the baby's heartbeats but, crucially, flow is sustained between each beat.

When the placenta is damaged, as in pre-eclampsia, this flow between beats disappears. Loss of flow, called 'absent end diastolic flow' (AEDF), is a sign of stress calling for close monitoring from then on.

However, in the worst cases, flow doesn't just stop but actually reverses very briefly between beats. This is a sign of *distress* which, like terminal traces on the CTG, calls for immediate delivery.

With advanced ultrasound technology it is now possible to carry out Doppler assessments of blood flow within the baby's body. For example, we can now look at how the stressed baby distributes the blood that is pumped from its heart. A severely stressed baby will maintain flow to its brain at a cost to other parts of its body, particularly the kidneys and digestive system.

Ultrasound can also show us how much fluid is surrounding the baby. A seriously reduced amount, called *oligohydramnios,* is usually a reliable sign of stress.

So there is a lot we can do to monitor the unborn baby's condition in pre-eclampsia. What is *less* easy is predicting how well the baby will survive preterm delivery, if that proves necessary.

Preparing preterm babies for delivery

Before the 1980s, babies delivered before about 30 weeks did not do well immediately after birth. The big problem was *hyaline membrane disease* – immature lungs that were too stiff to inflate properly for breathing. Babies with this problem who survived had to be maintained on artificial ventilators for the first few days until the situation improved. Sometimes this did not happen and affected babies faced long periods of recovery, requiring continuous oxygen support for up to a year or more.

The big breakthrough here was research showing that high doses of corticosteroids (also known as 'steroids'), given by injection to a mother at least 24 hours before preterm delivery, greatly improved the condition of her baby's lungs.

At first this treatment was not given routinely to women with preterm pre-eclampsia because of two concerns:

- that large doses of steroids might make their condition worse;
- that steroids would increase the risk of stillbirth, as suggested by one very early trial.

Happily these fears proved unfounded. Treatment with high-dose steroids is now standard with preterm delivery and has greatly improved the outlook for babies.

The crucial timing of the birth

We have known for almost a century that only delivery can resolve and ultimately cure pre-eclampsia. But big questions remain about *when* to do this. At or near full term there is no issue: delivery almost always guarantees an excellent outcome for both mother and baby, while delay only increases the risk of complications.

However, the less mature the pregnancy, the more difficult these decisions become, particularly in the 'middle ground' between 34 and 37 weeks.

Before 34 weeks most doctors favour a 'conservative', approach, aiming to keep the baby in the uterus for as long as possible but watching closely for a worsening in the condition of either mother or baby that would suggest the need for urgent delivery.

This approach should be used only in well-staffed specialist units where 24-hour monitoring is available. It should never be attempted at home.

The benefits of conservative management

Conservative management gives the baby extra time to mature. That time rarely exceeds two weeks, but still increases the baby's chances of survival without complications. It is important, though, for caregivers to recognise the point at which enough is enough and the only option is delivery.

There are various indications for delivery. From the mother's point of view, her signs and symptoms may become increasingly severe and difficult to control. From the baby's point of view, cries for help can be seen in the results of ultrasound and heart rate monitoring. Often SOS signals come from mother and baby at the same time. Waiting for these developments, especially when the baby is very immature (before 28 weeks), calls for great skill from doctors and midwives and courage and patience from mothers and families.

On the downside, while conservative management is often helpful for unborn babies, it increases the risk of serious complications for mothers. These include eclampsia, HELLP syndrome and placental bleeding. Balancing the sometimes conflicting needs of mother and baby is a tricky task, particularly between 34 and 37 weeks.

UK national guidelines recommend continuing the pregnancy to 37 weeks if possible. But some experts believe 35-36 weeks is a better cut-off point for conservative management. New research should help to decide who is right.

A confusing trial

The debate about the best time to deliver mothers with pre-eclampsia has been confused by a recent study from the Netherlands, known as the HYPITAT trial. The women in this trial, all at least 36 weeks pregnant, were suffering from what was called 'gestational hypertension'; this included gestational hypertension alone and pre-eclampsia.

Analysis of the trial results showed that outcomes were better in those who had immediate induction rather than conservative management. However, it is unfortunate that the trial failed to distinguish between gestational hypertension and pre-eclampsia. Although it makes good sense to deliver women with pre-eclampsia without delay after 36 weeks, not all women with gestational hypertension have a major problem and don't necessarily need delivery.

A test to look for placental problems, as described in Chapter 3 *(page 45)*, could be helpful here, and we hope that future studies will use such tests to distinguish between gestational hypertension and pre-eclampsia.

The problem of very early pre-eclampsia

The world record for early-onset pre-eclampsia is 16 weeks – a well-documented case of eclampsia. Such cases are extremely rare and fly in the face of the generally accepted rule that pre-eclampsia only happens after 20 weeks.

However, most specialist centres see women with pre-eclampsia between 20 and 26 weeks every year. These cases can be heart-breaking, with the extreme prematurity of the babies compounded by their poor growth.

Women in these situations find themselves in the middle of a nightmare. Typically a woman who feels completely well is found to have pre-eclampsia at a routine check. Suddenly she is rushed into hospital where her happy vision of a normal birth at 40 weeks is replaced by the terrifying prospect of immediate delivery. She feels her baby moving but the hard truth is that he or she has a very poor chance of survival before 24 weeks. Even between 24 and 26 weeks the outlook is poor, especially for babies who are very poorly grown.

Delivery can be delayed in the usual ways, by controlling blood pressure and watching for signs of deterioration. But if a crisis threatens, urgent delivery is the only option. When babies have no hope of survival, it is kinder and more sensible not to monitor them intensively. But these decisions need to be discussed fully and honestly. Parents need to understand the harsh reality of their situation – that it may not be possible to do anything to save their child.

Birth and after

Pregnant women have an increased risk of blood clots. These may occur in the leg veins or elsewhere in the circulation, particularly the lungs (*pulmonary embolism*). Women with pre-eclampsia are especially prone to blood clotting at or after birth, particularly after a long time in bed followed by a caesarean section.

For this reason, preventive measures may be offered to some women before the birth and to *all* women after a caesarean. This involves injecting an *anticoagulant* (anti-clotting) drug called heparin under the skin once or twice a day. The doses are low and the treatment is safe, effective and short-term, usually stopping when the woman goes home. It is also appropriate to wear compression stockings until normal activity is possible.

Serious problems after delivery

In the UK and probably most other developed countries, eclampsia and HELLP often come after rather than before birth. Sometimes they come more than a week later (although this is rare with HELLP syndrome) – sometimes with incredible speed and severity. Over the course of a few hours a seemingly well woman with a new baby can be transformed into a critically ill patient in intensive care.

In Chapter 2 we explained how pre-eclampsia is caused by the placenta. If this is true, how can we explain why the disease sometimes reaches a climax after the placenta is removed?

The disease of exceptions

Once again we see how pre-eclampsia is a 'disease of exceptions', which sometimes defies explanation. There are some plausible theories about these late cases, but they are hard to investigate. That's because it is almost impossible to research what is going on when these cases occur so rarely and unpredictably – often out of normal working hours.

And even if we could predict these crises, at present we have no idea how they might be prevented.

The dark before the dawn

The storm that is pre-eclampsia does not blow over immediately after the birth. Indeed, as we have explained, it may get worse before it gets better.

Blood pressure tends to rise in the first five days after birth, reaching a peak between five and seven days – a time when most mothers have gone home.

It is strange that the tight control of blood pressure used in most maternity units should be relaxed at a time when hypertension is likely to be at its worst. Policymakers really need to address this inconsistency in future.

For the moment all we can say is that continuing treatment of high blood pressure is important and may be needed for up to 3-6 months after birth. There are a wide range of treatments on offer that do no harm to breastfed babies.

Later problems for mothers

The experience of pre-eclampsia can be hugely traumatic, and many women remain emotionally distressed for some time afterwards; some even go on to develop *post-traumatic stress disorder* (PTSD), which we looked at in more detail in Chapter 4 *(see page 89)*.

Finally, as mentioned in Chapter 2, women affected by pre-eclampsia, particularly early-onset disease, are at increased risk of health problems in later life. These include high blood pressure, heart disease and diabetes; thyroid and kidney problems have recently been added to this list.

A reduced risk of breast cancer

We still don't know whether pre-eclampsia *causes* these later problems or simply gives early warning of them. Both of these theories are equally plausible. It's not all bad news though, since several studies suggest that women who have had pre-eclampsia may have a reduced risk of breast cancer.

At present there is no organised way of following up on the risks pre-eclampsia may pose to women's future health. But a pointer to the future has been given by the American Heart Association, which now recognises pre-eclampsia as a major risk factor for heart diseases. You can read more in Chapter 8.

Childbearing, with or without pre-eclampsia or other complications, can and ideally should be a time to reflect on how to make the best of your resources. A varied diet, moderate exercise and a reasonable balance between home and professional life are all important.

CHAPTER 7: THE MIDWIFE'S ROLE IN PRE-ECLAMPSIA

In the last chapter we looked at the management of pre-eclampsia, from diagnosis to delivery – and beyond.

This chapter focuses specifically on the role of midwives, who care for and support women and their partners before, during and after the birth of their babies. It covers similar ground to previous chapters but from a midwife's perspective.

All pregnant women benefit from midwifery care, although it is not available in all parts of the world. Where it is available, pregnant women regarded as 'low-risk' are able to receive most, if not all, of their care from midwives, with very little involvement from doctors.

Even those who need specialist supervision, including women at risk of pre-eclampsia, still benefit from the continuing care of midwives, who can help them understand and cope with what is happening as well as maintaining a focus on the normal and positive aspects of pregnancy and motherhood.

Preparing women: assessing and explaining the risks

In many countries antenatal care begins at the 'booking' visit, when a thorough assessment should alert a midwife to any factors that increase the risk of pre-eclampsia. While the pregnancy may turn out to be normal, awareness of risk factors allows midwives to step up the standard provision of antenatal care with extra visits and more screening tests.

All pregnant women are potentially at risk of pre-eclampsia, but where the chances of problems are clearly increased women should be referred to specialists for review and enhanced monitoring.

Factors that can increase a woman's risk of pre-eclampsia are listed in Chapter 2 *(page 33)*. But since pre-eclampsia cannot yet be reliably predicted, midwives need to remain vigilant even in the absence of risk factors.

Talking to women about pre-eclampsia

Providing the right level of information about risk is an important aspect of midwifery care. An Australian survey of women who had suffered pre-eclampsia found that almost eight out of 10 knew nothing about the illness before they were diagnosed and, once diagnosed, did not understand how serious their condition was. These women and their families placed a high value on access to information (1).

A sensitive midwife will want to give a woman at risk the information she needs about pre-eclampsia without threatening her confidence in her ability to achieve a healthy pregnancy and normal birth. An open relationship, based on mutual respect and trust, helps to build this confidence and also aids adjustment if complications set in.

Midwives are well placed to help women see why blood pressure and urine need to be checked at every visit, to understand the 'silent', stealthy nature of pre-eclampsia in its early stages and to recognise that it can appear any time after 20 weeks.

But it is important to strike the right balance between minimising and overstating the potential problems.

Talking after diagnosis

However seriously they are affected by pre-eclampsia, women still need to talk about and participate in their own care.

Most cases of pre-eclampsia result in delivery of a healthy, well-grown baby close to full term. But women with early-onset disease face more challenges and more complex management, while some need urgent delivery soon after diagnosis.

The level of information required will vary according to each woman's situation. Regular communication, including taking time to listen to her concerns, will help keep the focus on the mother-to-be rather than her condition.

Referring women to specialist care

Risk factors for pre-eclampsia can be elicited at the booking visit and midwives should refer women at risk for specialist care in accordance with their local guidelines and regulations.

The PRECOG and NICE guidelines in the UK and the SOMANZ guidelines in Australasia identify factors at booking that point to the need for specialist referral and suggest a plan of stepped-up care for women at increased risk, followed by a systematic assessment for signs of pre-eclampsia from 20 weeks. But other countries may differ in their approach.

Early specialist referral allows for consideration of possible preventive measures, such as low-dose aspirin and calcium supplementation *(see Chapter 3, page 47)*, as well as individual care planning to ensure the best possible outcome.

While early risk-rating and referral are crucial to safe care, it is important to keep in mind the unpredictable nature of pre-eclampsia, which can also occur unexpectedly in supposedly 'low-risk' women.

Spotting the early signs and symptoms

There are times when pre-eclampsia seems to appear like a 'bolt from the blue', leaving everyone shocked by the sudden onset of severe disease. This was the case with Leigh (New Zealand), who had enjoyed an apparently normal pregnancy and became very unwell a few hours after her baby was born.

> *'I rang the bell as I was starting to feel very uncomfortable with nausea and chest pain. My blood pressure was now 186/104 and a transfer was arranged back to the birthing suite. I was finally readmitted after an hour, crying in pain and vomiting, with a blood pressure of 190/115.'*

Leigh's experience *(see also Chapter 4, page 71)* was dramatic and unusual. But the fact that her baby was born very small may have been a clue that pre-eclampsia had developed, with the baby affected first.

Variability – the great challenge

The great challenge with pre-eclampsia – for doctors and midwives alike – is to reliably detect a condition that varies hugely in how and when it presents.

However, unlike with Leigh, warning signs usually appear some time before a woman begins to feel unwell. There is always a tension between emphasising the normal aspects of pregnancy and looking for potential problems, but women need to know about any concerns. Where there is real uncertainty it is always better to be safe than sorry.

The importance of blood pressure

A number of 'signs' of pre-eclampsia can be seen and measured. These include the classic signs of raised blood pressure and protein in the urine as well as blood changes and rapid weight gain associated with sudden swelling (oedema), particularly in the face.

The significance of changes in blood pressure is explained in great detail in Chapter 2 *(page 14)*, but we will offer a brief recap here. The booking blood pressure is an important baseline: while hypertension is defined as a systolic pressure of 140mmHg and/or a diastolic of 90mmHg, it is important to be aware that pressures in the higher range of normal (systolic of 130mmHg or more and/or diastolic of 80mmHg or more) in early pregnancy can be a clue that a woman will go on to develop pre-eclampsia.

Blood pressure in mid-pregnancy

Mid-pregnancy readings can provide another clue. These should be lower than at booking because of physiological changes that reduce blood pressure. If this does not happen, a wise midwife should be alert to possible risk and watch the woman closely for further changes.

At this stage of pregnancy, routine antenatal visits are often spaced a month apart, and more frequent blood pressure checks will help detect any increase in a timely manner. Any trend upwards, even if lower than 140/90, should be followed up. Pre-eclampsia may already be developing, even before the blood pressure rises, so it is wise to be aware of the multi-system nature of the disease and alert to subtle changes.

Checks on urine

Urine should be tested for protein at every antenatal visit. A 'trace' of protein is nothing to worry about, but any more, indicated by one or more 'plusses' on a dipstick test, must be followed up with laboratory tests, such as a urine protein:creatinine ratio (PCR), as described in Chapter 2 *(page 13)*.

Proteinuria can sometimes be due to a urine infection, which needs to be ruled out by a laboratory test on a midstream sample. However, this is very unlikely in the absence of bladder or kidney pain.

Proteinuria should never be ignored and *must* be followed up on the same day. The dipstick test produces a high rate of false positives, but complacency can put a woman and her baby at risk.

Don't make women responsible for testing

Reading the colour of the dipstick accurately can be challenging, particularly in poor light, and should always be the responsibility of the midwife rather than the mother-to-be.

Janis (New Zealand), talking about her experience of severe pre-eclampsia at 26 weeks, felt she should not have been asked to check her own urine.

> 'This should have been the responsibility of the maternity caregiver. Perhaps if they had read the urine stick instead of me it would have been caught earlier. I'm not stupid, I can match colours, but there isn't a huge difference between pale yellow and pale green.'

Sudden swelling

Sudden onset of oedema is usually obvious to women and their caregivers and is often linked with sudden excessive weight gain. Oedema alone is not a diagnostic sign of pre-eclampsia, but a steady weight gain of more than 1kg (or about 2lb) per week is a possible warning sign.

Blood testing for pre-eclampsia

A midwife who is concerned that a woman may be developing pre-eclampsia can arrange blood tests, including a full blood count and tests for kidney and liver function.

The full blood count includes the level of haemoglobin (Hb), packed cell volume (PCV or *haematocrit*) and platelet count. As the disease progresses, the lining of blood vessels (endothelium) throughout the body becomes damaged and leaks fluid. This makes the blood more concentrated, with haemoglobin and packed cell volume higher than normal, while the platelets, which are used to repair the damaged blood vessels, tend to reduce in number.

If blood levels of platelets and other clotting factors fall too low, a rare and serious complication known as disseminated intravascular coagulation (DIC) may develop *(see Chapter 2, page 26)*.

Kidney and liver function tests

Tests on kidney function are primarily concerned with blood levels of waste products such as urea, uric acid and creatinine. A build-up of these products in the bloodstream is a sign of kidney malfunction.

Liver function tests measure blood levels of certain enzymes whose levels are raised when there is liver damage. In pre-eclampsia the most significant liver enzymes are aspartate aminotransferase (AST) and alanine transaminase (ALT).

With HELLP syndrome *(see Chapter 6, page 126)*, high levels of liver enzymes are combined with low levels of platelets and a breakdown of red blood cells known as *haemolysis.*

When carrying out blood tests it is always important to look at the results in the context of pregnancy- and gestation-specific ranges.

Midwives must be guided by their clinical observations and their local protocols for recommended investigations. If there are clear indications of pre-eclampsia immediate specialist review is essential.

Negative results don't exclude problems

One very important thing to bear in mind when testing for pre-eclampsia is that while a positive result strengthens the diagnosis of pre-eclampsia, a negative result can never exclude it.

This is because pre-eclampsia is not a clearly-defined illness but a 'syndrome' – a cluster of features occurring together *(see Chapter 3, page 40)*. Because the components of the cluster are highly variable from woman to woman, the absence of such features as low platelet count, raised uric acid levels and even proteinuria cannot rule out the diagnosis of pre-eclampsia.

Monitoring the unborn baby

In women at risk of pre-eclampsia the baby's growth must be monitored carefully because poor placental function can lead to growth restriction and a reduced oxygen supply.

Fetal growth restriction is very common in early-onset pre-eclampsia. Sometimes the growth problems develop before the maternal signs, when detection can be enhanced by standardised measurements of the mother's fundal height, which can then be plotted on a computer-generated customised antenatal growth chart (2). This is in line with recommendations for general midwifery care of normal women in the UK NICE guidelines.

When fetal growth restriction is suspected, referral for ultrasound assessment of growth, liquor volume and Doppler flow is recommended. In late-onset pre-eclampsia, even if the fetus is not small for gestational age, it may still be suffering from circulatory stress, which can be detected by Doppler ultrasound measurements of different parts of its circulation. These tests look for 'brain sparing' – preferential diversion of the baby's blood flow to the brain, suggesting the need for delivery sooner rather than later.

Checking fetal movements

Mothers-to-be need to know that they can help their babies by contacting their midwives if there is any reduction in the usual frequency and strength of fetal movements. For some women, particularly first-time mothers, it is difficult to know what 'normal' feels like, so face-to-face discussion should be supported by clear written instructions.

There are excellent resources available to teach women and their caregivers about normal fetal movements, with evidence-based protocols for follow-up when reduced movements are reported. One such resource is the practice guideline published by the Australasian Stillbirth Alliance (3).

Delays in reporting and acting on reduced fetal movements can have tragic consequences, and women should be urged to act on their concerns immediately rather than waiting to see if the situation improves.

Variation in symptoms

As explained in Chapter 6 *(page 125)*, there is wide variation in the symptoms women with pre-eclampsia may experience. Most have no symptoms at all, while a few feel very ill towards the end of the illness. Some women feel generally unwell, tired and even 'flu-like for some time before diagnosis.

The classic symptoms of pre-eclampsia are listed in Chapter 2 *(pp 18-19)*. They include severe headache, visual disturbances, epigastric pain, nausea/vomiting, breathlessness and chest pain. When a woman presents with symptoms, a systematic approach is essential, keeping in mind the multi-system nature of the disease, the signs and symptoms relating to each system involved and the relevant clinical and laboratory investigations.

Teamwork between midwives and specialists

For some women the need for specialist care is obvious from the booking visit. In such cases midwives normally remain involved, working with obstetricians to provide appropriate care. This continuity of care, where possible, is a great benefit to women and their families, helping them to cope with the stress of a high-risk pregnancy. With complicated pre-eclampsia, other specialists may also be involved, including physicians, anaesthetists and neonatologists.

It is difficult for women initially assessed as low-risk to adjust to the reality of a complication. And all too often things are made worse for them when different health professionals offer different opinions and suggest different management plans. What women with pre-eclampsia need – in common with all pregnant women – is consistent care, reliable information and rapid access to checks when needed. Management plans should be set out clearly in the records, including notes carried by women, and all professionals have a duty to respect them.

Midwives and obstetricians are mutually dependent when caring for high-risk women and should make time to communicate regularly on relevant issues.

Referral guidelines

Midwives have to follow formal guidelines on care and referral. We do not attempt here to describe and compare the various international guidelines, but those from the organisations listed below are readily available online:

The National Institute for Health and Care Excellence (NICE – UK)
https://www.nice.org.uk
Action on Pre-eclampsia (PRECOG guidelines – UK)
http://action-on-pre-eclampsia.org.uk/professional-area/precog/
Royal College of Obstetricians and Gynaecologists (RCOG – UK)
https://www.rcog.org.uk
Society of Obstetric Medicine of Australia and New Zealand (SOMANZ)
https://somanz.org
American College of Obstetricians and Gynaecologists (ACOG)
https://www.acog.org
Guidelines at: http://www.acog.org/Resources-And-Publications/ Task-Force-and-Work-Group-Reports/Hypertension-in-Pregnancy
The Society of Obstetricians and Gynaecologists of Canada (SOGC)
https://sogc.org
The Society approved guidelines published by the Canadian Hypertensive Disorders of Pregnancy Working Group (4).

Later referrals

The case for referring women to specialist care in later pregnancy may not be entirely clear-cut. For example, a woman may not have the level of hypertension – 140/90 – that is an accepted indication for referral; nevertheless her blood pressure might have increased substantially from the booking level and there may be other signs that pre-eclampsia is developing.

It is better to refer as soon as problems appear rather than waiting for them to get worse. As a rule, in the absence of hypertension, referral is necessary with:

- proteinuria of more than 0.3g over a 24-hour period;
- a protein:creatinine ratio (PCR) of 30 mmol/mol or more;
- new proteinuria of 2+ on dipstick testing;
- symptoms of pre-eclampsia *(see Chapter 2, pp 18-19)*;
- abnormal full blood count, kidney or liver function tests;
- suspected fetal growth restriction.

Support through difficult times: the midwife's role after admission

Referral for assessment doesn't always lead to immediate hospital admission. Some women are seen as outpatients several times before being admitted. However, once pre-eclampsia is diagnosed, most women are admitted and will stay in hospital until after their babies are born.

Admission usually comes as a shock after the sudden appearance of severe pre-eclampsia, although in cases of gradual progression it is more predictable. Regardless of the circumstances, it is never easy for women to be separated from their partners, families, familiar routines and support systems, and confined to hospital – possibly for weeks.

How women feel

Women admitted to hospital with pregnancy complications regularly bemoan their loss of control over the pregnancy as well as their daily lives. Busy, active women who are often juggling the competing demands of work and family are suddenly told to put their lives on hold and 'rest' in hospital. This is far from easy, especially as most women in this situation still feel perfectly well and don't understand why they need to be there.

Midwives can offer crucial support with this adjustment. And while hospital midwives are responsible for assessment, self-employed or community midwives are sometimes able to help with handover of care and may even continue to visit afterwards.

However, from this point onwards the responsibility for providing physical and emotional support will shift to hospital midwives. Offering a warm welcome to the hospital and time to listen to and address concerns is an excellent start.

Making sense of the situation

Many women admitted to hospital with pre-eclampsia are acutely fearful – for their babies and themselves – even when there is no immediate risk. But sometimes the reverse is true and women facing serious risk but feeling well wonder what all the fuss is about.

Midwives need to acknowledge these different viewpoints by helping women to understand why they have been admitted, keeping them informed about what is happening and what is likely to happen, and giving them the opportunity to ask questions.

If staff always appear rushed, a woman may be reluctant to express her fears or ask questions for fear of being a 'nuisance'. She may also feel like a burden to her partner and family, especially if there are children at home or if giving up work sooner than expected is likely to cause financial problems. Making time to listen and talk is essential.

Involvement in decision-making

Some women want to be actively involved in making decisions about their care, while others prefer a more passive role. When the disease is progressing fast, most are happy to leave decision-making to the professionals; however, research has shown that involvement with their own care in high-risk pregnancy gives women a sense of responsibility for their own health and that of their babies, and may help them adjust emotionally after the birth.

Women need information about their condition and about the many tests and procedures that may be completely new to them. There will be frequent urine and blood tests, ultrasound scans, CTG monitoring, checks on blood pressure and reflex testing, among others. These can be very stressful, particularly for women who have never been seriously unwell, and explanations from midwives are very helpful.

These explanations probably need to be given more than once because at times of stress people often find it difficult to take in the information. It is helpful to involve partners and other family members and to acknowledge their varying fears and concerns. Taking the time to remember first names, offering to help in small ways and inviting questions can go a long way towards reassuring everyone involved.

The paradox of 'resting' in hospital

The main reason for admitting women with pre-eclampsia to hospital is not for rest but to maintain control of a complex, unpredictable condition, with the ability to deliver the baby urgently, at any time, if necessary.

While they will be encouraged to rest in hospital, this is often difficult on busy wards with multiple occupancy. Most women in this situation would prefer a single room, and midwives can sometimes arrange this for them. But for women with advanced pre-eclampsia there are advantages to sharing a room because there are always others around to raise the alarm if a crisis, such as an eclamptic convulsion, occurs.

Preparing for premature delivery

Many women enjoying a normal pregnancy feel some degree of nervousness as their due date approaches. But for women facing a premature delivery because of pre-eclampsia, the anxiety can be overwhelming because of the real risk that the baby might not survive.

For many women, a visit to the neonatal intensive care unit helps them prepare for the shock of seeing their baby in an incubator, attached to various monitors, oxygen and intravenous tubing.

The need for information

It is common for women with pre-eclampsia to complain that they were not given enough information about their illness, or that the information they *were* given was not pitched at the right level for them.

It takes time to really listen to a woman's fears, assess her understanding and give the appropriate information. But this is an important investment that has a really positive impact on a woman's wellbeing as she faces the myriad investigations leading up to the birth of her precious baby.

Provision of reading material may help, but it should never replace face-to-face discussion.

Keeping watch

After admission, mothers-to-be, midwives and medical staff need to be alert to possible symptoms of pre-eclampsia, since their onset can be more useful than laboratory tests in signalling the rapid progression of the disease.

Women need to know that they can call for a midwife or nurse *at any time* and that their concerns will be taken seriously. Midwives need to warn women about the particular symptoms that may herald serious complications *(see Chapter 2, pp 18-19).*

Listening to women

Women also need to be able to call for a midwife if they are worried about reduced fetal movements. It is important for midwives to listen to women and to trust their own instincts that something may be wrong.

Nadia (New Zealand), who had complained of upper abdominal pain, was about to be discharged after her blood test results came back normal. But her midwife suspected otherwise, as Nadia reports.

> '*I guess it was me saying I knew something wasn't right and she believed me and kept on to the doctors, saying "it must be something".*'

Repeat blood tests showed that Nadia was developing HELLP syndrome, and her baby was delivered by emergency caesarean section some hours later. Had her midwife not persisted, things might have gone a lot worse for Nadia and her baby.

The timing of delivery

While some women with pre-eclampsia go into labour spontaneously, it is more usual for induction to be planned at an optimal time for mother and baby.

Sometimes that decision has to be made urgently if either mother or baby become very unwell; but ideally decisions should be made in such a way that the woman and her partner are fully involved.

Support during labour

Support and reassurance from a midwife during labour or planned caesarean can help a woman feel more positive about the experience. Attention to important normal practices, such as 'skin-to-skin' contact immediately after the birth, is invaluable for mother and baby; but it often depends on the midwife acting as an advocate, particularly after a complicated labour and/or high-tech delivery.

Making sure mothers have time to touch, cuddle and even feed their babies before they are transferred to special care nurseries can be emotionally and physically beneficial for both, as well as creating treasured memories.

Every birth is special, and even the most difficult labour can be transformed into a positive and memorable experience with skilled and sensitive midwifery care.

The midwife's role in postnatal care

Even though pre-eclampsia is thought of as a placental disease which is 'cured' by delivery, women may still become quite unwell after the birth. It is not uncommon for pre-eclampsia to get worse – or even be diagnosed for the first time – after the baby is born. As pointed out in Chapter 6 (*page 139*), blood pressure tends to rise in the few days after delivery, reaching a peak between five and seven days.

This means that midwives must not drop their guard after the birth and should continue to monitor their patients very carefully for any increase in blood pressure or symptoms of worsening disease.

The psychological aftermath

Emotional distress after an experience of severe pre-eclampsia is very common, and women continue to need the support of their midwives. This may be particularly true for women who need to recover from caesarean sections on top of the illness, while still having to care for their newborn babies.

Immediately after the birth there is often a sense of elation or even emotional numbness, and it may take some time for a woman to feel the full emotional impact of her experience. Taking time to talk over and process that experience is an important part of recovery. Midwives can also provide details of further resources – including patient support groups – in case they are needed at a later stage.

Discharge from hospital

According to NICE (UK) guidelines, women should not be discharged from hospital after pre-eclampsia until their blood pressure has stabilised and is under control, there are no persisting symptoms and blood tests show an improving trend.

On discharge it is the responsibility of midwives and medical staff to make sure a new mother is clear about:

- who will provide follow-up care;
- how often blood pressure needs to be checked;
- symptoms to worry about – and report to the midwife;
- how to make urgent contact with the midwife.

Additionally midwives need to clarify with specialists:

- the plan for reducing or stopping antihypertensive medication, where relevant;
- indications for referral back to specialist care;
- the follow-up plan.

Support after discharge

During the early weeks of postnatal recovery, most women will continue to have some midwifery care. In New Zealand, the woman's own midwife often provides the follow-up care, while in other places care provision is more fragmented.

Ideally the midwife who provided antenatal care will continue visiting during the postnatal period to provide holistic support and help the woman come to terms with what has happened.

Post-discharge checks

After discharge, blood pressure should be checked every 1-2 days until it has returned to normal, and blood tests repeated as clinically indicated. Women with persisting hypertension and/or proteinuria at the six-week postnatal review should be referred back to specialist care.

The role of patient groups

In the immediate postnatal period, women may appreciate the support of patient groups like Action on Pre-eclampsia (APEC), where they can access appropriate information and talk to others who have been through similar experiences. *(For a full list of these groups see Chapter 8, page 173).*

For women who have been very sick and given birth very early there may be no time to think about the enormity of what has happened until some weeks later. At this point it can be very helpful for them to talk through their experience with their midwife as well as their specialist, and express their feelings.

Extra challenges of prematurity

Providing support after discharge may be particularly difficult after premature birth, when mothers often have to care for their babies in special care nurseries and may find it difficult to establish breastfeeding. But such support is hugely valuable at a time when care may have become very fragmented and the focus has shifted from the mother to the baby.

Support after loss

Pre-eclampsia can rob women of many of the normal aspects of pregnancy that are taken for granted. The sense of loss is likely to be greater for those diagnosed early and most acute for those whose babies don't survive.

For these women, the stress of recovery is compounded by grief. And recovery depends on professional and social support, which is often sadly lacking.

For Ruth (UK), the delivery and subsequent death of her baby at 27 weeks left her feeling desperately isolated:

> 'It was an awful and very lonely time. I didn't know anyone who had experienced anything similar and there was no local support available. No one knew how to be with me or what to say, and often what they did say was quite hurtful. My family just wanted me to "get back to normal", which ended up being an added pressure.'

Ruth needed to talk about her grief not put it away until it was no longer seen. She needed time to dwell with her grief in order to overcome it.

Midwives who have travelled the journey with women who suffer loss through pre-eclampsia are in the best position to acknowledge their feelings and offer genuinely helpful support. They can also refer women on for further professional or social support when necessary.

Thinking about the next pregnancy

Contemplating another pregnancy can be frightening after pre-eclampsia. Some women choose not to take the risk if they have suffered serious complications; others may be advised against it by their doctors. In some cases it is a woman's partner who cannot face the prospect of seeing her so seriously ill again.

A specialist review a few weeks after delivery is the best context for a debrief about what happened and discussion about the management of a possible next pregnancy. If this facility is not available – which sometimes happens in less severe cases – it may fall to midwives providing postnatal care to counsel women.

Even though thoughts of another pregnancy may be far from a woman's mind during the postnatal period, her midwife can recommend lifestyle changes – including healthy diet and exercise – that will help to keep her healthy and may reduce the risk of recurrent pre-eclampsia.

At this stage it is also important for midwives and doctors to check for and manage any underlying health issues that may predispose a woman to pre-eclampsia in the next pregnancy.

Support through the next pregnancy

The risk of recurrent pre-eclampsia increases in proportion to its severity in a previous pregnancy and how early it was diagnosed. Most women will have a normal pregnancy next time, and those who do develop pre-eclampsia will tend to get it later and less severely.

However, prediction of risk is not an exact science and caregivers need to remain vigilant. A pre-pregnancy specialist review or early specialist referral will allow for timely discussion of an appropriate care plan and the use of potentially preventive measures such as low-dose aspirin and calcium supplementation *(see Chapter 3, page 47)*.

A very anxious time

The stage at which pre-eclampsia developed in a previous pregnancy is often a very anxious time, particularly for women who went on to lose their babies. Extra antenatal support may be welcomed at these times.

While a multidisciplinary approach is essential for high-risk women, midwives also help to keep a focus on normality at times when bad memories dominate a woman's thinking and threaten the joyful anticipation of another baby.

Midwives must always be careful to avoid giving false reassurance, but helping women to celebrate signs of progress and the special nature of pregnancy is a valuable contribution they can make.

References

1. East C, Conway K, Pollock W, Frawley N, Brennecke S. Women's experiences of Pre-eclampsia: Australian Action on Pre-eclampsia Survey of Women and their Confidants. J Pregnancy. 2011; Article ID 375653, 6 pages

2. Roex A, Nikpoor P, van Eerd E, Hodyl N. Serial plotting on customised fundal height charts results in doubling of the antenatal detection of small for gestational age fetuses in nulliparous women. 2012; Australian and New Zealand Journal of Obstetrics and Gynaecology; 52:78-82

3. Preston S, Mahomed K, Chadha Y, Flenady V, Gardener G, MacPhail J, Conway L, Koopmans L, Stacey T, Heazell A, Fretts R and Frøen F for the Australia and New Zealand Stillbirth Alliance (ANZSA). Clinical practice guideline for the management of women who report decreased fetal movements. Brisbane, July 2010

4. Magee LA, Pels A, Helewa M, Rey E, von Dadelszen P; Canadian Hypertensive Disorders of Pregnancy (HDP) Working Group. Diagnosis, evaluation and management of the hypertensive disorders of pregnancy. Pregnancy Hypertens. 2014 Apr;4(2):105-45

Further reading

Berg M. A Midwifery Model of Care for Childbearing Women at High Risk: Genuine Caring in Caring for the Genuine. Journal of Perinatal Education. Winter 2005;14 (1) 9-21

Futura M, Sandall J, Bick D. Women's perceptions and experiences of severe maternal morbidity: A synthesis of qualitative studies using a meta-ethnographic approach. Midwifery. 2014; 30, 158-169

Hinton L, Locock L, Knight M. Maternal critical care: what can we learn from patient experience? A qualitative study. BMJ Open 2015; 5: e006676. doi:10.1136/bmjopen-2014- 006676

Leichtentritt R D, Blumenthal N, Elyassi A, Rotmensch S. High-Risk Pregnancy and Hospitalization: The Women's Voices. Feb 2005; Health and Social Work. 30 (1). 39-47

CHAPTER 8: HOW WOMEN CAN HELP THEMSELVES

Up to this point in the book we have focused on the role of professionals – family doctors, specialists, midwives and research scientists – in understanding, predicting, preventing, diagnosing and treating pre-eclampsia.

But what about the women at the centre of all this activity? Are they helpless victims of chance and passive recipients of care? Or do they have the power to influence events in their own interests and those of their unborn babies?

We are firm believers in the ability – indeed the obligation – of women to help themselves when it comes to pre-eclampsia.

They can do this by:

- understanding their personal risk of pre-eclampsia and its implications for antenatal care;
- recognising and reporting potential signs and symptoms of the illness;
- being prepared to challenge professional complacency but respect professional safeguards;
- taking expert advice about the next pregnancy.

This chapter takes a detailed look at all these aspects of self-care and addresses itself directly to women – and their partners, their families and anyone else who has an interest in their wellbeing.

As with chapters 2, 4 and 7, we illustrate our arguments with case history material derived from responses to our online survey of women with personal experiences of pre-eclampsia.

Understanding your personal risk of pre-eclampsia

There are a number of so-called 'risk factors' that increase your chance of getting pre-eclampsia. The more of these boxes you tick the more likely you are to have it to some degree. The main risk factors are identified in Chapter 2 *(see page 33)*, but it is worth repeating them here:

- being pregnant for the first time. This accounts for most women who get pre-eclampsia;
- having had pre-eclampsia in a previous pregnancy. This is an important risk factor, especially if the affected pregnancy ended early (before 34 weeks), but the number of women involved is relatively low;
- having a family history of pre-eclampsia;
- being pregnant for the first time by your current partner;
- conceiving after a short period (less than 6 months) of sexual relations;
- having a long interval (10 years or more) between the last pregnancy and the current one;
- being under 20 or over 35;
- being obese. This depends on your height:
    - If you are 5ft (1.52m) tall you are obese if you weigh more than about 154lb (11 stone, 69.85kg);
    - If you are 5ft 6 inches (1.68m) tall you are obese if you weigh more than about 188lb (over 13 stone, 82.55kg);
    - If you are 5ft 9 inches (1.75m) tall, you are obese if you weigh more than about 204lb (14 stone 6lb, 91.62kg). There is no threshold – the more overweight you are, the greater your risk of pre-eclampsia.
    There are plenty of online calculators that enable you to calculate your BMI precisely.
- needing help, such as IVF, to get pregnant;
- having one of a number of chronic conditions, including hypertension, kidney problems, diabetes, migraines, polycystic ovarian syndrome or antiphospholipid antibody syndrome (APS);
- having twins, triplets or more. The risk is increased by about three times in twin pregnancies and is even higher with triplets and quadruplets.

'I had many of the triggers for pre-eclampsia – IVF, previous high blood pressure brought on by weight gain, and advanced maternal age – but my specialist was never concerned and told me not to worry when I asked about pre-eclampsia. I wish he had reviewed with me the signs and symptoms and had me check my blood pressure at home daily. I mostly wish I hadn't trusted him so much and been more proactive about my concerns.'

Tracy, US

Know your family history

If your mother or one or more sisters had pre-eclampsia this increases your own risk, especially if the illness led to an early preterm delivery.

'Two sisters had pre-eclampsia before me so I knew a lot about it. I was very closely monitored during pregnancy because of these genetic risk factors.'

Anon, New Zealand

You may need to probe

You might assume you would automatically know whether your mother or sister(s) had pre-eclampsia, but that's not necessarily true. Pre-eclampsia has gone by different names – particularly 'toxaemia' – in the past. And the illness is not always recognised and named – even now.

'My mum's two aunties and her grandmother had pre-eclampsia but I didn't know that at the time. If I had realised it was in the family I would have paid much more attention to my symptoms.'

Sarah, UK

The key questions to ask the women in your family – including your maternal aunts and grandmother – if they are not sure whether they had pre-eclampsia are:

- Did you have high blood pressure?
- Did you have swelling – particularly of the hands and face?
- Were you very unwell?
- Did you have fits (seizures)?
- Did your baby have to be delivered early?

- Was your baby very small?
- Why did your baby die *(if relevant)*?
- Were you advised against further pregnancies?

Getting answers to these questions is likely to be particularly difficult for women who were adopted or whose mothers are no longer alive. But it is worth investing in a bit of detective work.

> *'My mother died shortly before I got married. I had no idea she had had pre-eclampsia when she was pregnant with my older sister. When I was recovering in hospital after my baby died, my dad said he remembered my mother having something similar. If I had known I was at risk I am sure my doctors would have been more on the alert and would have taken my symptoms more seriously.'*
>
> Anon, UK

Be clear about what risk means

Risk is a difficult concept to grasp. You might have every single one of the risk factors listed above – although that is highly unlikely – but that doesn't mean you will inevitably get pre-eclampsia. Conversely, you can't assume you won't get it if you have *none* of the risk factors.

> *'I had a perfectly normal (pretty wonderful) low stress pregnancy and this happened to me. Other than it being my first pregnancy I had no risk factors. I am 30, normal weight, very healthy, no family history. It's very scary – if it could happen to me it could happen to anyone.'*
>
> Nicole, US

Even if you were able to calculate a precise risk for pre-eclampsia – such as 1-in-3 – there are limits to the usefulness of that information. What everyone wants to know and no one can tell them is: will I be one of the lucky *two* or the unlucky *one*?

Knowing your risk simply tells you how alert you should be to the possibility of complications in your pregnancy and whether you might benefit from an enhanced level of antenatal monitoring delivered under specialist supervision.

Plan your care in relation to your risk

Many women pin their hopes and dreams on a perfect pregnancy and a natural delivery. But if you have a significant risk of pre-eclampsia, you might be unwise to plan for non-specialist antenatal care and a home birth.

> 'I had a natural water birth planned. To go from that to a two-week stay in a major hospital and having my son die in my arms and to not bring him home – it's been an absolute nightmare.'
>
> Laura, US

If you have read the preceding chapters you will be aware that pre-eclampsia is a dangerous, unpredictable, highly variable illness that is:

- difficult to predict with any degree of accuracy;
- impossible to prevent with any degree of certainty;
- tricky to diagnose;
- challenging to manage and control.

The need for specialist involvement

Your best hope for a safe and happy outcome lies in a personalised antenatal care programme that is tailored to your risk and overseen by specialists with skills and facilities that match your needs.

This vigilance needs to persist up to and beyond the birth itself. With pre-eclampsia there is never a point at which you can safely say: 'Okay, I've come this far and I'm clearly not going to get it now.' Some of the worst cases develop shortly after the birth. And if you are at home when that happens you are much more vulnerable than you would be in hospital, with specialist expertise and facilities at hand.

Your care in pregnancy

Do what you can to reduce your risk

Unfortunately it is not yet possible to reliably prevent pre-eclampsia, although researchers are constantly striving to push the boundaries, as described in Chapter 1 *(see page 9)*.

The first priority is to start antenatal care early, ideally at 8-10 weeks of pregnancy. This allows time for assessment and investigation of possible risks, referral to a specialist and discussion of preventive treatments *(see below)*.

Low-dose aspirin is the best established preventive treatment, although the benefits are small and not necessarily applicable to all women.

Daily treatment with low-dose aspirin is often recommended for women known to be at risk of pre-eclampsia and it may be worth discussing this with your midwife or specialist at a very early stage of pregnancy.

The case for dietary supplements

Calcium supplements are at the top of this list. It is now accepted that in some areas of the world where calcium intake is low, because of the water supply or a poor diet, calcium supplements help to prevent pre-eclampsia.

Other candidates for prevention, including vitamin D and selenium, remain unproven and are not recommended.

Being overweight is a risk factor for pre-eclampsia, but if you need to lose weight it is better to do this before rather than during pregnancy.

Once you are pregnant, there is little evidence that you can reduce your risk of pre-eclampsia through diet and lifestyle changes. However diet may be important for other reasons, especially if you are very overweight or prone to diabetes. There is every reason, therefore, to eat a moderate, mixed healthy diet, including plenty of fruit and vegetables.

Never miss an antenatal appointment

Antenatal check-ups can be tedious and time-consuming. And sometimes it can be tempting to skip an appointment, especially if you feel perfectly well and have something better to do with your time. But missing appointments can be dangerous, especially in the second trimester when they tend to be widely spaced.

Most women feel perfectly well

The reason we need antenatal checks for pre-eclampsia is precisely *because* most women feel perfectly well until the illness has reached a late and dangerous stage. You could have very high blood pressure and significant proteinuria without having a clue that anything was amiss. And if you missed an appointment at this stage, the illness could escalate into a crisis that might have been prevented by earlier recognition and intervention.

*'I skipped an appointment to go to my leaving party at work. I didn't
feel very well at the time but, in my ignorance, I thought that's how
pregnancy made you feel. A few days later I was rushed to hospital
by ambulance and my very premature baby had to be delivered almost
immediately to save my life.'*

Ruth, UK

Report signs and symptoms without delay

If an antenatal check shows your blood pressure is normal and there is no
protein in your urine, that's reassuring but no grounds for complacency. Pre-
eclampsia can evolve to crisis levels over a period of hours, and normality
today doesn't guarantee the same tomorrow. That's why you also need to
be alert to the appearance of signs and symptoms between checks.

The main signs and symptoms to look out for are:

- sudden swelling, particularly of the face and hands;
- excessive weight gain – more than 1kg (about 2lb) per week
  over several weeks;
- severe headache;
- disturbances of vision, such as 'flashing lights';
- severe pain below the ribs on the right side (sometimes the left),
  felt in the stomach, the lower chest or the back;
- increasing breathlessness;
- reduced or absent fetal movements.

You may feel reluctant to bother your doctor or midwife and it can be
tempting to just wait and see what happens. But with pre-eclampsia, as a
general rule, it is better to be safe than sorry.

*'Sometimes you feel like you're overreacting when something
worries you, especially if it is your first pregnancy. That's why it
is important to know the warning signs ahead of time and discuss
them with your health care provider. This will help diagnose pre-
eclampsia sooner in some cases.'*

Allison, US

*'Don't be afraid to ask your doctors lots of questions and trust your
gut feeling. If you feel something is wrong get to your doctor as soon*

as possible. Protect both yourself and your baby. Life is precious.'

Kristen, US

Challenge complacent professional attitudes...

Chapters 2 and 4 are littered with examples of women whose caregivers either failed to recognise signs and symptoms of pre-eclampsia or failed to act on them.

Professionals can get it wrong

For many people it is natural to defer to professional opinions and difficult to question or challenge them. But doctors and midwives can be wrong about pre-eclampsia for several reasons:

- The signs and symptoms can be vague and easily mistaken for other things.
- They may come at an unusual time (such as the second trimester) or in an unusual order (such as proteinuria before hypertension).
- The professionals concerned may have limited experience and understanding of pre-eclampsia.

In the end, every woman's health is her own responsibility. At the very least, you have the right to insist on having your blood pressure and urine tested and your baby's heartbeat checked if you have concerns between regular antenatal appointments.

If any of the results are abnormal, you should expect further assessment and investigation, ideally on the same day. You should *not* expect to have nothing happen for a week or more. Pre-eclampsia can evolve to crisis proportions much faster than that.

> 'The night before I was flown out of the county as an emergency I called [the hospital] and the midwife told me to "just take a bath and relax". I could have died if I had just listened to her and wrongly ignored my strong instincts. I am grateful that I took my own blood pressure and reached out to another professional who listened to my concerns and took them seriously.'
>
> *Laura, US*

'I had been feeling unwell for a few weeks with abdominal pain, a tingling sensation in my mouth, vomiting and headache. I saw my GP when my headache would not go away and was accompanied by visual disturbance. I told him I was concerned it was PE due to my family history. However, he reassured me it was a migraine and to go home and rest. My husband wasn't happy with this diagnosis and asked me to call the hospital. They brought me in and induced me just a few hours later.'

Kerry, UK

...but respect the need for safeguards

Once pre-eclampsia is diagnosed, the safest place for a woman and her unborn baby, up to and beyond the birth, is hospital.

This is *not* because there is any need for bed rest but because the illness will almost inevitably get worse; and both mother and baby need to be watched carefully for signs of deterioration that signal the need for early delivery. This monitoring usually needs to be carried out several times a day, which is simply not feasible outside a hospital or day assessment unit.

Don't fight the wrong battle

Hospital admission may well upset your carefully laid plans – it almost always does. You may be still working, or painting the nursery or enjoying some quality time at home before your life changes forever.

But resisting admission is fighting the wrong battle. From now on your main concern has to be the safety of you and your baby.

Change your expectations

Once in hospital with pre-eclampsia you need to adjust your expectations about your pregnancy and your baby's birth and accept a few unwelcome truths:

- You will probably have to stay there until your baby is born.
- Your pregnancy is unlikely to run its full normal course and you may have no choice over the mode of delivery.
- You will need to submit to an intrusive level of monitoring and, possibly, treatment before, during and for some days after your baby's birth.

- If your baby is premature, he or she may well need special care for some time after the birth.

Stay responsible

But being in hospital doesn't mean you should abandon all responsibility for your own wellbeing and that of your baby. Yes, you will have frequent checks. But things can change very suddenly with pre-eclampsia and you need to watch for any new or worsening symptoms that could indicate a turn for the worse, and report them immediately to your caregivers.

Care, support and information after the birth

Don't push to go home too soon

Your baby's safely delivered and is doing well. You're feeling exhausted but otherwise fine. So it's okay to go home now – right? WRONG!

Delivery always resolves pre-eclampsia but not necessarily straightaway – and things often get worse for a while before they get better:

- Hypertension tends to get worse in the few days after the birth, with the highest readings often found 5-7 days later. When blood pressure is very high there is a risk of stroke.
- Eclampsia can appear for the first time after birth – even several days later.
- HELLP syndrome often makes its appearance after birth.

'Five days after delivery I was very swollen and developed a headache. I spoke to a doctor on call who told me to take [painkillers] and call her in the morning if the headache had not gone. The next day I felt disoriented and my vision was off, with no depth of perception. I spoke to a nurse practitioner who thought I was tired. Shortly after that I had a seizure and was taken to the ER, where I had a second seizure.'

Vineeta, US

Crises are more dangerous out of hospital

These crises are much more dangerous if they happen at home. That's why the safest thing is to stay in hospital until all the signs and symptoms have either disappeared or (as with hypertension) are controlled by medication.

After you return home, it is important to continue having your blood pressure checked at intervals until at least six weeks after the birth.

While you remain in hospital – and even after you go home – it is important to remain alert to new or worsening symptoms that could mean a crisis is at hand, and report these immediately to your caregivers.

Piece together what happened

You could put some of your down time in hospital to good use by trying to understand exactly what happened to you. This process will help you to come to terms with your experience at the time, but it will also come in useful later on when you get round to thinking about the next pregnancy.

Talk to the specialist

Ideally you should talk to the specialist in charge of your care and it might be useful to have your partner, another family member or a friend with you when you do, perhaps to take notes for later reference. Here are some questions you might usefully address to the specialist:

- Did I have pre-eclampsia?
- How bad was it?
- Did I have any complications?
- If yes, what were they?
- How well is my recovery going now?
- Am I likely to have suffered any permanent damage?
- Has my baby suffered any permanent damage?

Get support where you can

Having pre-eclampsia can be a lonely, isolating and frightening experience. It may be that all your friends and family have enjoyed normal, uncomplicated pregnancies and can't understand what you've been through. People may say the wrong things while trying to be helpful. They may want you to get back to normal while you still need to work through your feelings about what happened.

In these circumstance it can often be helpful to seek support from a professional – your midwife, your family doctor, your health visitor or, if appropriate, a counsellor or therapist.

Think about patient support groups

Some of the best sources of information and support are the patient support groups that focus either on pregnancy issues in general or pre-eclampsia in particular. Your midwife, if you have one, should be able to direct you towards the most appropriate group, and may even have some literature to pass on. Patient support groups (*listed by country on page 173*) can usually offer a mixture of the following services:

- comprehensive information, both online and in print;
- telephone support;
- introductions to other local people who have had similar experiences;
- support from volunteer 'befrienders'.

> *'After months of feeling lonely, isolated and misunderstood I can't stress too much what a difference it made to talk to women who had been through similarly awful experiences. Finally I was no longer a freak but a member of a community.'*
>
> Anon, UK

Preparing for the next pregnancy

Find the right specialist

Most women don't get pre-eclampsia again, but some do, and the earlier you had it in your first pregnancy the more likely it is to recur in the next. So you will probably want to make sure you can access the best possible care for your next pregnancy.

Ideally this will be provided by a specialist who is a recognised expert on pre-eclampsia, with a lot of experience of managing the condition. Although your care plan should be directed by an expert, it may include specified checks by a local midwife.

If you are already under the care of such an expert, that's great. If not, you may want to seek advice from your family doctor and/or local support groups. Patient support groups are usually aware of the leading experts in their field and can sometimes advise on or facilitate referrals.

> *'I changed hospital and saw a professor at the biggest hospital in the state. He is an expert on pre-eclampsia and gave me a wealth of very*

thorough, intelligent, useful information.'

Katharine, Australia

'Prior to my diagnosis, I had seen a wonderful perinatal specialist at a different hospital from the one where I delivered, and after my first delivery I switched hospitals so that I would be in his care throughout my second pregnancy. He recommended testing for underlying conditions between my pregnancies. I was closely monitored by both the perinatal specialist and my new obstetrician during my second pregnancy and I did not develop pre-eclampsia. During this pregnancy I had doctors who provided me with information, listened carefully to my symptoms, explained their recommendations, were knowledgeable about pre-eclampsia and treated my concerns and questions with respect. If all health care providers would follow that example, babies and mothers would have a better chance of a safe and healthy delivery.'

Emily, US

Ask the right questions

If possible, it is a good idea to arrange an appointment with your chosen expert before you conceive again. You will have your own list of questions but you may like to include the following:

- How do you rate my chances of getting pre-eclampsia again?
- How would you advise me to reduce my risk?
- What sort of antenatal care programme will you provide?
- How often will I see you?
- How do I report concerns between appointments?
- What will happen if I do get pre-eclampsia again?

Relax and enjoy your pregnancy

It is almost impossible for a woman who has had severe pre-eclampsia – and possibly lost a baby – to approach the next pregnancy without some degree of fear or trepidation.

It is a modern mantra that 'pregnancy is not an illness'. But for those affected by pre-eclampsia, pregnancy is most definitely an illness and they may never again be able to think of it as a natural, joyful, life-enhancing experience.

However, if you have done everything in your power to surround yourself with the right kind of expertise and support, that should provide you with the reassurance you need to enjoy the normal aspects of your pregnancy and look forward to motherhood.

Ruth from the UK, whose first baby died after a very premature delivery, but who went on to have two healthy children, made this poignant but encouraging comment:

> *'I lived my second pregnancy in a state of abject terror until the third month when I found a specialist in whom I felt absolute confidence. The feeling that I had passed my burden of worry from my shoulders to his was almost a physical one. Amazingly, although I knew my risk of recurrence was high, I was able to enjoy my pregnancy because I trusted him to spot the earliest signs and do the right things. I thought: "if he can't save my baby then no one can" – and that thought was strangely comforting.'*

Look after yourself in the long term

In chapters 2 and 6 we explained that certain long-term health problems are more common in women who have had pre-eclampsia. These include chronic high blood pressure, heart disease, stroke and type 2 diabetes. It is good to be aware of these risks but not to worry unduly since treatments for these conditions are continuing to improve. For example, we now have safe and effective ways to treat high blood pressure, prevent hardening of the arteries and manage diabetes.

The risk of these long-term health problems increases with the severity of the pre-eclampsia which, in turn, increases with earlier time of onset. So mild pre-eclampsia at the end of pregnancy is much less of an issue than severe pre-eclampsia leading to delivery at 30-34 weeks or earlier.

There is general agreement that pre-eclampsia offers a unique opportunity to identify women whose future health could be protected and improved by appropriate medical supervision. How this should be done is still under discussion. But since the American Heart Association recently (2011) included a history of pre-eclampsia as a reason for such checks, there will be growing pressure on doctors to provide them.

You can play your part by adding to the pressure and by taking action to look after yourself well. This means leading a healthy lifestyle, including regular moderate exercise and a balanced and varied diet, which avoids excesses of any one food type, such as meat, fats or processed foods.

You could follow the DASH (Dietary Approaches to Stop Hypertension) diet, which has been developed with support from the US National Institutes of Health and is rich in fruit, vegetables and low-fat dairy products (1). It is not the only diet that can be useful, but it has been shown to significantly reduce the risk of heart disease.

References

1. Ravera A, Carubelli V, Sciatti E, Bonadei I, Gorga E, Cani D, Vizzardi E, Metra M, Lombardi C. Nutrition and Cardiovascular Disease: Finding the Perfect Recipe for Cardiovascular Health. Nutrients. 2016 Jun 14;8(6). pii: E363.

Patient support groups around the world

The following organisations offer varying combinations of information, support and education about pre-eclampsia:

Australia
Australian Action on Pre-eclampsia (AAPEC)
www.aapec.org.au

Canada
Preeclampsia Foundation Canada
www.preeclampsiacanada.ca

France
Association de Prevention et d'Actions contre la pre-eclampsie (APAPE)
administration@apape.fr

Germany
Arbeitsgemeinschaft Gestose-Frauen e.V.
www.gestose-frauen.de

Netherlands
Hellp Stichting
www.hellp.nl

New Zealand
New Zealand Action on Pre-eclampsia (NZ APEC)
www.nzapec.com

UK
Action on Pre-eclampsia (APEC)
www.apec.org.uk

USA
Preeclampsia Foundation
www.preeclampsia.org

CHAPTER 9: YOUR QUESTIONS ANSWERED

In this chapter, we offer clear simple answers to the questions most commonly asked by women who have been affected by pre-eclampsia.

For those who prefer to dip in and out rather than read the whole chapter, the section headings and the pages they begin on are listed below.

Questions about:

Questions about causes

I'm a fit, healthy woman who looks after herself and has a healthy diet and lifestyle. Why did I get pre-eclampsia?

Most women who get pre-eclampsia are completely healthy and are at risk of the illness only in their first pregnancies. The reasons for this are still not clear. There is growing evidence that pre-eclampsia may be caused by a problem within the mother-father partnership. The unborn baby is part 'foreign', in that half of its genes come from the father. In most partnerships it seems that the foreign aspects of a first baby are easily accepted by the mother's immune system. But in some cases they are not; and this may lead to faulty development of the placenta, the special pregnancy organ that nourishes the baby as it grows *(see Chapter 2, page 21)*. This is what seems to start at least some cases of pre-eclampsia.

Having said that, some health problems increase the risk of pre-eclampsia. These include chronic high blood pressure *(hypertension)*, kidney disease, diabetes and some rare autoimmune conditions related to lupus. Being overweight is also a risk factor. But most women with these problems don't get pre-eclampsia. The risk of getting pre-eclampsia may be influenced by lifestyle, but only marginally. So, to sum up, whether or not you get pre-eclampsia must be seen largely as an accident of nature.

I feel I let my baby down by getting pre-eclampsia. What did I do wrong?

As far as we know, nothing you did – or failed to do – before or during your pregnancy caused you to develop pre-eclampsia. It is not a 'lifestyle disease', and most of the risk factors – such as first pregnancy, being an older or younger mother, or having a family history of the illness – are entirely beyond your control. It is pointless and distressing to blame yourself.

Did I get pre-eclampsia because I am an older mother?

Being an older mother wouldn't have *caused* you to get pre-eclampsia. But there is evidence that age is a factor, since women under 20 and over 35 are at slightly increased risk. For women under 20, as explained in Chapter 2 *(see page 35)*, this may be because the time between first sexual intercourse and conception is too short for the mother's immune system to have learned to 'tolerate' the 'foreign' cells in which half the genes come from the baby's father.

We don't know exactly why older mothers are more at risk but we presume it is to do with the aging process. There is no doubt that a 40-year-old has fewer physical reserves than someone half her age and is usually less fit.

My blood pressure's been on the high side for years. Is this why I got pre-eclampsia?

Having chronic hypertension doesn't *cause* pre-eclampsia, although it does increase your *risk* of getting it for reasons that are not fully understood. However, it is important to remember that high blood pressure is only one aspect of pre-eclampsia, not the whole story. Most women who get it have no pre-existing blood pressure problems.

My first pregnancy was perfectly normal. Why did I get pre-eclampsia this time?

Although pre-eclampsia is most common in first pregnancies, some women get it for the first time in a second or later pregnancy. This is particularly likely to happen if you change partners between pregnancies, when your immune system has to learn to tolerate 'foreign' cells of a baby from a different partner. It can also happen if you stay with the same partner but leave a long interval – 10 years or more – between pregnancies. When this happens, your immune system may have 'forgotten' how to tolerate the foreign cells from your partner and has to start all over again.

Some health problems increase your risk of pre-eclampsia *(see the first answer in this section)*. But these would tend to lead to pre-eclampsia in *every* pregnancy rather than just second or later ones.

Is pre-eclampsia hereditary? Does that mean my daughter will get it?

Pre-eclampsia is not directly passed on to children by their parents in the same way as genetic diseases like cystic fibrosis or haemophilia. However, a family history of pre-eclampsia is an important risk factor. Women whose mothers and/or sisters have had pre-eclampsia are three times more likely to get it themselves than those without this family history. We don't know if the risk of pre-eclampsia keeps rising with the number of relatives who have had it.

If you have had pre-eclampsia, your daughter will not *inevitably* get it herself, but she and those looking after her in her first pregnancy need to understand that she is at increased risk, and her antenatal care should be organised accordingly.

My husband's first wife had pre-eclampsia. Does that mean I am at risk?

Although most of the risk factors for pre-eclampsia are maternal, it seems that fathers can also play a part. Research from Scandinavia suggests that men who experience pre-eclampsia with one partner are about twice as likely as other men to have the same problem with another partner. The fact that women whose mothers-in-law had pre-eclampsia are at very slightly increased risk themselves also suggests a paternal role in the illness.

Questions about signs and symptoms

Why is blood pressure raised in pre-eclampsia?

Rising blood pressure is often the first detectable sign of pre-eclampsia. What seems to happen at stage 2 of the illness (*see Chapter 2, page 24*) is that the placenta under stress releases substances that affect the inner lining of the mother's arteries, known as the *endothelium*. In response, the endothelium releases substances that powerfully constrict the small arteries of the body. In order to maintain blood flow through these narrowed vessels, the heart has to pump blood out at higher-than-normal pressures.

How come I felt so well when my blood pressure was so high?

As a rule high blood pressure causes no symptoms of illness at all unless it reaches very high levels – 200/130mmHg or more – when the arteries are in danger of bursting. Thankfully pressures of this level are very rare in pregnancy.

With pre-eclampsia it is normal to feel perfectly well until the illness reaches a late and dangerous stage, which can happen very suddenly. That's why you need to be in hospital once the condition has been diagnosed. In retrospect, some women recall feeling vaguely unwell for some time before very severe pre-eclampsia develops. But this is not a reliable sign of the illness.

Why was there protein in my urine? Was it anything to do with diet?

The leakage of blood proteins into the urine, one of the key diagnostic signs of pre-eclampsia, has nothing at all to do with diet. It is a sign that the kidneys, whose job is to filter waste into the urine and retain useful nutrients like protein in the blood, are not working properly. This is because of the damage to the inner lining of the blood vessels (*endothelium*), described in the first question in this section.

The kidney damage – and the resultant leakage of protein – tends to get worse as the disease progresses. Total kidney failure is one (thankfully rare) potential consequence of this damage.

Why did I need to do 24-hour urine collections?

The simple dipstick tests used by doctors and midwives to check urine samples are useful for flagging up the presence of protein in the urine. But they are not very good at measuring *how much* protein your kidneys are leaking. That's because the test is influenced by how concentrated or dilute your urine is; and this, in turn, depends on how much you have drunk in the few hours beforehand.

A sample collected over a 24-hour period or a protein:creatinine ratio (PCR) urine test gives a more accurate reflection of the amount of protein in your urine and hence the severity of the illness.

Wouldn't it be easier for women to check their own blood pressure and urine at home?

In theory this would save women the time and effort of attending a clinic. But in practice there are problems. The automated blood pressure machines available for home use are known to be less accurate than those used by doctors and midwives; so relying on them could cause unnecessary alarm in some cases and give false reassurance in others. You can buy urine dipstick tests for home use, but these are not very reliable, for reasons explained in the answer to the previous question.

If you are known to be at risk of pre-eclampsia, it might be useful for you to monitor your own blood pressure and urine between check-ups. But home tests are no substitute for antenatal checks carried out by skilled professionals.

My doctor told me I had high levels of uric acid in my blood. What does this mean?

This can be an early sign of pre-eclampsia, coming before the appearance of protein in the urine. Like protein in the urine, it is caused by problems with the kidneys' filtering mechanism. As well as allowing blood proteins to leak out into the urine in pre-eclampsia, the kidney filters also retain in the bloodstream waste products like uric acid, which should be excreted with urine. This causes no harm to mothers or babies except in the most severe cases.

A blood test showed my platelet levels were low. Is this serious?

Platelets are the specialised blood cells responsible for clotting. In normal pregnancy they tend to be busier than usual, making the blood more prone to clotting. In pre-eclampsia they are often even more 'reactive'. This means they get used up at a faster rate than normal and their concentration in the blood falls as a result.

Low platelet levels are another sign of the circulatory problems that are typical of pre-eclampsia. At its most extreme this evolves into the extremely dangerous crisis known as disseminated intravascular coagulation or DIC (*see Chapter 2 page 26*), when the clotting system explodes out of control so that normal vessels are randomly plugged by numerous small clots. This leads to dangerous loss of function in all parts of the body because of failure of the blood supply. But it also rapidly exhausts the many factors that sustain clotting, leading to uncontrollable bleeding.

Why did my hands and face swell up?

Swelling *(oedema)* is a common feature of normal pregnancy, particularly in the feet and ankles. In pre-eclampsia this swelling can be sudden and extreme, affecting the face and fingers too. The swelling is caused by leakage of fluid from the blood vessels into the tissues. It tends to be worse in pre-eclampsia because the illness affects the innermost lining of the blood vessels *(the endothelium)*, making them more prone to leakage. This severe swelling is usually linked with a rapid rate of weight gain, since water is a very heavy substance.

My doctor dismissed my epigastric pain as heartburn. Why didn't she know better?

Upper abdominal 'epigastric' pain is quite common in pregnancy. Only rarely is it a sign of the liver problems of HELLP syndrome, one of the more serious complications of pre-eclampsia. The pain of HELLP syndrome usually comes on suddenly and severely, and there is pain in the liver area when a doctor presses there. Pain in the liver area may also be a sign of gallstones, which is why the two conditions are sometimes confused.

Pregnant women with this kind of pain should always be thoroughly assessed and have their blood pressure and urine checked for the diagnostic signs of pre-eclampsia before it is ascribed to something else. Milder pain or discomfort *without* liver tenderness is common and usually caused by heartburn or the position and movements of the baby.

I had severe backache rather than pain below my ribs. Was this a symptom of pre-eclampsia?

Although epigastric pain is most commonly felt below the ribs, usually on the right hand side, some women feel it high up in the back instead. This is because the liver is large and extends round to the back of the abdomen.

Why was I told to watch out for 'flashing lights' and spots before my eyes?

These can be warning signs of impending eclampsia (convulsions). This is one of the most serious (but rare) complications of pre-eclampsia, triggered by abnormal activity in the nerve cells of the brain. Because it is difficult to predict which women with pre-eclampsia will progress to eclampsia, they are advised to watch out for these warning signs.

What caused my terrible headache?

Severe headache is a typical feature of late-stage pre-eclampsia, which can signal that a crisis is about to happen. Headaches are very common for all women at all stages of life. But the headache of pre-eclampsia tends to be very bad, often described as 'the worst headache of my life'. It may be felt anywhere in the head or at the back of the neck. The pain probably comes from irritated or inflamed blood vessels, much like the similar pain of migraine. It may also be caused by accumulation of fluid within the brain (*cerebral oedema*), which is associated with eclampsia.

Are there degrees of pre-eclampsia? My doctor said I had mild pre-eclampsia but later I became very ill.

Pre-eclampsia is 'progressive' and almost always gets worse once it has started. It is often labelled 'mild' or 'severe' but the labels are misleading because apparently mild pre-eclampsia can deteriorate very suddenly. Moreover the baby's illness may run its own course, independently of how well or badly the mother is doing.

Severe pre-eclampsia is an unstable condition. The blood pressure may vary from hour to hour and is hard to control – even with two or three different drugs; severe swelling may come on suddenly; kidney function may worsen from day to day; and the mother may feel very unwell. With 'mild' pre-eclampsia, the blood pressure is easy to control, the liver and blood clotting systems are not involved and the mother – but not necessarily the baby - is well.

My doctor didn't think I had pre-eclampsia at all at first because I had protein in my urine but normal blood pressure. Was he right?

High blood pressure is usually an earlier sign of pre-eclampsia than proteinuria. But if you have read the rest of this book you will know that pre-eclampsia is regarded as 'the disease of exceptions', which doesn't always follow a predictable pattern. Some women with pre-eclampsia develop proteinuria before high blood pressure, and in some cases the blood pressure doesn't rise *at all*. Unless there is some other obvious cause for the proteinuria it should be assumed to be pre-eclampsia and antenatal care stepped up accordingly.

My midwife thought I had pre-eclampsia but my doctor disagreed. Why wasn't it clear?

Unfortunately, there is no single diagnostic test that gives a yes/no answer to the question: does this woman have pre-eclampsia? The new Elecsys test, which measures the angiogenic factors mentioned in Chapter 2 *(see page 25)*, is increasingly being used around the world. It is only applicable to women who present with signs or symptoms before 37 weeks, but it is helpful in ruling out other problems masquerading as pre-eclampsia.

In the absence of a single reliable test, pre-eclampsia is recognised by a number of typical signs and symptoms. Because these signs and symptoms don't all come at the same time and can all be mistaken for other things, it is not unusual for health professionals to disagree over the diagnosis. However, any woman with new hypertension *and* proteinuria after 20 weeks of pregnancy should be assumed to have pre-eclampsia and treated accordingly.

My doctor said I needed to be admitted straight away but I didn't see why because I felt perfectly well. Why couldn't I just rest up at home?

There are two important points here:

1. The fact that you felt perfectly well was no indication of the severity of your disease. Most women with pre-eclampsia don't feel ill until they are on the verge of a crisis such as kidney failure or eclampsia. This can happen very suddenly, which is why it is best to be in hospital once pre-eclampsia is diagnosed.

2. The point of being in hospital is not to rest – most women could rest much more easily at home than in a busy hospital antenatal ward. Rather it is to keep you and your baby under the closest possible supervision, with frequent monitoring tests. The aim of this monitoring is to recognise the stage at

which delivery is necessary in order to avoid serious danger for mother, or baby, or both.

If my doctor or midwife had picked up the warning signs sooner, could the illness have been prevented?

At present there is no reliable way to prevent pre-eclampsia, so earlier detection would not have stopped the disease in its tracks. The point of early detection is to keep mother and baby as safe as possible, monitoring them closely and making sure that delivery is carried out before serious complications set in. It is possible, therefore, that your illness might have been less severe if your caregivers had picked up the warning signs sooner.

Questions about monitoring and treatment in hospital

In hospital they kept telling me to rest and relax when my blood pressure was high? Was it my fault it was high?

Absolutely not! In other situations, blood pressure can be influenced by how rested you are and how stressed or relaxed you feel. But the high blood pressure of pre-eclampsia is completely independent of your state of mind. It is caused by narrowing of the small arteries of the body; and this, in turn, is caused by the placental problem at the heart of pre-eclampsia. It is misleading – and unfair – of hospital staff to suggest that any of this is within your control.

My blood pressure was always highest in the morning when I'd been resting all night. Why was this?

Normally blood pressure is highest in the evening, falling dramatically overnight during sleep. But in pre-eclampsia the blood pressure tends not to drop overnight; and sometimes the normal pattern is completely reversed, with the highest readings recorded during sleep or first thing in the morning. We don't really know why this happens.

Why did I need to stay in hospital after the drugs brought my blood pressure back to normal?

It is a mistake to think of high blood pressure as being the central feature of pre-eclampsia. In fact it is just one of a number of outward signs that the circulatory system is disturbed and out of balance. It is vital for very high pressures to be controlled by 'antihypertensive' drugs because this can prevent stroke – a very serious, rare complication of pre-eclampsia. However, controlling the blood pressure does not make the underlying disease go away or stop it getting worse. Even with normalised blood pressure, you and your baby would still have been at risk of dangerous complications and definitely needed to stay in hospital.

Why did they need to do so many blood tests?

Blood tests are another way of tracking the progress and severity of pre-eclampsia and they need to be carried out regularly in hospital after the disease is diagnosed. The tests are looking for three main signs of advanced pre-eclampsia:

- worsening kidney function that could lead to kidney failure;
- abnormal liver function that could lead the liver to fail or even burst;
- blood clotting problems that could lead to blood vessel blockages and/or haemorrhage.

The results of these blood tests help doctors to determine when delivery needs to happen in order to avoid dangerous complications for mother and baby.

The blood tests showed my liver function was abnormal. What was going on?

Liver damage tends to be a fairly late feature of pre-eclampsia that is hard to detect except through blood tests, which can show leakage of the contents of damaged liver cells into the bloodstream. The damaged liver tends to swell, causing the 'epigastric' pain that often comes with late-stage pre-eclampsia. This liver damage often comes with blood clotting problems, leading to a complication called HELLP syndrome (see the first question of the next section).

In very rare cases the liver can swell so much that it bursts, which is a life-threatening situation. The main reason doctors carry out so many blood tests in pre-eclampsia is to check for these problems before they reach dangerous proportions.

The magnesium sulphate made me feel really ill. Why did I have to have it?

Magnesium sulphate, a chemical compound also known as 'Epsom salt', is given by mouth as a treatment for several minor medical problems, including constipation. It is now also known to help control and prevent the eclamptic convulsions (fits or seizures) that are a rare but dangerous complication of pre-eclampsia, when given in high doses.

Magnesium sulphate is regularly prescribed for women who have severe pre-eclampsia or have already had a convulsion. It has to be given, in hospital, by infusion into a vein or injection into a muscle, and can make you feel unwell. Possible symptoms include flushing, itching or tingling, nausea and/or vomiting, weakness that can cause breathing difficulties, thirst, palpitations, drowsiness or confusion. However, research has shown that any risks are greatly outweighed by the potential benefits of the treatment.

Questions about complications

I was told I had HELLP syndrome. What is this?

HELLP syndrome is a combined liver and blood clotting disorder which is a serious complication of pre-eclampsia. The letters stand for **H**aemolysis, **E**levated **L**iver enzymes and **L**ow **P**latelet count. Haemolysis is when the solid red cells in the blood burst and spill their contents into the plasma, the fluid portion of the blood; elevated liver enzymes are a sign of liver damage, while low platelets are a sign of overactive clotting. Some people get ELLP syndrome, which is similar but without the haemolysis.

The syndrome can only be detected through blood tests. Once HELLP is diagnosed it is important to deliver the baby as soon as possible to avoid life-threatening crises such as liver rupture and haemorrhage.

Why did I have fits even though my blood pressure was never very high?

Fits are a rare life-threatening crisis of pre-eclampsia. We know that they are not caused by high blood pressure because they can happen if your blood pressure is only slightly raised – or even normal. The fits are triggered by abnormal activity in the nerve cells of the brain, but we don't know exactly why that happens in some women with pre-eclampsia.

I was told I had signs of liver damage. How serious is this?

Liver damage is one of the potential complications of pre-eclampsia that can be detected in routine blood tests. Often it is detected as part of HELLP syndrome *(see first question in this section)*. The liver damage can be serious, even life-threatening, because the liver could fail or even burst. As long as these crises can be prevented or overcome, liver function returns to normal after delivery.

What caused my kidneys to fail?

Impaired kidney function is a standard feature of pre-eclampsia. With the normal filtering mechanisms not working properly, proteins that should remain in the bloodstream leak out into the urine; at the same time waste products like uric acid that should be excreted with the urine remain in the bloodstream.

Since pre-eclampsia is a progressive disease, the kidney damage usually gets worse, and complete failure of one or both kidneys is one possible consequence. This is a dangerous situation requiring treatment with an artificial kidney machine *(dialysis)*. Fortunately, though, in most cases the kidney function eventually returns to normal after delivery.

I was in intensive care after suffering pulmonary oedema. How did I get it?

Pulmonary oedema is one of the most dangerous complications of pre-eclampsia. Oedema affecting the feet, hands and face is not dangerous in itself. But if fluid leaks from the blood vessels into the air spaces in the lungs, you begin to drown, quite literally.

Most women need intensive care in this situation, and temporary life support from an artificial ventilator is often needed until the problem can be controlled. To do this, excess fluid needs to be removed from the blood vessels and the tissues. This 'drying out' process is straightforward if drugs can be used to stimulate urine production. But if the kidneys have failed there may be a need for short-term dialysis on a kidney machine.

I haemorrhaged badly after delivery and needed multiple transfusions. Why did this happen?

Childbirth itself can be a cause of massive haemorrhage after delivery when the placenta is removed. In pre-eclampsia, haemorrhage may be caused by failure of the mother's clotting system, known as disseminated intravascular coagulation (DIC). This is best described as a clotting tornado that rips through the mother's system and leaves tiny blood clots in all parts of her body (*see also page 180*). These can block blood flow to the organs, which is bad enough. But to make matters worse the blood still flowing has exhausted its ability to clot because it has lost nearly all its specialist clotting cells, known as platelets.

This is a very dangerous crisis, which can only be managed by replacing the missing clotting factors through multiple transfusions – sometimes as many as 20-30 – and delivering the baby if that has not already happened.

Questions about the baby

How are babies affected by pre-eclampsia?

Both mothers and babies can be affected by pre-eclampsia because it starts in the placenta – a shared organ. The main problem for the baby is a restricted blood supply from the placenta. This can lead to slower-than-normal growth (*fetal growth restriction, or FGR*). In extreme cases the baby can suffocate from lack of oxygen. These problems are most common when pre-eclampsia sets in early (before 34 weeks) and are rare after 37 weeks.

Could my high blood pressure have harmed my baby?

The baby suffers because of a restricted blood flow from the mother to the placenta. The mother's blood pressure goes up in a bid to keep the blood flowing. The raised pressure itself can be harmful to the mother but not the baby.

Could the drugs I was taking for high blood pressure and to prevent fits have harmed my baby?

As far as we know, all these drugs cross the placenta to the baby, but some are safer than others. Two classes of antihypertensive drugs, known as ACE inhibitors and angiotensin receptor blockers (ARBs), are never recommended in pregnancy because they can cause major problems for babies in the uterus. However, other drugs, including labetalol and methyl dopa, are known to be safe in pregnancy.

Calcium channel blockers, including nifedipine, and drugs called alpha- and beta-blockers are also safe to take over the short period of a pre-eclamptic illness. Magnesium sulphate, given to prevent convulsions, is well tested, and with standard doses there are very few side effects for the baby.

My baby was 'small-for-dates'. What does this mean?

It almost certainly means your baby was suffering from some degree of fetal growth restriction (FGR) and was therefore smaller than expected (*see first answer in this section*). Strictly speaking, small-for–dates is not necessarily the same as FGR, since some babies grow normally but remain small.

One of the reasons for routine scanning in pregnancy is to check that babies are growing properly in the uterus. A slow-down in growth can sometimes be an early sign of pre-eclampsia – or even the first sign. For this reason, if you had a growth-restricted baby that needed delivery by 34-36 weeks in one pregnancy, you would need to be monitored carefully for signs of pre-eclampsia in the next.

I was really ill but my baby was fine. How do you explain that?

Pre-eclampsia is a shared disease that can affect the mother or the baby, or both. Babies are most likely to be affected by pre-eclampsia that develops relatively early (before 34 weeks), when they still have a lot of growing to do. Babies whose mothers develop pre-eclampsia after 37 weeks, when they are fully grown, are usually fine. Mothers who get the problem immediately after the birth usually have totally normal babies.

Why did I have to monitor my baby's movements in hospital?

When women are admitted to hospital with pre-eclampsia there are two patients – the mother and the baby; and both have to be monitored for signs that the disease has progressed to the point where delivery is essential. Reduced – or absent – fetal movements can be a sign that the baby is under stress. Further tests are then needed to confirm whether this calls for early delivery.

What do the CTG tests show about the baby?

The cardiotocograph (CTG), known in the US as the non-stress test (NST), is a simple tool for checking on the baby's wellbeing when pre-eclampsia is suspected or diagnosed. It records the pattern of the baby's heartbeat, which is directly affected by the reduced blood supply to the placenta that goes with pre-eclampsia. Doctors checking the readings (traces) from these tests look for three warning signs of danger to the baby, of which the third is the most serious:

- no acceleration in the heart rate when the baby is active;
- slowing of the heart rate ('deceleration') when the uterus contracts;
- loss of 'variability' – normal fluctuations in the heart rate that are a sign of healthy brain activity.

A normal CTG shows that the baby is well *now*. It does not predict what will happen later, even over the next hour. So it is not unusual for the test to be repeated when there are changes in the mother's condition, such as a small bleed, abdominal pain or a sudden spike in the blood pressure.

What does the Doppler test show about the baby?

Doppler ultrasound measurement of blood flow through one of the arteries in the umbilical cord is a test used to show whether the baby is getting enough blood from the placenta. The flow of blood through the cord should be continuous, speeding up with each fetal heartbeat. If the flow is intermittent, stopping between beats, it means the baby's blood supply is under threat. The baby may not be in immediate trouble, but since this problem is likely to get worse, the baby will probably have to be born early. In the worst cases, the blood flow actually reverses (bounces backwards) between heartbeats. When this happens the baby is in trouble and usually needs to be delivered urgently. However, for extremely pre-term babies a policy of cautious delay is sometimes appropriate.

Questions about the birth

My baby had to be delivered very prematurely and had a lot of problems at first. Why couldn't they have waited longer?

When to end the pregnancy by delivering the baby is one of the most difficult decisions doctors have to make when caring for women with pre-eclampsia. Because it is a progressive disease, the pregnancy is usually on a short fuse (two weeks, on average) before delivery will be needed to prevent dangerous complications.

If pre-eclampsia is diagnosed in the last few weeks of pregnancy there is no major dilemma about delivery because the baby is likely to do very well. But decisions about delivery are more difficult before 32-34 weeks, when doctors have to balance the risks of prematurity against those of continuing the pregnancy. However, if continuing the pregnancy would pose real dangers to mother or baby, the responsible decision is to deliver the baby and trust neonatal care to help him or her weather the storms of prematurity.

I really wanted a natural birth. Why did I have to have a caesarean?

There are a number of reasons why caesarean section might be recommended for women with pre-eclampsia. The main ones are these:

- The mother is too ill to cope with labour.
- The baby is too premature to cope with labour.
- The baby is in distress. If the baby is distressed before labour contractions have started, this would almost certainly get worse during labour itself.

Any of the normal reasons for caesarean delivery may also apply in pre-eclampsia. These include:

- failure to progress in labour;
- breech baby, or one that is rotated to face the wrong way;
- the baby being disproportionately large for the mother's pelvis.

Most women who have one caesarean can try for a normal labour next time. But if you end up having a second section it is probable that any subsequent birth will also be by caesarean.

They said they'd try to keep me going for another two weeks then suddenly decided I had to be delivered the next day. What went wrong?

Pre-eclampsia is a dangerous, unpredictable disease that can progress with frightening speed. And the only known resolution is to end the pregnancy by delivering the baby. That's why it is safest to be in hospital, where doctors and midwives can keep mother and baby under constant supervision, watching out for signs of deterioration that would indicate the need for the baby to be born sooner rather than later.

Your doctors might well have thought that your pregnancy could last another two weeks but changed their minds when test results showed new dangers for you or your baby.

If pre-eclampsia is a pregnancy problem, how come I didn't get it until after my baby was born?

It is confusing that, while delivering the baby is known to resolve pre-eclampsia, the illness may appear for the first time *after* the birth. We aren't sure why this happens but it may be that the final contractions when the placenta is delivered squeeze out a parting shot of the substances that cause pre-eclampsia.

Another possible explanation, for which we don't yet have any direct evidence, is that the placenta produces some beneficial factors during pregnancy that protect the baby by restraining the mother's illness. This protection is suddenly lost when the placenta is delivered, allowing the disease to run out of control very quickly.

I thought delivery cured pre-eclampsia, but I got much worse for a few days afterwards. Why?

This answer relates to the previous one. Although delivery eventually cures pre-eclampsia by removing the placenta that was the source of the problem, the illness often gets worse for a few days before it gets better. The highest blood pressure readings are often found 5-7 days after the birth. In the UK and probably most other developed countries eclampsia is most common after birth, with cases reported as late as 7-10 days afterwards.

Why did I have to stay in hospital for such a long time after my baby was born?

Again this answer relates back to the previous one. Since pre-eclampsia often gets worse before it gets better, it makes sense for mothers to remain in hospital until all their test results are heading back towards normal and the dangers posed by the illness have passed.

Questions about feelings and how to cope

I felt isolated and depressed after my experience of pre-eclampsia. Everyone else I know had problem-free pregnancies. What can I do?

These feelings are perfectly normal and understandable. The best ways to cope with them might be:

- to talk about how you feel to your doctor, midwife, health visitor or other relevant caregiver – particularly if you are feeling seriously depressed;

- to make contact with a patient group that can offer information and support and contact with other women in a similar situation (*see page 173 for list of groups by country*).

I really want another baby but I am too scared to contemplate another pregnancy after my experience of pre-eclampsia. How can I resolve this?

This is a common reaction. Most women who have had pre-eclampsia are concerned about whether the problem will recur in future pregnancies. And for some women the fear is so great that they dare not risk another pregnancy. The good news is that most women don't get pre-eclampsia again, while those who do tend to have it less severely.

The best way for you to resolve your personal dilemma is probably to consult an expert on pre-eclampsia. The expert would be able to advise you about your personal risk of recurrence and how your next pregnancy should be managed if you do decide to go ahead. The patient groups referred to in the question above are likely to be good sources of advice on how to get an expert opinion.

I keep having flashbacks about the birth. Is this normal?

If you had a difficult pregnancy and/or birth, it is not unusual to run through the events like a film in your head for some days or weeks afterwards. But persisting, disturbing flashbacks can be a sign of a severe anxiety disorder known as post-traumatic stress disorder (PTSD), particularly if you also:

- have sleeping problems and bad dreams;
- feel tense, anxious or emotionally numb;
- are avoiding people or places associated with the bad experience.

If this is how you are feeling, you should seek help from your doctor as soon as possible.

I feel angry because no one listened when I said there was something wrong. Why don't doctors know more about pre-eclampsia?

It is understandable that you should feel angry if your valid instincts about your pregnancy were ignored. Unfortunately this is a common complaint from women with pre-eclampsia because many of the early signs and symptoms are vague and can be either overlooked or mistaken for other things.

The fact is that, although doctors have known about pre-eclampsia for hundreds of years, their understanding of the illness is still at quite a primitive level. Among the very many things they *don't* know are the following:

- what causes the disease;
- whether it is one disease with variable signs or several different diseases with similar signs;
- why some women get it early in pregnancy and others late;
- why some women get it again and others don't;
- why it sometimes gets worse after birth, which is supposed to cure it.

Only scientific research can fill these gaps in our knowledge and bring better care to women who need it. Until then, mistakes in diagnosis will continue to be made. That is all the more reason for women like you to be persistent when they know or suspect that something is wrong.

Questions about the next pregnancy

I had pre-eclampsia very badly. What are the chances of my getting it again next time?

The *good* news is that most women who have pre-eclampsia in their first pregnancy don't get it again. And if they do get it again, it is usually less severe than it was the first time. There is no accurate way to predict who will get it again, but we *do* know that the earlier it came on in the first pregnancy, the more likely it is to recur next time.

Changing partners or leaving a very long gap between pregnancies can increase your risk. Your risk of recurrence may also be higher if you have existing circulatory problems, including kidney disease, chronic hypertension and clotting disorders. You may want to rule out hidden problems by having a full medical check-up before you attempt to conceive again.

My baby died as a result of prematurity. How long do I need to wait before trying again?

There are no hard and fast rules about this, although in general it is advisable to leave at least six months between one birth – successful or otherwise – and the next conception. There is no particular medical advantage to waiting longer than that; but you might well want to wait longer to be sure you are in a strong and positive frame of mind before you embark on the next pregnancy.

What can I do to make sure I don't get pre-eclampsia again?

At present there is no reliable way for doctors or women themselves to prevent pre-eclampsia. It *may* help to make sure your diet is healthy, to lose weight if you are carrying too much, to take folic acid supplements and to take low-dose aspirin (always under medical supervision). But none of these interventions is guaranteed to make a difference.

One thing you should do, if possible, is to make sure your antenatal care is provided in a centre that specialises in high-risk pregnancy, where your risk can be assessed and you can be closely monitored for the earliest signs of recurrence.

I had an emergency caesarean. Does that mean I'll have to have one next time?

Not inevitably, but you will probably not be allowed to continue too long in labour, particularly in the second (pushing) stage, because of the (very small) risk of rupture to your uterus, which will bear the scars of the previous caesarean. If you end up having a second caesarean, you are almost bound to have a caesarean in any subsequent pregnancy.

How can I get the best care next time around?

Ideally you should arrange to be referred to a medical expert on pre-eclampsia before you conceive again. You can then be:

- tested for any underlying medical problems that might increase your risk of getting pre-eclampsia again;
- advised of your chances of recurrence and what, if anything, can be done to reduce them;
- offered a management plan for your next pregnancy.

Your doctor may be able to advise you about how to consult a relevant expert. Failing that, a relevant patient group in your country should be able to help (*see list on page 173*).

I now have a new partner. Will that increase my chance of getting pre-eclampsia again?

Having a new partner might well increase your risk – especially if you get pregnant within three months of starting sexual relations with that partner. The most likely explanation for this rests on the immune theory of pre-eclampsia. It is possible that some women get pre-eclampsia because their immune system hasn't learned to 'tolerate' the foreign cells in male semen that will contribute to half the genes of the baby. This process should be complete by the time of the next pregnancy, which may be why most women don't get pre-eclampsia again. However, with a new partner you have to start the process all over again.

It is more than 10 years since I had my last baby. Does that affect my chances of getting pre-eclampsia again?

It may – and for the same reasons given in the previous answer. After 10 years your immune system may have forgotten how to accommodate the foreign cells from your partner and has to start all over again. This 'tolerisation' is a form of immunity and, like all immunity, may be lost over time

I have been told that I must lose weight before becoming pregnant again. I am finding this very difficult. How important is it?

We know that being very overweight or obese increases a woman's risk of pre-eclampsia so it seems logical to assume that losing weight before conceiving again will reduce the risk. There is some evidence to prove that this will work; and there is definitely no harm in trying as long as you don't lose too much weight too quickly or put yourself under intolerable stress.

If I get my blood pressure absolutely normal before I start another pregnancy will that ensure that I do not get pre-eclampsia?

It is very important for blood pressure to be controlled during pregnancy, but normalising your blood pressure will not guarantee you protection against pre-eclampsia. It may be that in future, with better drugs, better outcomes will be possible. But the medication we have at present is certainly not the answer.

Questions about the long term

Will my blood pressure ever go back to normal?

Some women's blood pressure returns to normal within days of the birth, but in others the process takes weeks or even months, which can be very frustrating. A small minority of women are left with chronic hypertension after pre-eclampsia. That doesn't necessarily mean that pre-eclampsia is to blame. It may be that the illness simply 'revealed' an underlying tendency to high blood pressure that would have surfaced sooner or later. What we don't yet know is whether pre-eclampsia itself can lead to long-term changes in blood pressure.

Will I suffer permanent damage as a result of pre-eclampsia?

The vast majority of women make a complete recovery from pre-eclampsia, even when they have been seriously ill. However, an unfortunate few who have suffered complications are left with permanent health problems, which can include kidney or liver disease, visual or mental impairment. These problems tend to make themselves known at an early stage, though; so if you seem to have recovered completely, the chances are that you will stay well.

I was told I might be at risk of health problems in the future. What can I do to stay healthy?

Women who have had pre-eclampsia have a higher-than-average risk of developing serious later health problems. These include chronic hypertension, stroke, angina and heart attack. However, as explained in the first answer in this section, it may be that the illness reveals an underlying tendency to such problems rather than causing them.

You can reduce your risk of later health problems by having regular health checks with your GP, taking medical advice and making sure your diet and lifestyle is as healthy as possible (see Chapter 8, page 172).

My baby was very small. Will he catch up eventually?

Most babies do, but those who were extremely malnourished in the uterus may never achieve their full growth potential.

Will my baby have long-term health problems because of pre-eclampsia?

The illness itself doesn't seem to carry any long-term risks for babies apart from the consequences of prematurity and/or food or oxygen deprivation in the uterus. Severe oxygen deprivation can cause permanent brain damage such as cerebral palsy, while severe malnutrition can restrict growth.

There is increasing evidence that babies born prematurely, or who are small-for-dates, or both, are more at risk of later circulatory problems, such as high blood pressure, obesity and diabetes. Research on this is still at an early stage. Ways of preventing these kinds of health problems are getting better and better so it is good to be aware of the risks and to take appropriate medical advice.

Questions about research

Why can't pre-eclampsia be prevented?

The simple answer is that we don't know enough about it yet. Most illnesses become preventable once their causes are understood. With pre-eclampsia, although we know it usually starts with a problem in the placenta, we don't yet understand what *causes* the problem. If and when we do understand it, we can begin to develop treatments that can block the mechanisms responsible.

At present, most potential preventive treatments – including low-dose aspirin and various dietary changes – are based on a degree of guesswork and so are far from reliable. Current studies of low-dose aspirin may remove some of the guesswork and lead to more certainty about the appropriate dosage and the best stage of pregnancy to start taking it.

Why can't pre-eclampsia be cured without having to deliver the baby?

Pre-eclampsia is a progressive disease, which never gets better on its own and almost always gets worse. At present, the only way to resolve pre-eclampsia is to end the pregnancy by delivering the baby and, more specifically, the placenta. There is no resolution that will allow the pregnancy to be safely prolonged for more than 1-2 weeks in most cases. This relates back to the first answer in this question: we don't yet know exactly what causes pre-eclampsia and until we do it won't be possible to prevent the disease or stop it in its tracks.

How can I help with research?

This is a great question. People expect health professionals to be knowledgeable – but such knowledge can only emerge from well-conducted research. Getting involved with research is one of the best ways you can help to increase the sum of knowledge about pre-eclampsia and ultimately improve care. Specific ways you might be able to help include:

- donating tissue for research – *eg* your placenta after the birth;
- donating samples for genetic analysis;
- taking part in clinical trials or trials of management techniques.

When will there be a cure?

Definitely not within the next decade. But new knowledge will benefit certain groups of women so that their pregnancies will be easier for them and easier for their caregivers to manage. Here are just a few of the things we will need to know about pre-eclampsia before we can even *begin* to think about a cure:

- Is pre-eclampsia one disease that behaves differently in different women or several diseases that behave similarly?
- What stops the placenta from developing normally in women who go on to develop pre-eclampsia?
- Why do some women with an apparently normal placenta get pre-eclampsia?
- Exactly how does the placental problem translate into the maternal illness of pre-eclampsia?
- Why do some women get pre-eclampsia only once and others recurrently?

We can assure you that doctors and scientists all over the world are working on providing the answers to these questions.

Further Reading

Myklestad K, Vatten LJ, Salvesen KÅ, Davey Smith G, Romundstad PR. Hypertensive disorders in pregnancy and paternal cardiovascular risk: a population-based study. Ann Epidemiol. 2011 Jun;21(6):407-12.

GLOSSARY

Medical term	Explanation
Absent end-diastolic flow	This describes a worrying ultrasound Doppler finding, usually in a cord artery. Normally blood continues to flow through fetal arteries between heartbeats. But if the forward flow is restricted, as can happen with pre-eclampsia, it may flow abnormally and stop between beats. This is a serious problem for the baby that calls for close monitoring
Accelerations	Normal speeding up of the unborn baby's heartbeat when it is active, which can be detected in cardiotocography (CTG) tests. See also 'cardiotocography'
ACE inhibitors	A class of drugs to control blood pressure that can't be given in pregnancy because they are not safe for babies. See also 'antihypertensive drugs'
Angiogenic factors	Substances that control the health of the endothelium, which lines all the blood vessels of the body. When these are out of balance they contribute to the signs and symptoms of pre-eclampsia. In pregnancy, the placenta imposes huge changes on a woman's circulation by producing many angiogenic (and anti-angiogenic) factors. See also 'anti-angiogenic factors', 'endothelium'

Angiotensin receptor-blockers (ARBs) A class of drugs to control blood pressure that are very effective but can't be given in pregnancy because they are not safe for babies. See also 'antihypertensive drugs'

Antenatal care The systematic programme of screening and surveillance that is provided for pregnant women throughout the developed world. Also known as 'prenatal care'

Anti-angiogenic factors Substances released from the placenta in excessive quantities in pre-eclampsia that disturb the normal functions of the endothelium. See also 'angiogenic factors', 'endothelium'

Antihypertensive drugs Various classes of drugs used to reduce high blood pressure. See also 'ACE inhibitors', 'angiotensin receptor-blockers', 'beta-blockers, 'calcium channel-blockers', 'diuretics', 'labetalol', 'methyldopa'

Antioxidants Substances produced naturally in the body and available from the diet that reduce stress on overworked cells. See also 'oxidative stress'

Antiphospholipid antibody syndrome (APS) A rare variant of an autoimmune disorder called lupus, which puts women at increased risk of pre-eclampsia

Arteries Blood vessels that circulate oxygen-rich blood from the heart to all parts of the body

Beta-blockers A class of drugs to control blood pressure that work by blocking some of the actions of adrenaline (and its cousin, noradrenaline). Both hormones stimulate the circulation and raise blood pressure

Biomarkers Measurable substances in blood or other fluids that reflect the workings of specific bodily functions and are useful for diagnosing disease or assessing risk for that disease

Blood pressure	The pressure exerted by circulating blood on the walls of the arteries, which is usually measured in the upper arm. The result is given as two numbers: the highest pressure, when the heart is beating, and the lowest pressure, when the heart is at rest between beats. See also 'diastolic blood pressure', 'hypertension', systolic blood pressure'
Calcium channel-blockers	A class of drugs to control blood pressure that are commonly prescribed in pregnancy because they are safe for babies. See also 'antihypertensive drugs'
Cardiotocography (CTG)	A commonly-used technique for monitoring the unborn baby's heartbeat before and during labour. In North America this is known as a non-stress test (NST) when used before labour and Electronic Fetal Monitoring (EFM) when used during labour
Cerebral haemorrhage	A stroke caused by a bleed into the brain, which can be a complication of uncontrolled high blood pressure
Conservative management	A 'watchful waiting' approach used in early-onset pre-eclampsia to give the unborn baby as much extra time in the uterus as possible while monitoring mother and baby closely for danger signs that should prompt urgent delivery. Also called 'expectant management' in some places
Convulsions	Also known as seizures or fits, which are characteristic of eclampsia. See also 'eclampsia'
Corticosteroids	Drugs (also known as 'steroids') that are given to mothers, by injection in high doses, at least 24 hours before pre-term delivery to speed the maturation of the baby's lungs. See also 'hyaline membrane disease'

Creatinine	A waste product that is normally excreted in urine but may be retained in the bloodstream if the kidneys are not working properly
Cystitis	A painful inflammation of the bladder, caused by infection, which can sometimes cause proteinuria. See also 'proteinuria'
Day assessment units	Special clinics, usually staffed by midwives, supported by obstetric staff when required, where women with potential signs and symptoms of pre-eclampsia can be monitored intensively on a daily basis without being admitted to hospital. Not available in all countries
Decelerations	Abnormal slowing of the unborn baby's heartbeat when the uterus contracts, which can be detected in cardiotocography (CTG) tests. See also 'cardiotocography'
Diastolic blood pressure	The lowest blood pressure within the arteries when the heart is at rest between beats. See also 'blood pressure', 'systolic blood pressure'
Disseminated intravascular coagulation (DIC)	A late-stage complication of pre-eclampsia, causing dangerous blood clots and uncontrollable haemorrhage. See also 'platelets'
Diuretics	Drugs that stimulate the kidneys to excrete more urine and can also reduce blood pressure by small amounts. See also 'antihypertensive drugs'
Doppler scanning	Ultrasound measurements of the pattern of maternal blood flow to the placenta through the two main arteries that supply the uterus. It is also widely used to test whether blood is flowing normally through the baby's cord, to and from the placenta. This test is often called a 'cord Doppler'. See also 'absent end-diastolic flow'

Early-onset pre-eclampsia
Pre-eclampsia diagnosed before 34 weeks of pregnancy. Because the period between 34 and 37 weeks is regarded as a transition zone, cases diagnosed before 37 weeks are sometimes called 'early-onset'. See also 'late-onset pre-eclampsia'

Eclampsia
Convulsions (fits or seizures) that are one of several possible late-stage complications of pre-eclampsia

Ectopic pregnancy
An abnormal variant of pregnancy where the placenta and baby develop outside the uterus

ELLP syndrome
A partial form of HELLP syndrome, without the haemolysis. See also 'haemolysis', 'HELLP syndrome'

Endothelium
The inner lining of the blood vessels that is damaged in pre-eclampsia

Epigastric pain
Severe pain below the ribs on the right side (sometimes on the left), usually felt in the stomach, lower chest or back. This pain, caused by problems in the liver, can be a feature of late-stage pre-eclampsia. See also 'HELLP syndrome', 'liver function test'

Fetal growth restriction (FGR)
Unusually slow growth of the unborn baby, caused in pre-eclampsia by a reduced supply of nutrients from the placenta. Sometimes also called 'intrauterine growth restriction' (IUGR); See also 'small-for-gestational-age'

Fetal movements
Movements of the unborn baby within the uterus that can be felt by the mother from about mid-pregnancy. Reduced or absent fetal movements are signs of stress – or, more rarely, distress – in the baby

Fibrin
A substance that cements platelets together to seal off leaks in the circulation. See also 'platelets'

Fits
Also known as convulsions or seizures, which are characteristic of eclampsia. See also 'eclampsia'

Gestational hypertension   Raised blood pressure appearing for the first time in pregnancy, which may give early warning of pre-eclampsia. Sometimes also known as 'pregnancy-induced hypertension', or PIH. See also 'blood pressure', 'hypertension'

Haemoglobin   The pigment in red blood cells that carries oxygen around the body and gives blood its red colour

Haemolysis   Rupture of the red blood cells that can be a late-stage complication of pre-eclampsia. See also 'HELLP syndrome'

HELLP syndrome   A combined liver and blood-clotting disorder that is one of several possible late-stage complications of pre-eclampsia. The initials stand for Haemolysis, Elevated Liver enzymes and Low Platelet count. See also 'haemolysis', 'liver function test', 'platelets'

Heparin   A drug that may be given to women with pre-eclampsia before delivery to reduce the risk of dangerous blood clotting. In many countries low doses of heparin are offered to all women after caesarean section

Hyaline membrane disease   A serious complication of prematurity where the baby's lungs are too immature to inflate properly for breathing

Hydatidiform mole   A rare condition where the uterus contains an abnormal placenta but no baby

Hypertension   Abnormally raised pressure within the arteries that carry oxygen-rich blood around the body. A typical cut-off is 140 or higher for the systolic reading, or 90 or higher for the diastolic reading. See also 'blood pressure', 'diastolic blood pressure', 'systolic blood pressure'

Intrauterine growth restriction (IUGR)   See 'fetal growth restriction'

Intrauterine programming Conditions in the uterus that may predispose unborn babies to various health problems in later life, including diabetes

Labetalol A drug to control blood pressure that is commonly prescribed in pregnancy because it is safe for babies. See also 'antihypertensive drugs'

Late-onset pre-eclampsia Pre-eclampsia diagnosed after 37 weeks of pregnancy. In some cases this definition is applied after 34 weeks. See also 'early-onset pre-eclampsia'

Liver function test Measurement of blood levels of liver enzymes that are raised when there is liver damage

Low-dose aspirin Aspirin given in low doses that can reduce the risk of pre-eclampsia in some cases by making platelets less active and reducing the risk of clotting. See also 'platelets'

Magnesium sulphate A simple salt, given by injection or infusion, which can prevent eclampsia in women at risk as well as controlling eclamptic convulsions if they do occur. How it works is not yet understood. See also 'eclampsia'

Maternal pre-eclampsia The form of pre-eclampsia in which the mother is ill but there are no signs of poor placentation or fetal growth restriction. See also 'fetal growth restriction', 'placental pre-eclampsia', 'placentation'

Methyldopa A drug to control blood pressure that is commonly prescribed in pregnancy because it is safe for babies. See also 'antihypertensive drugs'

Mild pre-eclampsia A term that ideally should no longer be used. It refers to an apparently stable form of the illness that does not affect the mother's liver or blood clotting systems or the unborn baby. However, what looks like mild pre-eclampsia can progress to severe illness very suddenly. See also 'severe pre-eclampsia'

Normotensive pre-eclampsia	Features of pre-eclampsia without raised blood pressure
Oedema	Visible swelling in the feet, ankles, fingers or face that is caused by leakage of fluid from blood vessels into the tissues. See also 'pulmonary oedema'
Oligohydramnios	A major reduction in the amount of fluid surrounding the baby in the uterus that is a sign of severe stress in the baby
Oxidative stress	Damage to overworked cells. In pre-eclampsia this affects the placenta and the mother's circulation. See also 'antioxidants'
Packed cell volume	The proportion of red blood cells in total blood, also known as 'haematocrit'
Placenta	The special pregnancy organ that nourishes and protects the unborn baby throughout pregnancy
Placental abruption	Separation of the placenta from the wall of the uterus before delivery. This can cut off the baby's oxygen supply and cause serious haemorrhage in the mother
Placental malperfusion	An inadequate blood supply from the mother to the placenta. See also 'placentation'
Placental pre-eclampsia	The common form of pre-eclampsia in which maternal illness is combined with poor placentation and fetal growth restriction. See also 'fetal growth restriction', 'maternal pre-eclampsia', 'placentation'
Placentation	The process by which the placenta forms from the fertilised egg, grows in early pregnancy and sets up an ever-increasing blood supply from the mother by enlarging small arteries in the lining of the uterus. See also 'spiral arteries'
Plasma	The fluid part of the blood
Platelets	Specialised blood cells that help with clotting and can be overactive in pre-eclampsia. See also 'HELLP syndrome'

Post-traumatic stress disorder (PTSD) A severe anxiety disorder marked by flashbacks, avoidance behaviours and sleeping problems

Pregnancy-induced hypertension (PIH) A term that is becoming obsolete and is replaced by 'gestational hypertension'

Prenatal care See 'antenatal care'

Prostaglandins Hormone-like substances that are involved in a wide range of bodily functions, including platelet activity. See also 'platelets'

Protein:creatinine ratio A test for proteinuria that is more reliable than the simple 'dipstick' test because it is not affected by fluid intake. See also 'proteinuria'

Proteinuria Abnormal 'leakage' of blood proteins into the urine caused by impairment of the filtering function of the kidneys

Pulmonary oedema A dangerous late-stage complication of pre-eclampsia where the lungs fill with fluid and obstruct breathing

Risk factors Characteristics of a person or his/her lifestyle, family or medical history that increase the risk of getting a particular illness

Seizures Also known as convulsions or fits, which are characteristic of eclampsia. See also 'eclampsia'

Severe pre-eclampsia An unstable phase of the illness marked by hard-to-control blood pressure, worsening kidney problems and symptoms of illness in the mother. See also 'mild pre-eclampsia'

Small-for-dates A baby that is smaller than expected for the maturity of the pregnancy

Small-for-gestational-age A baby with a birth weight below the 10th percentile for babies of the same gestational age – meaning that it is smaller than 90 per cent of babies born at that age. See also 'fetal growth restriction'

Spiral arteries Small arteries in the uterus lining that expand massively during pregnancy to meet the ever-

	growing needs of the placenta and unborn baby. See also 'placentation'
Syncytiotrophoblast	The very fine cell structure covering the entire surface of the placenta, which promotes transfer of nutrients, oxygen and waste products between mother and baby and is vital to the success of pregnancy. See also 'trophoblast'
Systolic blood pressure	Peak pressure within the arteries when the heart beats. See also 'diastolic blood pressure'
Tolerisation	The process whereby the maternal immune system learns to be helpful rather than hostile to foreign cells from the father, so allowing the pregnancy to flourish
Toxaemia	An outdated term for pre-eclampsia, arising from the belief that the condition was caused by toxins (poisons) in the blood. In the UK, pre-eclampsia is still often referred to as 'pre-eclamptic toxaemia', or PET
Trophoblast	Specialised cells of the placenta that form the interface between mother and baby and are responsible for placentation and the exchange of oxygen, nutrients and waste products between mother and baby. See also 'placentation', 'syncytiotrophoblast'
Uric acid	A waste product that is normally excreted in the urine but can be retained in the bloodstream if the kidney filters aren't working properly. See also 'creatinine'
Variability	Normal fluctuations in the unborn baby's heart rate, as detected in cardiotocography (CTG) tests, which are a sign of healthy brain activity. See also 'cardiotocography'
Vascular headache	A severe migraine-like headache that throbs with each heartbeat and may be accompanied by visual disturbances. See also 'visual disturbances'

Ventricles	The two separate pumps of the heart that work in tandem – one to send blood to the lungs to pick up oxygen and the other to circulate oxygen-rich blood around the body
Villi	The extremities – or microscopic 'leaves' – of the placental 'tree' that absorb oxygen and nutrients for the baby from the mother's blood and filter out the baby's waste products into the mother's circulation
Visual disturbances	Bright flashing lights or loss of vision that can signal an approaching crisis in pre-eclampsia but can also feature in other conditions, such as migraine
White coat hypertension	Blood pressure that is higher when measured in a clinic or hospital than at home. See also 'blood pressure', 'hypertension'

Index

THE
Servant King

To my brothers, Stanley and Kenneth,
and their wives, Heather and Linda

THE
Servant King

T. D. Alexander

The Bible's
portrait of the
Messiah

inter-varsity press

INTER-VARSITY PRESS
38 De Montfort Street, Leicester LE1 7GP, England

First published 1998

British Library Cataloguing in Publication Data
A catalogue record for this book is available from the British Library.

ISBN 0–85111–575–6

Set in Garamond
Printed and bound in Great Britain by The Guernsey Press Ltd., Guernsey,
Channel Islands

*Inter-Varsity Press is the book-publishing division of the Universities and Colleges
Christian Fellowship (formerly the Inter-Varsity Fellowship), a student movement linking
Christian Unions in universities and colleges in the United Kingdom, and a member
movement of the International Fellowship of Evangelical Students. For information about
local and national activities write to UCCF, 38 De Montfort Street, Leicester LE1 7GP.*

Contents

Foreword

Since I have already benefited from other books by Desmond Alexander – notably his excellent Tyndale Commentary on *Jonah* – I came with a well whetted appetite to this present work and I was not disappointed.

This is an important book in many ways, but to me its chief attraction, and indeed its greatest value, lies in the fact that it not only leaps over but demolishes the gap which opens up for so many Christians between the Old and New Testaments. In Desmond Alexander's skilled hands the Bible is seen as it truly is: one book with one supreme, controlling theme.

Sometimes neat formulae dredged up from the distant past seem naive and simplistic to our sophisticated ears, and in dismissing them we lose sight of the important truth their simplicity enshrined. I was brought up to believe that the Old Testament is Jesus foretold, the gospels are Jesus come, the letters are Jesus explained and the Revelation is Jesus expected. Simple certainly, but deeply, centrally true! Much, much later, in his book *The Authority of the Old Testament*, Professor John Bright taught me to think of the Bible as a two-act play. In such a play each act brings its own information and perspective to the story, but without the second the first is going nowhere, and without the first the second lacks background and explanation.

I have no doubt that Dr Alexander would express the ruling principle of his book much more perfectly than I have done. But as I see it, both the simplicity of my early mentors and the depth of John Bright's understanding are fully justified in what you are about to read. *The Servant King* is written with the sort of authority that only a leading Old Testament specialist can command; but its deep learning is not allowed to obtrude, and the book has all the charm and helpfulness of a piece of enthusiastic Bible study, presented with freshness and accuracy.

The Bible is still our tutor to lead us to Christ, and Desmond Alexander is a true 'servant of the Word' in the interest of that great cause. Certainly, as we read, we see Christ more clearly; please God, having read, we will also love him more dearly.

Bishopsteignton   *Alec Motyer*
November 1997

Preface

The concept of the Messiah is central to both the Old and the New Testament; indeed, it is the theme which unites them. While we shall try to follow the more important brushstrokes in the biblical portrait of the Messiah, not every stroke will be discussed. Our focus will be primarily on what the Bible has to say about God's promises concerning the coming of a special king and how these promises find their fulfilment in the person of Jesus of Nazareth. Parts of the portrait are likely to be familiar to most readers of this book. I hope that what follows will offer new insights.

Some of the material in chapters 4 and 5 first appeared in my 'Genealogies, Seed and the Compositional Unity of Genesis', *Tyndale Bulletin* 44.2 (1993), pp. 255–270. It has, however, been partially revised for inclusion in this study. In quotations from the Bible, I have normally used the NIV. Where indicated, I have made my own translation.

For reading the original manuscript of this book and offering helpful and constructive comments I am especially grateful to Kathy Rendle, Ian Hart, James McKeown, Alec Motyer and Paul Williamson; naturally, they cannot be held responsible for any shortcomings that remain. Mark Smith and his colleagues at Inter-Varsity Press are to be thanked for their help in preparing for publication a less than perfect manuscript. I am also deeply indebted to my wife Anne and our children Jane and David for their encouragement throughout the writing of this book; their love is a constant source of pleasure. To my brothers, Stanley and Kenneth, and their wives, Heather and Linda, this book is dedicated with affection.

In writing this book it is my prayer that those who gaze upon the biblical portrait of the Messiah will come to a fuller appreciation of the one who brings God's blessing to all the families of the earth.

Soli Deo gloria.

Introduction

As a child, I used to watch the Australian entertainer Rolf
Harris paint striking scenes on an enormous canvas. At the
start, his bold brushstrokes conveyed little. But gradually, as
more paint was added, the picture emerged with greater clarity.
For the artist, the very first stroke, initially meaningless to me,
was as important for the creation of the picture as the last.

In certain respects, the biblical picture of the Messiah is
drawn in a similar way. In the chapters that follow, we shall
trace, stage by stage, how the Bible's portrait of the Messiah
develops, beginning in Genesis and ending with Revelation.

Overview

Genesis sets the agenda for what follows. After describing how
humanity is alienated from its Creator, Genesis focuses on a
unique family line. God promises to restore a spoiled creation
to its original, pristine condition through this family line. Its
course is traced through many generations, from Adam to
Judah, intimating that it will eventually give rise to a royal
dynasty.

The lineage highlighted in Genesis is closely linked to the
establishment of a holy nation from the descendants of the
patriarchs, Abraham, Isaac and Jacob. The creation of this
nation is described in the books of Exodus to Judges. In
fulfilment of earlier promises, God delivers the Israelites from
slavery in Egypt and later enables them to take possession of
the land of Canaan by overthrowing the nations already there.

As we move through the books of Genesis to Kings,

attention is gradually focused on those who are divinely appointed to lead Israel. Through his obedience to God, Joshua helps the Israelites to take possession of Canaan. When they fail to obey the Lord, however, the process of conquering the land is reversed in favour of their enemies. The book of Judges narrates how God, in response to the repentance of the Israelites, endows particular individuals with his spirit in order that they may rescue his people. While these leaders, designated 'judges', function like kings, they are prohibited from establishing royal dynasties. The best qualities of these divinely appointed and spirit-empowered judges exemplify the type of leadership favoured by God.

A significant development occurs when Saul is anointed by Samuel as the first king of Israel. Unfortunately, after initially displaying the characteristics of a good king, Saul soon departs from the true way. When this happens, God instructs Samuel to anoint David, the son of Jesse, as king over Israel. This marks an important step towards the fulfilment of the earlier promises concerning the family line in Genesis: a dynasty is now established, and it is descended from Judah.

While the books of Samuel and 1 Kings emphasize the positive characteristics of David and his son Solomon, their shortcomings are also highlighted. As a result of Solomon's selfishness and idolatry, his kingdom is later divided. Tracing what developed, 1 and 2 Kings provides a general picture of kingship at that time which is far from encouraging. Indeed, such is the decline that first the northern kingdom of Israel and then the southern kingdom of Judah experience defeat at the hands of their enemies. Their kings are deposed and significant elements of their population are carried into exile.

In spite of these developments, an expectation runs throughout 1 and 2 Kings that the divine promises made in Genesis, echoed and expanded upon elsewhere, will yet be fulfilled. This emphasis upon the coming of a future king appears in other Old Testament writings; we shall see it in the books of Amos, Isaiah, Jeremiah, Ezekiel and Daniel.

When we come to the New Testament writings, we find

that an important transformation takes place. The New Testament affirms that God's earlier promises are fulfilled, or are in the process of being fulfilled, in the person of Jesus Christ; he is the special king anticipated in the Old Testament. The final chapters of our study will explore some of the ways in which the New Testament presents Jesus Christ as a king through whom all the nations of the earth will be blessed. We shall see how the New Testament itself foresees the ultimate restoration of the whole universe through the life, death, resurrection, exaltation and future return of Jesus Christ.

Conclusion

Our survey will reveal that the Bible's portrait of the Messiah is constructed gradually, with earlier ideas being filled out in greater detail. One aspect of this is that the term 'Messiah' is introduced only at a late stage. No attempt will be made here to try to establish when precisely this happened. The timing is not too important, for our study suggests that belief in a future divinely appointed king existed long before the term 'Messiah' was used to designate him.

As we study how the portrait of the Messiah develops across the books of Genesis to Revelation, I would encourage you to interact with the biblical text itself. At the start of each chapter you will find two sets of Bible references: the passages or books reviewed in the chapter, and key texts which you might wish to consult before reading the chapter itself. At the end of each chapter you will find questions for reflection and discussion.

1
Humanity:
the crown of creation

Genesis 1 – 3

Summary

In the beginning human beings were created by God to govern the earth, initially enjoying a close and harmonious relationship with him. As a result of wilfully disobeying him, they were expelled from his presence and forced to live in a hostile world. In condemning the serpent who encouraged the first human couple to rebel against their Creator, God intimated that ultimately the 'seed of the woman' would overcome the 'seed of the serpent'.

Key texts: Genesis 1:26–31; 3:1–24

The Bible's portrait of the Messiah is part of a much larger picture involving the whole of creation. For this reason it is appropriate to begin with the opening chapters of Genesis. Fundamental to the biblical account of creation is belief in a single God who, by merely speaking, brings into existence the entire universe. Genesis 1 speaks of a universe constructed according to plan. Each stage is briefly summarized, the process coming to a climax with the making of human beings, both male and female. According to Genesis 1, human beings are the pinnacle of God's creative activity; nothing is made after them.

The special status of humanity is underlined by God's comment that they are to be made in the 'divine image' (*cf.* Gn. 1:26–27). This bestows upon humanity a tremendous dignity, distinguishing humans from all other living creatures. The modern idea that humankind is merely a more highly evolved form of animal, and nothing more, cannot be reconciled with the claim of Genesis 1 that each person resembles the divine creator.

Created to govern

The supremacy of human beings in relation to the rest of creation is further emphasized by God's directive that they are to 'fill the earth and subdue it' (1:28). As the crown of God's creation, humanity is commanded to rule the entire earth. Unfortunately, the traditional translation 'subdue' conveys for most readers an imperialistic attitude. But such an approach towards the earth is not endorsed here. As God's vice-regents, human beings are expected to govern the earth in the very manner that God himself adopts towards the whole of creation.

Genesis 1 is complemented by a further and much fuller picture of how God created human beings. In Genesis 2 we see God, as it were, rolling up his sleeves and shaping the first man from clay. Having moulded the man into the right form, God breathes life into him (2:7). In contrast to Genesis 1, this chapter highlights the close personal relationship that existed between God and the first human being, an intimacy that explains why God provides both an ideal environment and a suitable companion for the newly created man.

Although the theme of 'governing' is less evident in Genesis 2, the man displays the authority delegated to him by God when he names all the creatures (2:20). Previously, God had named different parts of creation (*cf.* 1:5, 8, 10). Now, reflecting the one in whose image he has been made, the man gives names to all the animals.

Failure and hope

The initial harmony of Eden, where God and humanity interact in complete harmony, is disrupted when Adam and Eve, encouraged by the serpent, eat from the tree of the knowledge of good and evil (3:6). By yielding to the serpent's temptation, the human couple not only disobey God, but more importantly they display both their inability to trust God and their desire to be equal with him. For them the serpent's words – 'you will not surely die' (3:4); 'you will be like God' (3:5) – are more appealing than God's instruction not to eat from the tree.

Although the consequences of these events are summarized only briefly in the biblical narrative, their significance for the whole of human history is enormous. Alienation replaces harmony throughout creation. No longer will the human couple meet God gladly face to face; they hide because of their shame. No longer will the man enjoy the bountiful produce of his God-given environment; humanity and nature will struggle to co-exist. No longer will the woman fulfil with ease her divinely given role to be the 'mother of life'; pain and grief will be an integral part of motherhood. No longer will the human couple be perfectly matched; tension will exist in relationships between men and women. And, as if to underline the horror of all this, the narrative concludes with God expelling the human couple from the Garden of Eden, thus denying them access to the tree of life (3:22–24).

17

In the midst of these tragic events, however, there are brief indications that all is not lost. In spite of their wilful disobedience, God provides clothes to cover the shame and nakedness of Adam and Eve (3:21). More importantly, he announces that the 'seed of the woman' will eventually defeat the 'seed of the serpent' (3:15). Such an outcome is appropriate given the serpent's role in destroying the harmony of creation.

Some commentators argue that the narrative speaks here only about the peculiar antagonism which human beings have towards snakes. But a much deeper meaning is intended, one which has great importance for the rest of Genesis, and indeed the whole Bible. The serpent represents those forces within creation that oppose the purposes of God. When God speaks of the 'seed of the woman' and the 'seed of the serpent', he is not simply contrasting human beings and snakes. Rather, he is contrasting two types of creature: those who display a positive attitude towards God and those who are fundamentally opposed to him. Within the overall context of Genesis the 'seed of the woman' refers to those who are righteous, whereas the 'seed of the serpent' denotes those who are wicked.

In Christian theology there has been a very long tradition identifying 'the seed of the woman' with Jesus Christ. On account of this, Genesis 3:15 has been known as the *protevangelium* – the first announcement of the gospel. Many modern theologians reject this understanding of the passage. They do so largely because they do not read Genesis as a coherent story that focuses on a unique family line which enjoys a special relationship with God. This line of 'seed', as we shall observe in our next two chapters, is the beginning of a royal dynasty through whom God will bring his judgment upon the 'seed of the serpent'. That the one who will bring this judgment and reverse the consequences of the first couple's disobedience will be of kingly standing is not surprising when we bear in mind the vice-regent status earlier conferred on Adam and Eve.

Conclusion

Although Genesis 3:15 hints at a reversal of the alienation arising from the disobedience of Adam and Eve, for the fulfilment we must read further. Here, however, we find the first brushstroke on the biblical canvas concerning a future king through whom God's salvation will come to humanity.

Questions for reflection and discussion

How does the account of Genesis 1 suggest that the world, as initially created by God, was perfect?

In what ways do human beings demonstrate that they are created in the image of God?

How has the divine image in human beings been distorted as a result of the disobedience of Adam and Eve?

What forms of alienation are most apparent in society today?

2

The line of seed

Genesis 3 – 50

Summary

The book of Genesis traces from one generation to the next the history of an exceptional line of human beings. In each generation one individual is highlighted. The members of this lineage often act in similar ways or display common characteristics, usually of a commendable nature. Contrary to expectation, this lineage does not always proceed through the eldest son.

Key texts: Genesis 4:25–26; 5:1–32; 11:10–26;
21:1–7; 25:21–26

G od's promise that the 'seed of the woman' will eventually overcome the 'seed of the serpent' draws attention to a conflict that will last for centuries between those who are righteous and those who are wicked. The reality of the conflict is encountered in the episode immediately following the expulsion of Adam and Eve from the Garden of Eden. Displeasure at God's approval of his brother's actions causes Cain to kill Abel (Gn. 4:1–8). Jealousy, hatred, murder and lying are the hallmarks of the serpent's seed.

In spite of having murdered his brother, God treats Cain leniently, merely exiling him from the land and forcing him to live a nomadic existence. From the description of his descendants, however, we see that Cain's evil nature lives on in his children. This is especially so with Lamech, who boasts of killing a man for striking him (4:23). From all that is recorded about the family line of Cain, there seems little hope that God's promise concerning the defeat of the 'seed of the serpent' will be fulfilled this way.

A new line of seed

Yet, before despair sets in completely, the narrator jumps back in time to tell of the birth of another son, Seth, to Adam and Eve. Seth fills the void created by the death of Abel, for Eve comments, 'God has granted me another seed in place of Abel' (4:25, my translation). With Seth, a new line of 'seed' begins, and immediately it is associated with the worship of God: 'At that time men began to call on the name of the LORD' (4:26). So, while the killing of Abel jeopardized the fulfilment of God's promise regarding the 'seed of the woman', God himself raised up another 'seed' in place of Abel.

The mention of Seth's birth is immediately followed by a genealogy which passes quickly over ten generations (5:1–32). The structure of this genealogy is distinctive, with only one individual being named in each generation. This reveals the existence of a special line of descendants, the continuation of which is carefully traced through the rest of Genesis. This unique lineage lies at the heart of the book of Genesis and is central to the understanding of how Genesis contributes to the portrait of the Messiah.

Several literary features should be noted. First, there is the heading, 'These are the generations of ...', which introduces new sections in the book. Some of these headings function like a zoom lens on a camera (*cf.* 2:4; 6:9; 11:27; 25:19; 37:2). They focus the reader's attention on a particular individual and his immediate children. This enables the author of Genesis to trace the fortunes of one family without having to follow in detail the lives of all other relatives. In this way Genesis highlights the importance of the lineage which, beginning with Adam, is traced through his youngest son Seth to Noah, the father of Shem, Ham and Japheth. The next stage of the line runs from Shem to Terah, the father of Abraham, Nahor and Haran. We then move from Abraham to Isaac, from Isaac to Jacob, and, finally, to Jacob's twelve sons (see Table 1 over the page).

Throughout Genesis the line of descent is always traced through the males and successive members are always clearly indicated. Great care is taken to establish accurately the line of succession, especially when, contrary to expectation, it does not continue through the first-born son. Thus, Seth the third-born is favoured over Cain the first-born (4:1–25); Isaac, Abraham's second-born son, enjoys priority over Ishmael, the first-born (16:1–16; 17:18–21; 21:9–20); Esau, the first-born of Isaac, takes second place to his younger twin brother Jacob (25:23).

Genesis emphasizes that this line of descendants owes much to divine activity. This is apparent in two main ways. On the one hand, when the wives of certain members of the line are barren, God enables them to have children. This is so in the cases of Sarah (21:1; *cf.* 17:16; 18:10–14), Rebekah (25:21) and Rachel (30:22–24; *cf.* 29:31; 30:1–2). Even when there are no obvious barriers to the birth of children, God's role in giving new life is often acknowledged (*e.g.* 4:1; 29:33; 30:6). These points suggest that the lineage traced in Genesis is no ordinary line; it is established by God.

23

Table 1: The main family lineage in Genesis

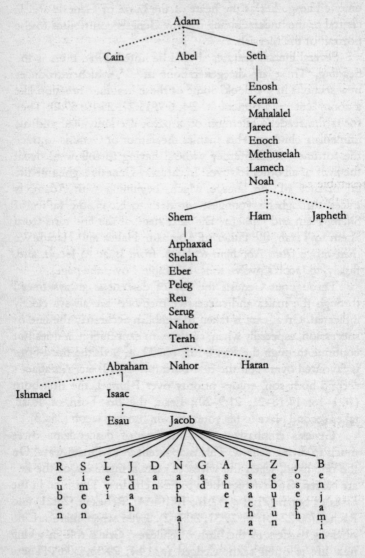

A second literary feature by which attention is drawn to the family lineage is the use of the word 'seed' (a word we have already encountered in 3:15 and 4:25). *zera'*, the Hebrew for 'seed', is a key word in Genesis, appearing fifty-nine times. It can denote either a single seed (*e.g.* Ishmael is Abraham's seed, 21:13) or many (*e.g.* the seed of Jacob will be as numerous as 'the dust of the earth', 28:14). Also, *zera'* implies a close resemblance between progenitor (the one who produces the seed) and progeny (what the seed becomes). This is underlined initially in Genesis 1:11–12, where attention is drawn to the fact that plants and trees produce seeds 'according to their various kinds'.

It is in keeping with this concept of resemblance between progenitor and progeny that members of the family line often resemble each other. We see this, for example, when we compare the account of Isaac's stay in Gerar (26:1–35) with that of Abraham (20:1 – 22:19). Isaac's behaviour mirrors his father's: each pretends that his wife is his sister (20:1–18; 26:1–11); each is involved in a dispute over the ownership of wells (21:22–34; 26:17–22); each enters into a covenant relationship with Abimelech king of Gerar (21:22–34; 26:26–31). Throughout Genesis other resemblances between members of the same seed may also be observed. This has at least one important implication. It establishes characteristics by which members of the line may be recognized, and creates the expectation that future 'seed' will display them; some will be noted in the next chapter.

Conclusion

Two main types of human 'seed' are highlighted in Genesis. On the one hand, there are those who enjoy a positive relationship with God and experience his blessing. On the other, there are those who distance themselves from God by their evil actions and, as a consequence, experience God's displeasure. The existence of these two types is perhaps most evident in the story of Cain and Abel (4:1–16). This conflict reappears throughout Genesis, however, being particularly apparent in the patriarchal narratives. We see it in God's comment to

Abraham: 'I will bless those who bless you, and whoever curses you I will curse' (12:3). This reveals that people will react towards Abraham either positively or negatively. The narrative in Genesis 25 – 35 develops around the strife that exists between Jacob and Esau. Similarly, the Joseph story centres on the hatred which Joseph's brothers have towards him. Indeed, many of the conflicts highlighted in Genesis occur between brothers.

The preceding observations reveal that the book of Genesis takes a special interest in tracing the development of a righteous line of 'seed'. This family line forms the backbone of Genesis and, as we shall observe in our next chapter, contributes in a very significant way to the Bible's portrait of the Messiah.

Questions for reflection and discussion

What features suggest that Genesis is particularly interested in tracing a unique family lineage?

In what ways is God portrayed as taking an active role in establishing this line of 'seed'?

What distinguishes the two main types of 'seed' highlighted in Genesis?

How does Genesis demonstrate that the two types of 'seed' are not determined by purely genetic factors?

3

Intimations of a royal line

Genesis 3 – 50

Summary

The family lineage which forms the backbone of Genesis is closely linked to various divine promises, the most important of which involves the mediation of God's blessing to all the nations of the earth. There are also indications that the line of 'seed' which is traced to Judah, the fourth-born son of Jacob, will eventually give rise to a royal dynasty.

Key texts: Genesis 12:1–3; 22:15–18; 38:1–30; 49:8–12

Genesis traces the history of a particular family line, beginning with Adam and ending with the sons of Jacob (also known as Israel). Why does Genesis focus on this line of 'seed'? To answer this question, it is important to note several features associated with it.

A special relationship exists between God and the members of this family line. Sometimes it is highlighted in the briefest of comments. For example, we read that 'Enoch walked with God; then he was no more, because God took him away' (Gn. 5:24). Elsewhere the special relationship is revealed in considerably more detail. This is so in the accounts concerning Noah, Abraham, Isaac, Jacob and Joseph. In the cases of Noah and Abraham, God not only reveals future plans but also establishes eternal covenants with them. Isaac and Jacob also receive revelations from God confirming, in particular, promises which were previously made to Abraham. Although God never reveals himself directly to Joseph, he enables him to discern future events by interpreting dreams. Furthermore, the account of Joseph's time in Egypt highlights God's providential care of him.

While the members of the special line of 'seed' enjoy God's favour and blessing, their failings are never disguised. We see Noah becoming drunk (9:20–21), Abraham being less than truthful concerning his marriage to Sarah (12:10–13), and Jacob deceiving his father (27:1–40), to mention the more obvious shortcomings. Nevertheless, in spite of such faults, they are viewed as more righteous than others. This is most obvious with Noah, who is introduced as 'a righteous man, blameless among the people of his time' (6:9) and who, with his family, is not destroyed in the flood like the rest of his generation. Abraham's righteousness is emphasized in various ways. It is first mentioned specifically in Genesis 15:6: 'Abram believed the LORD, and he credited it to him as righteousness.' Later, the extent of Abraham's righteousness is revealed by his willingness to obey God and sacrifice his much loved son Isaac (22:1–19). Although little information is given about Isaac, the fact that he enjoyed God's favour suggests that he too was viewed as righteous (*cf.* 26:12–14, 23–24). Jacob's relationship with God develops over a long period of time, and, although Genesis focuses initially on his deceptive behaviour (27:1–29), we see him eventually taking steps to rid his household of foreign gods (35:1–5). Like Abraham and Isaac, Jacob too knows God's blessing. Furthermore, all three actively worship God by building altars and offering sacrifices (12:7–8; 13:18; 22:9; 26:25; 35:1–7).

For the blessing of the nations

In Genesis, the line of 'seed' is closely associated with various divine promises. First, God promises the land of Canaan to the 'seed' of Abraham. This is mentioned specifically when Abraham first arrives in Canaan: 'To your seed I will give this land' (12:7). It is repeated on various occasions to Abraham, Isaac and Jacob (*e.g.* 13:15; 26:3; 35:12 among many). Secondly, it is frequently stressed that the 'seed' of Abraham will be very numerous. Different images highlight the extent of the 'seed'; they are compared to the dust of the earth (13:16; 28:14), the stars of the heavens (15:5; 22:17; 26:4) and the sand of the seashore (22:17; 32:12). Taken together, the divine promises concerning land and descendants focus on the establishment of the Israelites as a nation living in the land of Canaan. The fulfilment of these promises, however, clearly lies beyond the book of Genesis, indicating that Genesis records the beginning of something that will be completed only later.

Genesis records a third major divine promise: the nations of the earth will be blessed through Abraham and his 'seed' (*e.g.* 12:3; 18:18). The idea that humanity should experience God's blessing stands in sharp contrast to the trend found in Genesis 3 – 11. In those chapters the picture is of a rebellious humanity struggling to survive under God's curse. The promise of divine blessing, especially prominent in the call of Abraham (12:1–3), marks an important turning point within the Genesis narrative.

God's promise to bless the nations of the earth is closely linked to Abraham (12:3) and his 'seed' (22:18; 26:4). A careful study of Genesis suggests that this blessing will come primarily through those who belong to the special line of 'seed'. Thus, the promise is linked to Isaac, and not Ishmael (22:18; 26:4). Subsequently, Jacob, and not his older brother Esau, appears to be the one through whom God's blessing is mediated. The pronouncement of the first-born blessing on Jacob by his father Isaac is obviously significant (27:27–29). A similar picture comes in Genesis 37 – 50 where Joseph is highly favoured by his father (*cf.* 1 Ch. 5:1–2), and in turn imparts God's blessing to others.

Although Genesis speaks of 'all the nations' being blessed, this is no guarantee of universal blessing. God says to Abraham, 'I will bless those who bless you, and whoever curses you I will curse' (12:3). This introduces the idea that only those who respond positively towards Abraham and his 'seed' will experience God's favour. Abimelech, the king of Gerar, appears to recognize this, and so enters into a covenant first with Abraham and then later with Isaac (21:22–32; 26:26–31). God's blessing is also evident in the lives of those who come into contact with Jacob and Joseph. Indeed, the presence of the latter in Egypt enables many nations to survive a terrible famine (41:56–57). These observations suggest that God intends the line of 'seed' to play an important role in reversing the terrible consequences of Adam and Eve's disobedience in the Garden of Eden.

The promise of a royal line

There are strong grounds for believing that the main line of descent in Genesis is viewed as anticipating the creation of a royal line. This possibility is implied by the divine promise made to Abraham that 'kings will come from you' (17:6), echoed in a similar statement concerning Sarah that 'kings of peoples will come from her' (17:16). Moreover, although Abraham is never directly designated a king, he is sometimes portrayed as enjoying royal status. We see this in his defeat of the eastern kings in Genesis 14, in Abimelech's determination to make a covenant with him (21:22–34), and, finally, in the title 'mighty prince' (literally, 'a prince of God') given to him by the Hittite inhabitants of Hebron (23:6).

While there are only a few allusions to kingship in the next section of Genesis, chapters 25 – 36, these are nevertheless noteworthy. Isaac's importance is reflected in Abimelech's wish to make a treaty with him (26:26–31), as he had previously done with Abraham. In a divine promise which echoes Genesis 17:6, 16, Jacob is promised that 'kings will come from your body' (35:11). Finally, the brief comment in Genesis 36:31, 'These were the kings who reigned in Edom before any Israelite king reigned', indicates that whoever wrote this account either anticipated or already knew of a royal dynasty within Israel.

The subject of kingship is prominent in the Joseph story. At the outset his brothers interpret Joseph's first dream as implying that he will be a king: 'Do you intend to reign over us? Will you actually rule us?' (37:8). His second dream reinforces this idea (37:9–11). Later, we witness the fulfilment when Joseph rises from the obscurity of an Egyptian prison to hold the office of governor of Egypt, second only to Pharaoh (41:39–43). While Genesis indicates that the future monarchy will not be descended from Joseph, it is interesting that his life parallels that of the divinely promised future king: exalted from humble surroundings, he imparts God's blessing to the nations of the earth.

Although Joseph enjoys the spotlight in chapters 37 – 50, Judah also plays an important role (*e.g.* 43:8–9; 44:16; 44:18–34; 46:28). This is particularly so in Genesis 38, where we have one of the more unusual episodes in the book. The inclusion of this story can best be accounted for by noting its interest in the theme of 'seed'.

When Judah's first son Er dies, custom dictates that his second son Onan should 'produce children for his brother' by sleeping with Er's widow, Tamar. This fails, and Onan too dies. The duty now falls to the third son, young Shelah. But Judah does not want to give him to Tamar; what if he dies too?

Judah's reluctance to take the action necessary to maintain the family line is at the heart of the story. When Tamar eventually becomes pregnant by deceiving Judah (by now a widower himself), he is forced to acknowledge the righteousness of her actions (38:26). It is especially significant that the account concludes with the birth of Perez (and his twin brother Zerah), from whom the future king David is descended.

Judah's importance is further indicated by the special blessing which he receives from his father. While the poetic language of Jacob's blessing upon Judah makes it difficult to interpret every detail with confidence, his words clearly associate royal characteristics with the line of Judah.

> Judah, your brothers will praise you;
>> your hand will be on the neck of your enemies;
>> your father's sons will bow down to you.
> You are a lion's cub, O Judah;
>> you return from the prey, my son.
> Like a lion he crouches and lies down,
>> like a lioness – who dares to rouse him?
> The sceptre will not depart from Judah,
>> nor the ruler's staff from between his feet,
> until he comes to whom it belongs
>> and the obedience of the nations is his.
> He will tether his donkey to a vine,
>> his colt to the choicest branch;
> he will wash his garments in wine,
>> his robes in the blood of grapes.
> His eyes will be darker than wine,
>> his teeth whiter than milk.
>
> (Gn. 49:8–12)

When compared with the blessings pronounced by Jacob upon his other sons, the length and content of this one clearly suggests that Judah enjoys a special relationship with his father; only Joseph receives a comparable blessing. Jacob states that

Judah and his descendants will exercise leadership over his other brothers and their descendants (verse 8). We see this especially in the comment, 'Your father's sons will bow down to you' (verse 8), and in the reference to the sceptre and the ruler's staff not departing from Judah (verse 10). Jacob also possibly anticipates that there will come in the royal line of Judah one to whom the nations will submit in obedience (verse 10) and whose reign will be marked by prosperity and abundance (verse 11).

Conclusion

The association of royalty with Judah is unexpected, partially because of the way in which Genesis earlier links the theme of kingship with Joseph. The choice of Judah, however, is a further sign that the royal line is determined by God rather than by human preference. Genesis suggests that each patriarch would have selected someone else as principal heir: Abraham speaks out in favour of Ishmael (17:18); Isaac seeks to bless Esau (27:4); Jacob idolizes Joseph (37:3). On every occasion, however, the line of descent is traced through another son.

Beginning with the 'seed of the woman' in Genesis 3:15 and traced to Judah, this lineage anticipates the enthronement of a king through whom God's blessing will be mediated to all the nations of the earth. With these brushstrokes, Genesis initiates the Bible's portrait of the Messiah.

Questions for reflection and discussion

What suggests that the members of the line of 'seed' enjoyed a special relationship with God?

In what ways is God's promise to bless the nations of the earth linked to the central line of descendants in Genesis?

In spite of the prominence given to Joseph in Genesis 37 – 50, what features point to the importance of Judah and his 'seed'?

How does Genesis indicate that the line of succession traced through Judah will eventually give rise to a monarchy?

4

Promises and warnings

Exodus, Leviticus, Numbers and Deuteronomy

Summary

Although the books of Exodus to Deuteronomy are primarily interested in the deliverance of the Israelites from slavery in Egypt and their journey towards the promised land, two differing passages anticipate the creation of a monarchy in Israel. The first of these comes in a series of blessings pronounced under divine influence by a pagan prophet, Balaam. They recall the divine promises made to the patriarchs. The second passage, coming in a speech by Moses to the Israelites, underlines the importance of appointing the right type of king.

Key texts: Numbers 24:1–25; Deuteronomy 17:14–20

Although Genesis never uses the term Messiah, we have observed how it anticipates the coming of a future king from the line of Judah. Associated with this king is the restoration of harmony between God and humanity, and between humanity and the natural environment. In this way God's blessing will come to all the nations of the earth.

A future king

The coming of this future king is intimately linked to the divine promise that Abraham's descendants will possess the land of Canaan. The origins of this promise can be traced back to the time when God summoned Abraham to leave his own family and homeland.

> Leave your country, your people and your father's household and go to the land I will show you, so that I may make you into a great nation and bless you and make your name great. Be a blessing, so that I may bless those who bless you, and curse the one who disdains you, and so that all the families of the ground may be blessed through you (Gn. 12:1–3, my translation).

The promise that Abraham will become a great nation is later guaranteed by God in a covenant (Gn. 15). This divine promise, however, will not be fulfilled immediately, but only after a period of four hundred years, during which time a foreign nation will enslave and ill-treat the Israelites (Gn. 15:13).

The story of the Israelites' release from bondage under the Pharaoh of Egypt, and their subsequent journey towards the promised land, dominates the books of Exodus to Numbers. These books record in graphic detail how God reveals himself to the people in the signs associated with the punishment of the Egyptians and in the laws given at Mount Sinai. They also focus on the unbelieving and rebellious nature of the Israelites. Numbers reveals that out of all the adults to have left Egypt at the time of the exodus, only Caleb and Joshua will actually enter the promised land; all the other Israelites, including Moses himself, will die in the wilderness.

In Numbers the account of the death of the first generation of adult Israelites is placed alongside a series of unusual incidents involving a non-Israelite prophet called Balaam. Summoned by Balak, the king of Moab, to curse the Israelites, Balaam unexpectedly pronounces blessings upon them. These echo the divine promises found in Genesis concerning numerous descendants, possession of the land and the blessing of the nations. Thus Balaam focuses on the distinctive nature of the Israelite nation and its enormous size (Nu. 23:9–10). He sees it as invincible, like a devouring lion (23:24; 24:9) or a wild ox (24:8). He also portrays, using poetic imagery, the prosperity that the Israelites will enjoy under God's blessing (24:5–7). Finally, he focuses on a future king.

> I see him, but not now;
>   I behold him, but not near.
> A star will come out of Jacob;
>   a sceptre will rise out of Israel.
> He will crush the foreheads of Moab,
>   the skulls of all the sons of Sheth.
> Edom will be conquered;
>   Seir, his enemy, will be conquered,
>   but Israel will grow strong.
> A ruler will come out of Jacob
>   and destroy the survivors of the city.
>
> (Nu. 24:17–19; *cf.* 24:7)

Balaam's words regarding this coming king are noteworthy, for at this stage in their history the Israelites have no monarch. Yet his words closely parallel comments found in Genesis that highlight how a future royal descendant of Abraham will exercise authority over other nations.

The account of the blessings Balaam pronounced upon the Israelites plays an important role within Numbers. It indicates that, in spite of God's punishment upon the unbelieving

37

generation who came out of Egypt, the divine promises to the patriarchs, Abraham, Isaac and Jacob, will yet be fulfilled. The Israelites will possess the land of Canaan and become a great nation. Moreover, a monarch will arise from among them and defeat those opposed to God and his righteous people. Thus the Balaam story marks a turning-point in the account of the Israelites' prolonged sojourn in the wilderness.

Future temptations

Shortly afterwards, in Deuteronomy, Moses addresses the Israelites as they stand on the border of the promised land, poised to take possession of it. As an elder statesman encouraging his people at a crucial point in their history, Moses underlines how important it is for the Israelites to obey the Lord their God. Only through obedience will they occupy the land and prosper abundantly. Yet, as Deuteronomy concludes, a shadow hangs over all that is recorded. In spite of his words of encouragement, Moses anticipates that the Israelites will, by their disobedience, forfeit the land that they are about to enter. As we shall observe later, these events will have important consequences for the fulfilment of the divine promises concerning the future king.

As part of his speech to the Israelites, Moses foresees that after they enter the land the people will desire, like other nations, to have a king. Addressing the topic of kingship, Moses draws attention to factors which are important for the success of the monarchy. Foremost among these is the necessity of appointing 'the king the LORD your God chooses' (Dt. 17:15). He also lists dangers confronting any future monarch:

> The king, moreover, must not acquire great numbers of horses for himself or make the people return to Egypt to get more of them, for the LORD has told you, 'You are not to go back that way again.' He must not take many wives, or his heart will be led astray. He must not accumulate large amounts of silver and gold (Dt. 17:16–17).

These comments are followed by others which emphasize how important it is for the king to obey all of God's instructions. Only by doing this will he and his descendants 'reign a long time over his kingdom in Israel' (Dt. 17:20).

In contrast to the other passages we have already considered, Moses' comments regarding the monarchy contain no reference to the king's special role in bringing God's blessing to the nations of the earth. While this is perhaps surprising, it is in keeping with what Moses says to the Israelites throughout Deuteronomy. Although they will enter the promised land and take possession of it, failure in the future to obey God will eventually lead to their being exiled from the land. Such an event will obviously include their king. By focusing on the temptations facing the monarchy, Moses indicates that there may come a time when future kings will fail to revere and obey God fully.

Conclusion

The significance of Moses' comments about the monarchy will become clearer as we follow the account of its rise and decline. These words of warning, however, do not undermine God's intention that all the nations of the earth will be blessed through a future king descended from Abraham. Rather, in conjunction with what Moses has to say about the future of Israel as a nation, they indicate that the completion of the portrait of the Messiah lies beyond the creation of the Israelite monarchy.

Questions for reflection and discussion

How do the blessings pronounced by Balaam echo the divine promises in Genesis?

Why is it significant that these are repeated at this stage in the biblical account of Israel's history?

In what ways does Moses' warning about kingship fit in with all that he has to say to the Israelites regarding their future?

5

Prelude to the rise of the monarchy

Joshua and Judges

Summary

Whereas the book of Joshua focuses mainly on the success of the Israelite occupation of the promised land, Judges provides a contrasting picture. Central to both books is the role played by those appointed by God to lead the people. While Joshua is portrayed as an ideal leader, the subsequent judges are presented as providing less and less effective leadership. The expectation is created that the nation's troubles will be reversed only with the establishment of a royal dynasty.

Key texts: Joshua 23:1–16; Judges 2:16 – 3:6; 9:1–57

With the death of Moses the mantle of leadership passes to Joshua, and a new phase begins. As we move towards the establishment of a monarchy in Israel, the books of Joshua and Judges set the stage for its beginning. Although both books focus on how the Israelites take possession of the land of Canaan, a sharp contrast exists between them. Whereas the book of Joshua records that the first generation successfully takes control of the promised land, Judges reveals that subsequent generations fail to consolidate the process of occupation and find themselves opposed by other nations. Against this background of opposition, the monarchy is created.

A successful invasion

Throughout the book of Joshua the successful invasion of the land of Canaan is associated with divine activity. At the outset this is reflected in the extraordinary way in which God enables the people to cross the River Jordan and capture the walled city of Jericho. Much later, the success of the whole venture is summarized in these words:

> So the LORD gave Israel all the land he had sworn to give their forefathers, and they took possession of it and settled there. The LORD gave them rest on every side, just as he had sworn to their forefathers. Not one of their enemies withstood them; the LORD handed all their enemies over to them. Not one of all the LORD's good promises to the house of Israel failed; every one was fulfilled (Jos. 21:43–45).

God's actions on behalf of the Israelites are closely linked to their willingness to obey him. When, during the sacking of Jericho, Achan fails to obey the divine command to place 'the silver and gold and the articles of bronze and iron into the treasury of the LORD's house' (Jos. 6:24), the Israelites suffer a severe defeat at the hands of the inhabitants of Ai. Only after the discovery of Achan's sin and his punishment are the Israelites empowered by God to capture the city of Ai (Jos. 8:1–19).

Central to the successful occupation of the land is the example that Joshua sets the people. As their leader he recognizes the importance of observing all that is recorded in the 'Book of the Law' (Jos. 1:7–8), and from beginning to end he is exemplary in his obedience to God. This is reflected, in part, by his concern to circumcise the people and keep the Passover (Jos. 5:1–12). As a result, the Israelites, under his leadership, defeat so many kings that an entire chapter is given over to listing them (Jos. 12:1–24). The achievements of Joshua are an important reminder that victory does not depend upon the Israelites having a king like other nations. Rather, the successful invasion is dependent upon their obedience to God.

For Joshua, it is so important to obey God that towards the end of his life he assembles the Israelites in order to encourage them to continue doing so.

Be very strong; be careful to obey all that is written in the Book of the Law of Moses, without turning aside to the right or to the left. Do not associate with these nations that remain among you; do not invoke the names of their gods or swear by them. You must not serve them or bow down to them. But you are to hold fast to the LORD your God, as you have until now. The LORD has driven out before you great and powerful nations; to this day no-one has been able to withstand you. One of you routs a thousand, because the LORD your God fights for you, just as he promised. So be very careful to love the LORD your God (Jos. 23:6–11).

While the book of Joshua describes how the Israelites come to possess the promised land, Joshua's final speeches to the people suggest that he anticipates a future in which they will disobey God. Echoing the concluding chapters of Deuteronomy, he warns the Israelites:

But if you turn away and ally yourselves with the survivors of these nations that remain among you and if you intermarry with them and associate with them, then you may be sure that the LORD your God will no longer drive out these nations before you. Instead, they will become snares and traps for you, whips on your backs and thorns in your eyes, until you perish from this good land, which the LORD your God has given you (Jos. 23:12–13).

Although the book of Joshua presents a very positive view of the initial stage of the Israelite occupation of the promised land, it anticipates trouble ahead. For an account of this we must move on to the book of Judges.

Disobedience and failure

The opening verses of Judges echo the success story of the book of Joshua. Soon, however, there are indications that the occupation of the land is beginning to falter. We read that the men of the tribes of Judah and Benjamin are unable to dislodge those living in the plains and in Jerusalem respectively (Jdg. 1:19, 21). An important contrast is then made between Joshua's generation and that which follows:

After that whole generation had been gathered to their fathers, another generation grew up, who knew neither the LORD nor what he had done for Israel. Then the Israelites did evil in the eyes of the LORD and served the Baals. They forsook the LORD, the God of their fathers, who had brought them out of Egypt. They followed and worshipped various gods of the peoples around them. They provoked the LORD to anger because they forsook him and served Baal and the Ashtoreths (Jdg. 2:10–13).

As a result of their apostasy, the Israelites no longer enjoy success against their enemies. On the contrary, they find themselves being oppressed by 'raiders who plundered them' and 'sold them to their enemies all around.' Yet God does not abandon the Israelites completely:

> Then the LORD raised up judges, who saved them out of the hands of these raiders. Yet they would not listen to their judges but prostituted themselves to other gods and worshipped them. Unlike their fathers, they quickly turned from the way in which their fathers had walked, the way of obedience to the LORD's commands. Whenever the LORD raised up a judge for them, he was with that judge and saved them out of the hands of their enemies as long as the judge lived; for the LORD had compassion on them as they groaned under those who oppressed and afflicted them. But when the judge died, the people returned to ways even more corrupt than those of their fathers, following other gods and serving and worshipping them. They refused to give up their evil practices and stubborn ways (Jdg. 2:16–19).

This summary towards the beginning of Judges is followed by a cycle of stories which illustrate the pattern described here. Each section begins with the observation that 'the Israelites did evil in the eyes of the LORD' (Jdg. 3:7, 12; 4:1; 6:1; 10:6; 13:1) and then focuses on a 'judge' who is empowered by God to deliver the Israelites from their oppressors. In all there are six main sections, which focus on the following individuals: Othniel, Ehud, Deborah and Barak, Gideon, Jephthah, Samson. A careful comparison of the accounts of these judges reveals a number of striking features.

First, those chosen to deliver the Israelites from their enemies are sometimes empowered by the Spirit of the Lord coming upon them. This is true of Othniel (3:10), Gideon (6:34), Jephthah (11:29) and, especially, Samson (13:25; 14:6, 19; 15:14). Here, for the first time in Scripture, we read about the Spirit of the Lord enabling individuals to accomplish special feats of leadership. A similar endowment of the Spirit is later associated with the monarchy and the future Messiah.

Secondly, some of these judges are described as bringing

rest to the land; this occurs with Othniel (3:11), Ehud (3:30), Deborah and Barak (5:31) and Gideon (8:28). After Gideon, however, there is little evidence that the activities of either Jephthah or Samson enabled the Israelites to enjoy peace in the land.

This observation points to a third and particularly important feature regarding the overall portrayal of the judges. As we progress from one judge to the next, there are strong indications of a worsening moral and political situation among the Israelites. This is even reflected in the actions of the judges themselves. Gideon is the first judge to attack fellow Israelites (8:4–17); then Jephthah is responsible for the death of forty-two thousand Ephraimites (12:1–6). In a similar vein the later judges engage in unworthy religious activities. While Gideon initially destroys his father's altar to Baal and the Asherah pole beside it (6:25–32), he is later instrumental in making a golden ephod that becomes an object of false worship for the Israelites (8:22–27). Due to a hasty and unnecessary vow, Jephthah finds himself sacrificing his only child, a daughter (11:34–40). When we come to Samson, the last in this series of judges, we discover that his behaviour does not befit one set apart to follow the consecrated life of a Nazirite. Moreover, his desire for foreign women, a recurring theme in the Samson story, mirrors the Israelites' yearning after other gods. It is highly ironic, therefore, that the very one who was meant to deliver Israel from her enemies should end up being imprisoned in a Philistine jail and dying in a pagan temple. In these ways attention is drawn to the ever deteriorating situation regarding the security of the Israelites within the land of Canaan.

Fourthly, Judges emphasizes that those empowered by God to deliver the Israelites from oppression are not chosen by God to establish a hereditary monarchy. This is highlighted especially in the story of Gideon, when one of his sons, Abimelech, seeks to become king over Israel. The topic of kingship dominates Judges 9, as Abimelech, whose name means 'my father is king', murders some seventy brothers in an attempt to establish a royal dynasty. The narrative reveals, however, that Abimelech's actions merely contribute to the failure of the Israelites to possess the land. Acquiring a king in this manner does not bring rest to the people.

The picture of moral and spiritual decline portrayed in the cycle of stories involving the judges is painted in still stronger colours in the final four chapters of the book. Here, a contrast is made with the situation described earlier in the book of Joshua. First, we have a series of related events involving a shrine containing a silver idol erected by Micah and paid for by money which he stole from his mother. In due course the items associated with this shrine are taken by the Danites to become objects of false worship in the town of Laish (which they capture from its unsuspecting inhabitants and afterwards rename Dan). As a final comment on these events the narrator observes that the priest associated with this shrine is none other than Jonathan, a grandson of Moses (Jdg. 18:30). Secondly, there is a lengthy account involving the Benjamites of Gibeah who rape and kill a young woman from the tribe of Judah. Such is the revulsion which the other tribes feel that they decide to punish the Benjamites. As a result, the tribe of Benjamin is almost annihilated. Before this happens, however, the Israelites are filled with remorse, and, in spite of having made an oath prohibiting the giving of their daughters to the Benjamites, they arrange by murderous and devious means to provide wives for five hundred men. All these events underline the extent and seriousness of the moral decline that has come upon the Israelites.

The final chapters of Judges are opened and concluded by the words, 'In those days Israel had no king; everyone did as he saw fit' (17:6; 21:25). The first part of this statement is repeated in 18:1 and 19:1. This refrain suggests that the author of Judges views the lack of a king as a major factor in the nation's problems. Moreover, by focusing on the fate of the Benjamites and two individuals from 'Bethlehem in Judah', these chapters anticipate developments in 1 Samuel concerning the first two kings of Israel: Saul from the tribe of Benjamin and David from Bethlehem in Judah.

Conclusion

Israel's failure to possess the promised land is clearly not due to God's inability to overcome the nations already resident there. Rather, it results from the disobedience of the Israelites themselves. While God provides judges to 'save' them from their enemies, these judges have a tendency to reflect the failings of the people. In the light of this, the refrain of the concluding chapters of Judges, 'In those days Israel had no king', seems to imply that only with the establishment of a monarchy will the situation be changed. Alongside this, however, the story of Abimelech reveals that the monarchy must originate with God in order to know his blessing. Moreover, the success of any leader is dependent upon obeying God's law and being empowered by the Spirit of the Lord.

By emphasizing these ideas, the books of Joshua and Judges contribute in a distinctive way to the biblical picture of the Messiah. While the faults of Israel's judges are fully described, their role – as divinely empowered deliverers – foreshadows that of the Messiah. Moreover, echoing Genesis, attention is drawn to the tribe of Judah and the special part which it will play in establishing a monarch through whom the nations of the earth will be blessed.

Questions for reflection and discussion

What pattern is evident in Judges regarding the Israelites' occupation of the land of Canaan?

How does this compare with the book of Joshua?

How does Judges anticipate the establishment of the monarchy in Israel?

In Judges, what types of activity provoke God's displeasure?

6

The story of Ruth:
from Judah to David

Ruth

Summary

The story of Ruth forms an important bridge between the books of Judges and Samuel. Set in the context of the former, it anticipates the creation of the Davidic dynasty. Parallels between Ruth and Tamar (*cf.* Gn. 38), together with the genealogy at the end of the book, indicate that Ruth's marriage to Boaz is important for the continuation of the line of 'seed' highlighted in Genesis.

Key text: Ruth 4:9–22

Bef' efore focusing on the birth of the monarchy in ancient
Israel, as described in the books of 1 and 2 Samuel, we
shall consider briefly the story of a young Moabitess
called Ruth. Although this story forms one of the shortest
books in the Bible, it contributes in a special way to the portrait
of the Messiah.

At the very outset, the events described in Ruth are placed
in the period of the judges. This is underlined by the opening
words of the book: 'In the days when the judges ruled ...'
While this creates a chronological link with the book of Judges,
there is also a geographical link, in that the opening verses of
Ruth refer twice to 'Bethlehem in Judah', echoing identical
references in the two main stories that conclude Judges (17:7, 8,
9; 19:1, 2, 18). This connection is striking, given that the
expression 'Bethlehem in Judah' occurs elsewhere in the Old
Testament only in 1 Samuel 17:12. The prominence of
Bethlehem in the final chapters of Judges and the book of Ruth
is undoubtedly due to the fact that it is the village where David
was born and to which the prophet Samuel comes in order to
anoint David as king over Israel (1 Sa. 16:1; *cf.* 17:12).

The link with David

This link with the family of David is made explicit in the
conclusion to Ruth where we have two references to Jesse, the
father of David (4:17, 22; *cf.* 1 Sa. 16:1; 17:12). While the author
of Ruth does not state directly that David founds a royal
dynasty in Israel, there can be little doubt that the composition
and preservation of the story of Ruth owes much to this
connection.

The story of Ruth also provides an interesting contrast
with Judges. Whereas the latter depicts a situation of moral
decline within the nation of Israel, the former focuses on the
exemplary behaviour of both Ruth and her husband-to-be,
Boaz. While the Judges narrative provides a solemn reminder
of the danger posed by Israelites taking foreign wives, linking
this with religious apostasy, the story of Ruth centres on the

marriage of a pious Israelite man to a foreign woman who embraces the Israelites as her people and, more importantly, the Lord as her God. Throughout the book of Ruth the piety and faithfulness of its two main characters are presented as a source of blessing and hope. This is especially so for Naomi, Ruth's mother-in-law from her first marriage, who, having lost her husband and both sons, is on the brink of destitution. In this regard, the role of Ruth and Boaz in bringing God's salvation to an Israelite widow may be compared and contrasted with that of the judges.

We have already noted that a major reason for the significance of the book of Ruth is its link to the Davidic dynasty. As the story draws to a conclusion, we learn that the son born to Ruth and Boaz will in due time become the grandfather of Israel's most famous monarch, David. Lest this fact should slip the reader's notice, it is stated twice, first in 4:17 and then in the final verse of the book. As a result, this story, which begins with a man from Bethlehem called Elimelech, meaning 'my God is king', ends by naming another Bethlehemite who is chosen by God to be king over Israel.

The link with Judah

While the book of Ruth anticipates the start of the Israelite monarchy, it also highlights important links with the past, especially with events recorded in Genesis. The most obvious connection comes in the genealogy recorded in Ruth 4:18–22. This list of descendants, which ends with David, begins with Perez, whose birth to Judah and Tamar is described in Genesis 38:29. The heading used to introduce this genealogy, 'These are the descendants of' (RSV), is reminiscent of similar headings in Genesis (Gn. 11:10; 25:12, 19; 36:1, 9). As well as using this genealogy to reveal that Boaz is a direct descendant of Perez, however, the narrative earlier records how the 'elders and all those at the gate' of Bethlehem pronounce a blessing upon Boaz:

May the LORD make the woman who is coming into your home like Rachel and Leah, who together built up the house of Israel. May you have standing in Ephrathah and be famous in Bethlehem. Through the offspring the LORD gives you by this young woman, may your family be like that of Perez, whom Tamar bore to Judah (Ru. 4:11–12).

Here also Perez is mentioned, as are his parents Tamar and Judah. By recording these comments, the author of Ruth picks up the idea, central to Genesis, that the royal line of 'seed' is to be traced through the descendants of Judah.

This link with the 'seed' of Genesis is further highlighted by the way in which the story of Ruth's marriage to Boaz shares a number of striking features with the account of Tamar's relationship with Judah. Tamar and Ruth are both foreign women who marry Israelite men. Unfortunately, both are soon widowed without having borne children. In both cases the custom of levirate marriage – the marriage of a childless widow to her husband's brother in order to provide an heir for the dead brother – proves problematic. As regards Tamar, her husband's brother evades his duty and in the end is divinely punished. With Ruth, her husband and his only brother both die, each leaving a childless widow. Confronted by somewhat similar situations, Tamar and Ruth take unusually bold steps in order to secure the continuation of their husband's family line. Tamar, putting off her widow's clothes and disguising herself with a veil, encourages her father-in-law Judah to believe that she is a prostitute and so to sleep with her. Ruth, adorning herself with perfume and her best clothes, goes during the night to Boaz in order to seek his help and protection, an action that could easily have been misinterpreted. These similarities are striking, especially given that they concern the continuation of the ancestral line of King David.

Since Tamar and Ruth play a vital role in continuing the family line of Judah, from which the royal house of David is descended, it is hardly surprising that their actions are remembered by later generations. As we shall observe later, both women are selected for special mention in Matthew's genealogy of Jesus.

The kinsman-redeemer

One further feature of the book of Ruth deserves consideration in the light of our interest in the biblical picture of the Messiah. The concept of 'kinsman-redeemer' plays an important part in the story. It is associated not only with Boaz (2:20; 3:9, 12–13; 4:4) and an unnamed relative (3:12–13; 4:1, 3–4, 6, 8), but also with Obed (4:14), the son born to Ruth. Elsewhere in the Old Testament, someone performing this role acts in a special way on behalf of relatives who are confronting a crisis, possibly involving financial hardship or injustice. In such circumstances the 'kinsman-redeemer' helps those in need or ensures that justice is done. Such actions are an important expression of loving kindness, righteousness and family solidarity.

Although the concept of kinsman-redeemer is not associated with the Israelite king elsewhere in the Old Testament, it is highlighted as an aspect of God's activity on behalf of Israel. In Exodus 6:6 God describes his deliverance of the Israelites from Egypt in terms of redemption and judgment: 'I will redeem you with an outstretched arm and with mighty acts of judgment.' Since this is how the divine king rescues his people, it might be expected that his royal servant would fulfil a similar role.

Conclusion

In spite of its brevity, the book of Ruth contributes in a special way to the Bible's portrait of the Messiah. Chiefly, it links the name of David with the divine promises in Genesis concerning a future king from the line of Judah. Moreover, the portrayal of Boaz as a pious and faithful kinsman-redeemer underlines the righteous nature of this line of descendants. Also, the exemplary behaviour of Ruth the Moabitess, paralleling in certain regards that of Tamar, adds to the impression that through this line of 'seed', God's promise regarding the blessing of the nations will find fulfilment. In the light of this promise, it is surely fitting that the two women who play a crucial role in ensuring the continuation of the royal line of 'seed' come from other nations.

Questions for reflection and discussion

How may the characters in Ruth be contrasted with those encountered in Judges?

List the ways in which the book of Ruth provides a bridge between the line of seed in Genesis and the Davidic dynasty.

How is Boaz a model for future kings?

7

The beginnings of
the monarchy

1 Samuel 1 – 12

Summary

The opening chapters of 1 Samuel continue the picture of national decline found in Judges. Although Samuel is raised up by God to deliver the people, the shortcomings of his sons prompt the people to ask for a king. In spite of being divinely warned of the dangers that may come through the abuse of royal authority, the people insist on having a monarch. Subsequently, God instructs Samuel to anoint Saul, the son of Kish, from the tribe of Benjamin, as the first king over Israel.

Key text: 1 Samuel 8:1–22

Throughout the books of Exodus to Judges, prominence is given to the fulfilment of God's promise to Abraham that his descendants will possess the land of Canaan. During this same period, however, the promise to bless the nations through a royal descendant of Abraham recedes into the background. In the books of Samuel and Kings, attention is focused again on this latter promise as we read of the creation of a royal dynasty descended from the tribe of Judah. With this the biblical portrait of the Messiah begins to take fuller shape.

Although there are two books of Samuel in English translations of the Bible, they were composed as a unified account, describing God's choice of the house of David to form a royal dynasty to rule Israel for future generations. The story of David becoming king is recorded in considerable detail, with much attention given to those factors which make him suitable as the founder of a royal line. To accentuate these qualities the narrative contrasts David's success with the tragic failure of Saul. Before focusing on David's reign, however, it is helpful to observe how the early chapters of 1 Samuel build on the stories recorded in Judges.

A nation in decline

The initial episodes of 1 Samuel provide an interesting sequel to the Judges account of Israel's ever worsening moral and political situation in Canaan. The opening description of Samuel's birth suggests that he is yet another divinely appointed deliverer or judge. This suggestion comes through parallels drawn with the birth story of Samson. At the outset, the fathers of Samson and Samuel are introduced in very similar ways (Jdg. 13:2; 1 Sa. 1:1). Samuel's mother, like Samson's, is initially unable to have children. From birth, Samson and Samuel are both consecrated as Nazirites; their hair is not to be cut (Jdg. 13:5; 1 Sa. 1:11), and, while the circumstances differ, their mothers are warned against drinking wine (Jdg. 13:7; 1 Sa. 1:14). In these ways, the narrative implies that Samuel is a new Samson.

Although the birth accounts have noteworthy parallels, Samuel is confirmed as a 'judge' only much later, following a surge of repentance among the Israelites (1 Sa. 7:2–9). In this regard, the early chapters of 1 Samuel continue the cycle of events found in Judges: due to their sin God causes the Israelites to be oppressed by a foreign nation; when they cry out to God for help, he raises up a 'judge' to deliver them. For this reason, prior to describing Samuel's role as a judge, the narrative focuses in part on the moral decline of Israel's priesthood and in part on the oppression of the Israelites by the Philistines, the former being the cause of the latter.

Regarding the Philistine oppression, there are strong echoes of Judges, especially of the Samson story. The most striking parallel comes in the account of the capture of the ark of the Lord (1 Sa. 5:1–2). Whereas the extent of Israel's decline in Judges is marked by the Philistine imprisonment of Samson, the Israelites' divinely empowered leader, the capture of the ark signifies an even more terrible disaster. Now the very symbol of God's presence, his divine throne, has been taken by the Philistines. God himself, so it appears, is imprisoned by his enemies. The impact of this is highlighted in the brief account of the death of Eli's daughter-in-law as she gives birth to a son. Naming him Ichabod (meaning 'no glory'), she laments, 'The glory has departed from Israel' (1 Sa. 4:21). Yet, just as Samson's presence in the temple of Dagon in Gaza resulted in the death of many Philistines, so too does the presence of the ark of the Lord in the temple of Dagon in Ashdod.

When the Israelites eventually cry out to God for help, he responds by giving them Samuel as a 'judge'. The record of Samuel's successful leadership is summarized briefly and positively, with particular attention being given to his success against foreign oppressors (1 Sa. 7:7–14) and his concern for justice within Israel itself (1 Sa. 7:15–17). While Samuel is portrayed as an excellent judge, the narrative records how in his old age he inappropriately appoints his sons as judges. They, unfortunately, do not follow in his footsteps, but rather pervert the course of justice by accepting bribes (1 Sa. 8:1–3).

The demand for a king

The shortcomings of Samuel's sons prompt the elders of Israel to ask Samuel for a king to rule over them 'such as all the other nations have' (1 Sa. 8:5). This marks a watershed in the narrative, setting the stage for the transition from the period of the judges to the beginning of the monarchy in ancient Israel.

The response of both Samuel and the Lord to the elders' request is recorded. Samuel's reaction is one of displeasure (1 Sa. 8:6), apparently because he views this proposal as a rejection of his leadership. The Lord, however, comments that 'it is not you they have rejected, but they have rejected me as their king' (1 Sa. 8:7). This observation is hardly surprising, however, since it reflects a pattern repeated since the Israelites were delivered from Egypt.

In reply to the Israelites' request for a king, God outlines the negative consequences of having a king as ruler:

This is what the king who will reign over you will do: He will take your sons and make them serve with his chariots and horses, and they will run in front of his chariots ... He will take your daughters to be perfumers and cooks and bakers. He will take the best of your fields and vineyards and olive groves, and give them to his attendants. He will take a tenth of your grain and of your vintage and give it to his officials and attendants ... He will take a tenth of your flocks, and you yourselves will become his slaves. When that day comes, you will cry out for relief from the king you have chosen, and the LORD will not answer you in that day (1 Sa. 8:11–18).

Ignoring this divine warning, the people still insist that they want a king.

We want a king over us. Then we shall be like all the other nations, with a king to lead us and to go out before us and fight our battles (1 Sa. 8:19–20).

Without further comment the narrative records that God accedes to their request and instructs Samuel to give them a king.

The subsequent narrative describes in two different but complementary ways how Saul is anointed by Samuel as the first king of the Israelites. Whereas 1 Samuel 9:1 – 10:16 focuses upon a private anointing involving only Samuel and Saul, 1 Samuel 10:17–27 describes the public selection of Saul as king from among all the men of Israel. While these accounts are distinct, they share two noteworthy features.

First, in both episodes the choice of Saul is made by God. This is most apparent on the first occasion, for Samuel is divinely instructed to anoint Saul (1 Sa. 9:16). This private anointing confirms that the later selection of Saul is no accident.

Second, both episodes give evidence of Saul's personal humility. In the first, this is reflected in Saul's comments concerning his family ('But am I not a Benjamite, from the smallest tribe of Israel, and is not my clan the least of all the clans of the tribe of Benjamin?' 1 Sa. 9:21), and in his unwillingness to tell his uncle anything about his anointing when he returns (1 Sa. 10:16). Later, when all the people assemble before Samuel, Saul hides among the baggage in order to avoid being made king (1 Sa. 10:22–23). In these ways attention is drawn to God's choice of Saul as king and Saul's own reluctance to exalt himself over his fellow Israelites.

Throughout the story of Saul's appointment as king over Israel, various comments suggest that his role largely continues that undertaken by the judges. This is clearly implied in God's brief description to Samuel:

He will deliver my people from the hand of the Philistines. I have looked upon my people, for their cry has reached me (1 Sa. 9:16).

Saul's association with the judges is also emphasized by the reference to the 'Spirit of God' coming upon him in power (1 Sa. 10:6; *cf.* verse 10). Further, Saul's rescue of the men of

Jabesh Gilead from the threat of the Ammonites not only is typical of what the judges did, but provides an interesting contrast with the earlier story of the Benjamites of Gibeah (Saul's home town) being punished for raping and killing a young woman from Bethlehem. On that occasion, pieces of the woman's body were sent to the Israelite tribes in order to summon them to war against the Benjamites. Then, out of a sense of remorse for having almost totally annihilated the tribe of Benjamin, the Israelites attacked and killed the men of Jabesh Gilead in order to provide wives for those Benjamite men who have not been put to death. Now, in marked contrast, Saul, a Benjamite, sends the pieces of a slaughtered ox throughout the tribes of Israel in order to muster support for the people of Jabesh Gilead. By rescuing the inhabitants of Jabesh Gilead from the Ammonites, Saul is clearly portrayed as seeking to atone for past wrongs. In these ways he is depicted as an exemplary 'judge'.

While the episodes relating to Saul's appointment and confirmation as king show him in a very positive light, bringing deliverance to the Israelites as the judges did, the prophet Samuel in a lengthy speech reminds the people that their request for a king is 'evil' (1 Sa. 12:17). Moreover, he emphasizes that the establishment of a monarchy within Israel will not, of itself, guarantee peace and security for the people. Fundamental to their future prosperity is the need to obey God; without this they and their king 'will be swept away' (1 Sa. 12:25). In stating this, Samuel points to an important tension which runs throughout the biblical account of the Israelite monarchy. Although it is established by God and may be used to fulfil his purposes, its success in terms of ensuring the well-being of the people is directly related to the faithfulness of the king and his people in obeying God. Tragically, after starting well, Saul soon forfeits through disobedience his right to be king over Israel.

Conclusion

The anointing of Saul as the first king of Israel marks an

important stage in the outworking of God's purposes for Israel and all the nations of the earth. Focusing on both the positive and negative aspects of kingship, the story is filled with tension. In this way an important contrast is drawn between kingship as commonly exercised and kingship as approved by God. This distinction will be explored further in our next chapter as we contrast the fate of Saul with that of David. This same distinction is also important as regards the biblical picture of the Messiah, for, as we shall observe in future chapters, the Messiah is viewed as a perfect or ideal king.

Questions for reflection and discussion

How do the early chapters of 1 Samuel connect with the book of Judges? What is the significance of these links?

What ambiguities surround the creation of the Israelite monarchy?

What positive characteristics does Saul display in 1 Samuel 9 – 11?

8

The characteristics of divinely appointed royalty

1 Samuel

Summary

God's choice of Saul and then of David to be king over Israel confirms Hannah's remarks regarding the poor and humble being exalted to royal office. Hannah also affirms that God prospers those who trust and obey him, and this too is demonstrated, both positively and negatively, in the lives of Saul and David. Attention is also drawn to the concept of anointing – the term Messiah literally means 'anointed one' – and to the empowering activity of the Spirit of the Lord.

Key texts: 1 Samuel 2:7–10; 13:5–15; 16:1–13

While the early chapters of 1 Samuel ·recount the transition from the period of the judges to the appointment of Saul as Israel's first king, the immediately succeeding chapters focus on the gradual displacement of Saul by David the son of Jesse. The story of Saul's demise and David's rise to power highlights a number of important characteristics which distinguish true, or God-appointed, kingship from false. By contrasting David's behaviour with that of Saul, the narrative constructs a vivid picture of the ideal king. Although Saul and David in very differing ways fall short of this ideal, the accounts of their lives instruct us about the nature of true kingship.

Kingly humility

The most striking kingly quality emphasized in the books of Samuel is humility. While this is probably the last characteristic normally associated with royalty, it is portrayed as essential in order to be a successful king. The reason for this lies in the idea that God exalts the humble but brings down the proud.

The importance of humility within the books of Samuel is reflected in the prominence given to it in Hannah's prayer. Placed after the story of Samuel's birth, Hannah's prayer performs a special function by encapsulating themes which permeate the books of Samuel. Prior to the appointment of any king over Israel, Hannah powerfully expresses in poetry the principle that God raises up the poor and needy to royal heights:

> The LORD sends poverty and wealth;
>   he humbles and he exalts.
> He raises the poor from the dust
>   and lifts the needy from the ash heap;
> he seats them with princes
>   and has them inherit a throne of honour.
>
> (1 Sa. 2:7–8; *cf.* 2:4–6)

In the subsequent accounts of the choice and appointment of Saul and David as kings, their humble origins receive special mention. For his part, Saul stresses the insignificance of his own family: 'But am I not a Benjamite, from the smallest tribe of Israel, and is not my clan the least of all the clans of the tribe of Benjamin' (1 Sa. 9:21)? In saying this, he recalls the decimation that the Benjamites suffered at the hands of the other tribes (Jdg. 20:1–48). Saul's humility is later revealed when he hides himself in the baggage during the selection of the king (1 Sa. 10:22–23), and when he deals kindly with those who mock his appointment as king (1 Sa. 10:27; 11:12–14).

Like Saul, David is exalted from lowly origins. When Samuel visits the house of Jesse, even David's own father does not consider him a likely candidate for anointing; as the youngest of Jesse's eight sons, he is merely a lad assigned to tending the sheep. A similar picture emerges in the account of David's defeat of Goliath. David is portrayed as a youth who does not have the physical strength to wear a soldier's armour. Nevertheless, God enables him to defeat the Philistine champion.

The theme of David's humility reappears when Saul invites David to marry his eldest daughter Merab. David replies, 'Who am I, and what is my family or my father's clan in Israel, that I should become the king's son-in-law?' (1 Sa. 18:18). When Saul later makes a similar offer, David responds: 'I'm only a poor man and little known' (1 Sa. 18:23). The irony of this is noted by the narrator, who, shortly afterwards, observes David's fame (1 Sa. 18:30). Still later, when Saul pursues David in order to kill him, David compares himself to a 'dead dog' and a 'flea' (1 Sa. 24:14; *cf.* 26:20).

We observe something more of David's humility when his son Absalom seizes the throne (2 Sa. 15:1–37). During his flight from Jerusalem David is cursed and abused by Shimei. This, however, he accepts as part of God's judgment for his involvement in the death of Uriah (2 Sa. 16:5–14). By responding in this way, David differs enormously from Saul, because, having wrongly used his position of power for personal ends, he willingly acknowledges that his apparent removal from the throne is a form of punishment. For David, this is no less than he deserves, and he graciously accepts his public humiliation. In the light of this, it is no surprise that he should later be reinstated as Israel's king.

Trust and obedience

Another characteristic of good kingship, and one that goes hand in hand with humility, is the ability to trust and obey God. One aspect of this is the recognition that great achievements are accomplished only with divine assistance. Yet again, this is a quality commended by Hannah in her song of praise.

> He [the LORD] will guard the feet of his saints,
>   but the wicked will be silenced in darkness.
> It is not by strength that one prevails;
>   those who oppose the LORD will be shattered.
> He will thunder against them from heaven;
>   the LORD will judge the ends of the earth.
> He will give strength to his king
>   and exalt the horn of his anointed.
>
> (1 Sa. 2:9–10)

While the presence of this quality is noted in the earliest stage of Saul's reign, its absence is a feature of his later years. When, immediately after his anointing, Saul delivers the men of Jabesh Gilead from the Ammonites, he publicly acknowledges that 'this day the LORD has rescued Israel' (1 Sa. 11:13). Later, as his trust in God is tested by a Philistine invasion, he panics and hurriedly offers up a burnt offering, usurping the priestly role of Samuel (1 Sa. 13:7–14). Samuel's condemnation of Saul is telling:

You acted foolishly … You have not kept the command the LORD your God gave you; if you had, he would have established your kingdom over Israel for all time. But now your kingdom will not endure; the LORD has sought out a man after his own heart and appointed him leader of his people, because you have not kept the LORD's command (1 Sa. 13:13–14).

Saul's failure to obey God also surfaces in the story of his defeat of the Amalekites. Although ordered by God to destroy everything, Saul spares 'Agag and the best of the sheep and cattle, the fat calves and lambs – everything that was good' (1 Sa. 15:9). Further evidence of Saul's lack of faith in God comes when he consults in Endor a woman who is a medium (1 Sa. 28:4–25). This signals his rejection of the Lord, and, not surprisingly, heralds Saul's death.

The qualities of trust and obedience which Saul so sadly lacks in the later part of his reign are, in contrast, very evident in David. This is not to say that David always trusts and obeys God completely. On the contrary, the narrative of 2 Samuel focuses fully on his adulterous association with Bathsheba and his role in the death of her husband, Uriah the Hittite. David is squarely condemned and duly punished. He regrets his immoral actions, however, and his reinstatement as king, following the rebellions of Absalom and Sheba, indicates God's forgiveness.

Nowhere is David's trust in God more evident than in his willingness as a mere lad to confront Goliath, the three-metre-tall champion of the Philistines. David's remarks to Saul exemplify his trust: 'The LORD who delivered me from the paw of the lion and the paw of the bear will deliver me from the hand of this Philistine' (1 Sa. 17:37). Elsewhere, there are frequent examples of David regularly consulting God before undertaking military activities (1 Sa. 23:2, 4; 30:8; 2 Sa. 2:1; 5:19, 23). In this way he acknowledges the importance of God's role in overcoming his enemies.

A further demonstration of David's trust in God is his reluctance to kill Saul when the opportunity arises. Although Saul makes many attempts to murder David, and actually slaughters those who aid him – all of which is presented as a reason for his removal from the throne – David displays an altogether different attitude. Although David is encouraged by his men to slay Saul, he consistently refuses to kill 'the LORD's anointed' (1 Sa. 24:6, 10; 26:9–11, 23; *cf.* 2 Sa. 1:1–16). In spite of having been appointed as king-in-waiting by Samuel (1 Sa. 16:13) and being openly acknowledged by others, including Saul, as the next monarch (1 Sa. 21:11; 23:17; 24:20), David patiently waits for God to establish him as leader over the nation. He makes no attempt to grasp power by unlawful means. Remarkably, this fact is picked up by Abigail, a woman who provided food for David and his men:

> … the LORD will certainly make a lasting dynasty for my master [*i.e.* David], because he fights the LORD's battles. Let no wrongdoing be found in you as long as you live. Even though someone is pursuing you to take your life, the life of my master will be bound securely in the bundle of the living by the LORD your God. But the lives of your enemies he will hurl away as from the pocket of a sling. When the LORD has done for my master every good thing he promised concerning him and has appointed him leader over Israel, my master will not have on his conscience the staggering burden of needless bloodshed or of having avenged himself (1 Sa. 25:28–31).

This determination to wait on God to act is one of the main characteristics that sets David apart from Saul. It also distinguishes David from his own son Absalom and, later, Sheba son of Bicri, each of whom seeks to usurp the king's position and establish himself as the ruler of Israel.

To the qualities of humility and dependence upon God we could add righteous behaviour. Once again Saul's actions are contrasted with those of David. Saul's deceitful and murderous attitude towards David and those who assist him are contrasted with that of David towards Saul and the members of his family. Whereas Saul uses all sorts of devious means in his attempts to end David's life, David, in spite of having several opportunities to kill Saul, always acts in a submissive manner towards Saul as the Lord's anointed. We also see something of David's righteous behaviour in his grief at the news of the deaths of Saul and Jonathan, and in his generous treatment of Mephibosheth, Saul's crippled son.

Anointing

Two other features specifically associated with the divine appointment of Saul and David as kings ought to be noted; unlike the qualities of humility and dependence upon God, these are associated primarily with kings.

First, Saul and David are both anointed with oil. In the books of Samuel, anointing is mentioned first by Hannah at the conclusion of her prayer.

> He [the Lord] will give strength to his king
> and exalt the horn of his anointed.
>
> (1 Sa. 2:10)

From the poetic nature of this passage it is clear that the expression 'his anointed' is another way of saying 'his king'. This association between kingship and anointing is even more apparent in Samuel's anointing of Saul and then of David. On these occasions, the action of smearing oil on the head of the individual designates that person as chosen by the Lord to be king over Israel. This anointing is clearly very significant, setting the individual apart from others. On account of this, David consistently refuses to take Saul's life; the one appointed by God as king must be respected, even when, as in the case of Saul, he appears by his evil deeds to have forfeited that right.

Since anointing designates an individual as God's choice to rule over Israel, the designation 'anointed one' is often used as a synonym for 'king'. We derive our term 'Messiah' from the Hebrew word for 'anointed one'. Thus the passages which describe the anointing of Saul and David are very important for understanding the royal connotations underlying the word 'Messiah'.

69

The Spirit of the Lord

A second feature associated with the divine appointment of kings in 1 Samuel is the coming of the Spirit of the Lord in power. After anointing him, Samuel predicts that Saul will 'prophesy' and 'be changed into a different person' (1 Sa. 10:6). Later this is fulfilled in a highly visible and dramatic manner (1 Sa. 10:10–12). The account of David's anointing concludes with the comment: 'From that day on the Spirit of the LORD came upon David in power' (1 Sa. 16:13). This is almost immediately followed by the observation that 'the Spirit of the LORD had departed from Saul, and an evil spirit from the LORD tormented him' (1 Sa. 16:14). There follows an interesting passage which describes how David is brought to play the harp to Saul in order to bring him relief from this evil spirit. Not only does this episode bring the two main protagonists together for the first time, but it highlights the very contrasting effects produced by the different spirits sent from God (1 Sa. 16:23; *cf.* 18:10; 19:9). While references to the Spirit of the Lord are limited, these episodes indicate that the 'anointed one' is empowered by God to fulfil the task of leadership. This unique assistance, however, clearly depends upon the king's maintaining a harmonious relationship with God – otherwise, as in the case of Saul, the Spirit of the Lord may depart from him.

Conclusion

We have focused on a variety of qualities highlighted in the books of Samuel as important characteristics of the one appointed by God to rule over Israel. In particular, the narrative envisages the ideal king as one exalted from humble origins who demonstrates absolute trust in and obedience to God. Moreover, the one chosen by God is anointed with oil and empowered through the coming of the Spirit of the Lord to fulfil his role of leadership. These same qualities will be evident in the future king who brings to fulfilment God's plans for Israel and all the nations of the earth.

Questions for reflection and discussion

Why is the act of anointing important for understanding the term 'Messiah'?

In what ways do Saul and David resemble the earlier judges?

How is humility portrayed as an important characteristic of the king/Messiah?

What do the stories of Saul and David teach us about how Christian leaders should behave?

9

God's promises concerning the house of David

2 Samuel

Summary

David's position as king over Israel is consolidated following the death of Saul. The arrival of the ark of the Lord in Jerusalem draws attention to the special relationship that exists between God and David. This is confirmed through the covenant which God makes with David, in which he promises to establish David's 'house' or dynasty for ever. Although David desires to build a 'house' or temple for the Lord, God entrusts this task to David's son.

Key texts: 2 Samuel 6:1–23; 7:1–17

Amajor feature of the books of Samuel is Saul's displacement as king by David, the son of Jesse. This transition is highly significant, for David comes from the tribe of Judah and is descended from the line of Perez. Consequently, his enthronement represents a major step towards the fulfilment of the promises in Genesis. In this chapter we shall observe how the books of Samuel stress the importance of the royal line established through the appointment of David as Israel's king.

The royal line established

We have noted already the prominence given in Genesis and elsewhere to the tribe of Judah, and especially to the line of Perez. Not only is David descended from this line, as the book of Ruth confirms, but interestingly he names one of his daughters Tamar (2 Sa. 13:1), undoubtedly out of respect for her earlier namesake. Moreover, David's appointment as king has parallels with the process by which the line of 'seed' is established in Genesis. We observed there the importance of God's choice regarding participation in the line and how the principle of firstborn succession is often ignored in favour of a younger brother. Similarly, David, the youngest of eight brothers, is chosen by God to be anointed as king.

These connections, especially the genealogical, suggest that the divine promises in Genesis will be fulfilled through David and his descendants. Further support for this idea comes in a covenant which God makes with David, confirming that his 'seed' will reign over Israel 'for ever'. Before focusing on the details of this covenant, it is important to observe the context within which it occurs.

The early chapters of 2 Samuel recount how, following the deaths of Saul and Jonathan, a division occurs among the Israelites. While the 'men of Judah' appoint David as their king (2 Sa. 2:1–4), the remaining tribes support the claim of Ish-Bosheth, one of Saul's sons, to be ruler. After some time, Abner, probably the most influential of Ish-Bosheth's supporters, deserts him, siding with David. This leads to confusion and results in Ish-Bosheth being murdered by two of his generals, Recab and his brother Baanah. Following this, all the tribes of Israel rally behind David and anoint him as king (2 Sa. 5:1–3).

With his position as king consolidated, David proceeds to capture from the Jebusites the city of Jerusalem and establish it as his capital, renaming it 'the fortress of Zion, the City of David' (5:6–16; esp. verse 7). Then, after a successful campaign against the Philistines, David brings the ark of the Lord, God's earthly throne, to Jerusalem (6:1–23). The record of this journey, describing Uzzah's untimely death and the blessing bestowed upon the house of Obed-Edom, dramatically illustrates the dangers and benefits associated with God's holy presence. While Uzzah's death makes David angry and delays the journey towards Jerusalem, the ark is eventually brought up into the city amid great rejoicing.

The arrival of the ark of the Lord in Jerusalem marks a climactic point in David's career, vividly portraying the close relationship that exists between the Lord, the king of heaven and earth, and David, the king of Israel. Indeed, a common theme running through the account of David's appointment as king is the idea that the Lord is with him (1 Sa. 16:18; *cf.* 18:12, 14, 28). Moreover, David's rise to power and his confirmation as king have depended totally upon the active support of the Lord. This fact is confirmed by the brief comment that 'the LORD had given him rest from all his enemies around him' (2 Sa. 7:1). It is, therefore, most apt that David should bring the ark of the Lord into the city where he himself lives.

The covenant with David

With his position as king over Israel consolidated, David becomes uneasy with the contrast which he observes between his own 'palace of cedar' and the tent which houses the ark of the Lord. For David it is inappropriate that the earthly dwelling-place of the divine king should appear inferior to his own royal residence. Motivated by a concern for God's dignity and honour, David hints to the prophet Nathan that he wishes to replace the Lord's tent with a temple made of more permanent materials (2 Sa. 7:2). Although Nathan's immediate response is favourable, that very night the Lord intervenes, prohibiting David from fulfilling his plan.

The Lord's response to David is very significant, for, although he rejects David's offer to build a temple, he promises to establish David as the head of a royal dynasty that will continue to rule the nation of Israel for ever. Interestingly, David's wish to build a temple for God and the Lord's promise to establish David's family as a royal dynasty complement each other. This is reflected in the use of the Hebrew word *bayit*, which means 'house' and, as in English, can refer to either a building or a family (as in 'the house of Windsor'). Thus David's desire to build a house for God results in God building a house for David.

Something of the importance of the house promised to David is reflected in God's comments concerning it. First, the Lord affirms that he himself will raise up one of David's own sons and establish him as ruler over the nation. Whereas previous attempts by Abimelech and Ish-Bosheth to establish royal lines were hindered by God, David is assured that one of his sons will succeed him as king. Here, for the first time, God sanctions the creation of a royal dynasty within Israel.

Secondly, David's son will be responsible for building a house for the Lord. Although God stops David from constructing a temple in Jerusalem, he indicates that David's wish will be fulfilled through his son. This confirms the special nature of the relationship existing between God and the royal line of David. Moreover, it has important implications for how the city of Jerusalem will be perceived by future generations of Israelites.

Thirdly, God promises that the dynasty headed by David 'shall be established for ever'. By stating this promise twice (2 Sa. 7:12, 16), the Lord emphasizes that the Davidic monarchy will never come to an end. Elsewhere, Ethan the

Ezrahite, a wise man from the generation after David, expresses in poetry the duration of the dynasty promised to David:

> I [the LORD] will establish his line for ever,
>   his throne as long as the heavens endure ...
> Once for all, I have sworn by my holiness –
>   and I will not lie to David –
> that his line will continue for ever
>   and his throne endure before me like the sun;
> it will be established for ever like the moon,
>   the faithful witness in the sky.
>
> (Ps. 89:29, 35–37)

Fourthly, a special relationship will exist between God and the Davidic king: 'I will be his father, and he shall be my son' (2 Sa. 7:14). This father–son image captures well the idea of the intimate bond that exists between the Lord and the king. Yet, although God assures David that his dynasty will be established for ever, this does not automatically guarantee a peaceful and prosperous future. On the contrary, as a father disciplines his son, so too God will discipline any king who does wrong. The inclusion of this comment strongly suggests that such measures will become necessary in the future. Nevertheless, God promises never to remove the throne from David or his descendants, as he did with Saul.

Conclusion

While the books of Samuel do not describe God's message to David as a covenant, this is how other passages designate it. In Psalm 89, the term 'covenant' is used twice to denote God's promises to David. This designation not only underscores the importance of these divine promises, but possibly indicates that the covenant made earlier with Abraham, and established with Isaac and then with Jacob, is now, centuries later, being established with David and the royal line descended from him.

In the light of David's descent from the tribe of Judah and God's remarkable promises concerning him and his dynasty, it is hardly surprising that the house of David came to be viewed as playing a central role in the outworking of God's purposes for Israel and all humanity. As we shall observe in later chapters, the royal line of David becomes the focus of attention regarding the restoration of humanity's broken relationship with God.

Questions for reflection and discussion

What is the significance of the links between Jerusalem/Zion, the temple and the Davidic dynasty?

Why are God's promises to David concerning his dynasty especially important?

What do they reveal about how God's purposes will be worked out in the future?

10

Solomon: a model of ideal kingship?

1 Kings 1 – 11

Summary

The reign of Solomon reveals how a king, divinely endowed with wisdom, may bring justice, prosperity and security to his subjects. While Solomon achieves this ideal for part of his reign, he incurs God's wrath in his later years by following other gods. His failure to remain faithful to the Lord leads to the division of the kingdom of Israel, with Solomon's son retaining control of only a small portion.

Key texts: 1 Kings 3:4–15; 9:1–9; 11:9–13

The appointment of David as king over Israel marks an important step in the outworking of God's purposes for both Israel and the nations. With this, the fulfilment of the divine promise to bless the nations through a royal descendant of Abraham comes closer. The actual fulfilment still lies some distance in the future, however, as suggested by God's remarks to David regarding the disciplining of future kings (2 Sa. 7:14–15). Further evidence concerning this delay is found in the books of 1 and 2 Kings, which continue the story of the Davidic dynasty.

In this chapter we shall focus on the account of Solomon's reign as recorded in 1 Kings 1 – 11. These chapters are important, not only because they set the scene for the rest of the material in 1 and 2 Kings, but because they shed more light upon the nature of the future king through whom the nations will be blessed.

Solomon becomes king

The opening chapters of 1 Kings recount how David is succeeded by his son Solomon. Solomon's accession to the throne, however, does not occur automatically. The story begins by telling of David's impotence in his old age (1 Ki. 1:1–4). Such is his frailty that he is unable to have intimate relations with his very attractive female attendant Abishag. Against this background, David's son Adonijah prepares to claim the title of king. 'Now Adonijah ... put himself forward and said, "I will be king"' (1 Ki. 1:5). Not only is Adonijah very ambitious, but he appears to have the attributes necessary to be a king, including being 'very handsome' (1 Ki. 1:6; *cf.* 1 Sa. 9:2; 10:23–24; 2 Sa. 14:25–26). As on previous occasions, however, the one who strives after royal office is denied it, and, without taking any action on his own behalf, Solomon finds himself being anointed by Zadok as the next monarch, with David's approval (1 Ki. 1:39). Solomon's enthronement is masterminded by the prophet Nathan, suggesting that he is indeed God's choice (*cf.* 1 Ki. 1:11–14, 22–27).

After Solomon's dramatic appointment as king, Adonijah fears for his life and seeks refuge by clinging to the horns of the altar (1 Ki. 1:50–51). On learning of this, Solomon announces: 'If he shows himself to be a worthy man, not a hair of his head will fall to the ground; but if evil is found in him, he will die' (1 Ki. 1:52). While Solomon's words are undoubtedly meant to reassure Adonijah, their inclusion by the narrator suggests that this threat may indeed come to pass. In the light of this, it is no surprise that soon afterwards Adonijah is executed by Solomon (1 Ki. 2:13–25), although, as we shall observe below, the grounds for his death – he merely asks to marry Abishag – are somewhat questionable.

Close to death, David addresses Solomon:

> Be strong, show yourself a man, and observe what the LORD your God requires: Walk in his ways, and keep his decrees and commands, his laws and requirements, as written in the Law of Moses, so that you may prosper in all you do and wherever you go, and that the LORD may keep his promise to me: 'If your descendants watch how they live, and if they walk faithfully before me with all their heart and soul, you will never fail to have a man on the throne of Israel' (1 Ki. 2:2–4).

David's remarks underline the importance of observing what the Lord requires, and remind Solomon of God's promise regarding the Davidic dynasty. It is important to notice that, as expressed here, God's promise that David's descendants will occupy the throne is conditional upon their behaviour. Yet, earlier, God promised David that the Davidic dynasty would be established for ever (2 Sa. 7:12–16). As we shall observe in more detail below, the slightly differing wording of 2 Samuel 7:12–16 and 1 Kings 2:4 introduces a tension that runs throughout the books of Kings.

Apart from reminding Solomon to obey God, David also warns him about two individuals, Joab and Shimei, whose previous actions merited punishment. David tells Solomon to deal with them 'according to [his] wisdom' (1 Ki. 2:6; *cf.* 2:9). While the narrator does not deny the guilt of Joab and Shimei, doubts are raised regarding Solomon's treatment of them. Joab is killed, still holding the horns of the altar (1 Ki. 2:28–34), an action that clearly contravenes the instructions of Exodus 21:12–14 which require that a guilty party be taken away from the altar before being executed. In a similar fashion, the account of Shimei's death strongly implies that Solomon overreacts when he accuses Shimei of breaking an oath prohibiting him from leaving Jerusalem (1 Ki. 2:36–46). Whereas the original wording of the oath refers to Shimei's leaving Jerusalem by crossing the Kidron Valley (that is, travelling eastward), Shimei in fact goes to Gath, west of Jerusalem. Strictly speaking, Shimei does not break his oath to Solomon. Moreover, even if Shimei is truly guilty, the punishment announced by Solomon seems overly severe. Both of these incidents raise doubts about Solomon's ability to govern wisely.

Two other factors reinforce this initial picture of Solomon's failure to be a wise king.

First, the hasty execution of Adonijah, because he asks to marry Abishag, suggests a considerable lack of magnanimity on the part of Solomon (1 Ki. 2:13–25). This is especially so because Adonijah comes peacefully to Bathsheba, acknowledging Solomon as king and asking the queen mother to intercede on his behalf. Furthermore, in spite of having promised his mother that he would not refuse her request, Solomon disregards it completely (1 Ki. 2:20–25). Finally, Solomon's action appears to contradict the oath that he takes before God. Why, one might ask, should Solomon fear Adonijah when, as he states, the Lord has established him securely upon the throne of his father David (1 Ki. 2:24; *cf.* 2:12)?

Secondly, we are informed briefly that 'Solomon made an alliance with Pharaoh king of Egypt and married his daughter' (1 Ki. 3:1). The full significance of this event becomes clearer later in the Solomon story (1 Ki. 11:1–13). Marriage to a foreigner is normally viewed in the books of Genesis to Kings with some foreboding.

In these ways the opening episodes of Solomon's reign paint a less than perfect picture of the new king. This is not to say that he is portrayed as a villain; on the contrary, the presentation is quite subtle, focusing chiefly on minor but telling flaws, rather than on major shortcomings. For this reason, the narrator can still legitimately affirm that 'Solomon showed his love for the LORD by walking according to the statutes of his father David' (1 Ki. 3:3). Yet, even this observation may suggest an element of failure on the part of Solomon; it is the statutes of David that he follows rather than the statutes of the Lord. Moreover, the narrator's remark about Solomon's love for the Lord is immediately qualified by the observation that 'he offered sacrifices and burned incense on the high places' (1 Ki. 3:3). References to 'high places' are often interpreted negatively within the books of Kings, frequently being associated with idolatry (1 Ki. 22:43; 2 Ki. 12:3; *cf.* 1 Ki. 11:7–8).

Solomon's wisdom

While the initial picture of Solomon shows up his personal strengths and weaknesses, an important development occurs when God appears to him in a dream (1 Ki. 3:5–15). God invites him to ask for whatever he wishes. Solomon's response is noteworthy:

> Now, O LORD my God, you have made your servant king in place of my father David. But I am only a little child and do not know how to carry out my duties. Your servant is here among the people you have chosen, a great people, too numerous to count or number. So give your servant a discerning heart to govern your people and to distinguish between right and wrong. For who is able to govern this great people of yours? (1 Ki. 3:7–9)

These words please the Lord and so he promises Solomon 'a wise and discerning heart' (1 Ki. 3:12). Although Solomon has requested only wisdom, God will also give him 'both riches and honour' and, if he walks in God's ways, a 'long life'.

Confirmation of Solomon's new, God-given wisdom comes in the account immediately following.

First, he skilfully resolves a dispute between two women over the ownership of a young baby. The concluding comment captures well the significance of this event: 'When all Israel heard the verdict the king had given, they held the king in awe, because they saw that he had wisdom from God to administer justice' (1 Ki. 3:28).

Secondly, Solomon appoints officials to govern the different regions of the land, bringing harmony and prosperity within his kingdom. As a result, 'the people of Judah and Israel were as numerous as the sand on the seashore; they ate, they drank and they were happy' (1 Ki. 4:20).

Thirdly, apart from ruling successfully over all Israel, Solomon also controls 'all the kingdoms from the River to the land of the Philistines, as far as the border of Egypt' (1 Ki. 4:21), thus ensuring national security for the Israelites: 'during Solomon's lifetime Judah and Israel, from Dan to Beersheba, lived in safety, each man under his own vine and fig tree' (1 Ki. 4:25). In passing it should be noted that the extent of Solomon's empire, probably matching that of his father David (*cf.* 2 Sa. 8:1–14; 10:1–19), corresponds with what God promised to Abraham in Genesis 15:18–21.

Fourthly, Solomon becomes internationally renowned because of his knowledge and understanding: 'Men of all nations came to listen to Solomon's wisdom, sent by all the kings of the world, who had heard of his wisdom' (1 Ki. 4:34). In these ways, the narrative highlights how a king endowed with God-given wisdom may bring great blessing to others.

Having indicated the extent of Solomon's wisdom and the benefits flowing from it for both the Israelites and other nations, 1 Kings focuses next on the building and commissioning of the temple in Jerusalem (1 Ki. 5:1 – 8:66).

This marks the fulfilment of God's earlier promise to David that his son would build a 'house' for the Lord in Jerusalem (2 Sa. 7:12–13; *cf.* 1 Ki. 8:15–21, 24).

An important aspect of the account is the prayer which Solomon addresses to the Lord when the temple is completed (1 Ki. 8:22–54). For Solomon, its construction fulfils part of what the Lord had earlier promised his father David. In the light of this, he says:

> Now LORD, God of Israel, keep for your servant David my father the promises you made to him when you said, 'You shall never fail to have a man to sit before me on the throne of Israel, if only your sons are careful in all they do to walk before me as you have done.' And now, O God of Israel, let your word that you promised your servant David my father come true (1 Ki. 8:25–26).

Solomon's words, like those of David in 1 Kings 2:4, imply that the fulfilment of God's promise regarding the Davidic dynasty is conditional upon the behaviour of future kings. A subtle but important distinction in the wording exists between what the Lord promises in 2 Samuel 7:13–16 and what David and Solomon say God promises in 1 Kings 2:4 and 1 Kings 8:25–26 respectively. Whereas the Lord's words in 2 Samuel 7 speak of the Davidic dynasty being established for ever, the divine promise mentioned by David and Solomon speaks of there being a Davidic descendant upon the throne subject to that individual obeying the law of Moses.

While these two forms of the divine promise are sometimes taken to be contradictory, it is possible to reconcile them. Taken together, they allow for the possibility that there may be a period when the throne will not be occupied by a member of the Davidic line. This, however, would be only a temporary situation, for God would reinstate a descendant of David upon the throne at a later stage. Support for this interpretation comes later in Solomon's prayer, in which he anticipates that the Israelites, due to their sin, will be taken into captivity by their enemies (1 Ki. 8:46–51). Such an event would surely also herald the end of the Davidic monarchy's control over Israel. Solomon's prayer, however, also mentions a return from exile.

This reading of the divine promise regarding the future of the Davidic dynasty best explains the remainder of the narrative, which remarks on the disobedience of successive generations of Davidic kings and concludes dramatically with Jehoiachin, king of Judah, living in exile in Babylon (2 Ki. 25:27–30). After Jehoiachin, David's throne remains unoccupied. There are, however, indications within 1 and 2 Kings that the throne will be restored to a descendant of David. On this we shall have more to say in subsequent chapters.

Disobedience sets in

Although the middle section of the Solomon narrative offers much by way of encouragement, focusing on the king's great wisdom and his construction of the Lord's temple, the concluding chapters provide a chilling reminder of how good intentions can easily be undermined. The first major indication that all is not well comes when the Lord appears to Solomon a second time (1 Ki. 9:1–9). By reminding Solomon of the importance of obedience and warning him especially against the worship of other gods, the Lord's words have an ominous ring to them.

This is borne out as we read of the great wealth that Solomon acquires (1 Ki. 9:10 – 10:29), including horses imported from Egypt (1 Ki. 10:28–29), and then of his many foreign wives who turn his heart after other gods (1 Ki. 11:1–8). This strongly echoes Deuteronomy 17:16–17, which outlines the dangers associated with kings:

The king, moreover, must not acquire great numbers of horses for himself or make the people return to Egypt to get more of them, for the LORD has told you, 'You are not to go back that way again.' He must not take many wives, or his heart will be led astray. He must not accumulate large amounts of silver and gold (Dt. 17:16–17).

From these brief observations it is clear that, in spite of the positive description of the middle part of his reign, Solomon's latter days are marked by a departure from the Lord's statutes. The situation is summarized as follows:

The LORD became angry with Solomon because his heart had turned away from the LORD, the God of Israel, who had appeared to him twice. Although he had forbidden Solomon to follow other gods, Solomon did not keep the LORD's command. So the LORD said to Solomon, 'Since this is your attitude and you have not kept my covenant and my decrees, which I commanded you, I will most certainly tear the kingdom away from you and give it to one of your subordinates. Nevertheless, for the sake of David your father, I will not do it during your lifetime. I will tear it out of the hand of your son. Yet I will not tear the whole kingdom from him, but will give him one tribe for the sake of David my servant and for the sake of Jerusalem, which I have chosen' (1 Ki. 11:9–13).

Having pronounced this judgment upon Solomon, the Lord instructs the prophet Ahijah to inform Jeroboam, one of Solomon's officials, that he will rule over ten of the twelve Israelite tribes (1 Ki. 11:27–39).

Very briefly the narrative tells us that Solomon 'tries to kill Jeroboam' (1 Ki. 11:40). Jeroboam escapes and takes refuge in Egypt. The reader, however, has reason to believe that Jeroboam's stay in Egypt will only be temporary. This is suggested by the immediately preceding account of King Hadad's temporary exile in Egypt, from where he returns to Edom to become an adversary of Solomon (1 Ki. 11:14–25). Concerning Jeroboam's return we shall learn more in our next chapter.

Conclusion

The Solomon narrative adds several important elements to our developing picture of the Messiah. First, the narrative suggests that the future ideal king will be endowed with exceptional wisdom. This will enable him to govern justly, bringing prosperity and security to his subjects, and imparting God's blessing to the nations of the earth. Secondly, while the Solomon narrative affirms the importance of the Davidic dynasty in God's purposes, we are introduced to the possibility that failure to obey the Lord's commands will result in the throne of Israel being temporarily unoccupied. Solomon himself would have lost control of the kingdom due to his idolatry but 'for the sake of David'. Future generations of Davidic kings will struggle to retain possession of the throne, and eventually it will be removed from them. Nevertheless, the hope remains that in the future God will restore one of David's descendants to Israel's throne. This latter theme takes on special prominence as we read the remainder of the narrative in 1 and 2 Kings.

Questions for reflection and discussion

How does the biblical narrative portray the life of Solomon?

What benefits do Solomon's subjects enjoy as a result of his wisdom?

What causes Solomon to fall short of being an ideal or perfect king?

How does the account of the lives of David and Solomon contribute to the Bible's picture of the future Messiah?

11

The demise of the Davidic dynasty

1 Kings 11 – 22 and 2 Kings

Summary

A tension exists between the Lord's promise to establish David's dynasty for ever and the failure of David's descendants to obey the Lord fully. Eventually, due to their wrongdoing, God deposes the Davidic kings in Jerusalem. Nevertheless, the expectation exists that God will raise up a future ruler from the line of David.

Key texts: 1 Kings 11:26–40; 2 Kings 21:1–15

The reigns of David and Solomon mark a high point in the biblical narrative from Genesis to 2 Kings. During this period the Israelites experience God's blessing in an unprecedented manner. For the first time since their entry into the promised land, they possess the whole region covenanted by God to their forefather Abraham. Under the rule of Solomon, especially, the people are no longer threatened by other nations, they benefit from a just administrative system, and enjoy great economic prosperity. All this, however, will not last; it is merely a foretaste of a much greater kingdom to be established in the future. Nevertheless, we have here a picture, admittedly with limitations and imperfections, of the type of king and kingdom which God intends to establish through the royal 'seed' of Abraham.

The kingdom divided

In the account of Solomon's reign in the books of Kings, the concluding episodes introduce a tension. Solomon, due to his idolatry, no longer deserves to rule over the nation of Israel. Nevertheless, the Lord delays punishing him 'for the sake of David my servant and for the sake of Jerusalem' (1 Ki. 11:13). While God does not punish Solomon immediately, he nevertheless reduces the extent of the kingdom controlled by Solomon's son Rehoboam. As we shall see, this initiates a process that continues until, by the end of 2 Kings, the entire kingdom is removed from the house of David.

Although Solomon governs all Israel until his death, the kingdom is afterwards torn from his son Rehoboam and given to Jeroboam, God's new choice as king. While most Israelites follow Jeroboam, two tribes acknowledge Rehoboam as king. According to the Lord, this occurs 'so that David my servant may always have a lamp before me in Jerusalem, the city where I chose to put my Name' (1 Ki. 11:36). Thus the kingdom established under Solomon is divided into two parts. Jeroboam controls the larger northern portion, which retains the name 'Israel', and Rehoboam governs a much smaller region in the south, centred on Jerusalem, known as 'Judah'.

For his part, Rehoboam is portrayed as arrogant and foolish for refusing the advice of 'the elders who had served his father Solomon during his lifetime' (1 Ki. 12:6). This is why the majority of Israelites rejected him as king, preferring Jeroboam. While the tribe of Judah remained loyal to Rehoboam, his reign is marked by religious apostasy, with the people turning away from the Lord to worship the gods of other nations (1 Ki. 14:22–24).

A striking feature in the account of Jeroboam's call to be king is God's promise to establish his dynasty for ever. The fulfilment of the promise is conditional upon obedience:

> If you do whatever I command you and walk in my ways and do what is right in my eyes by keeping my statutes and commands, as David my servant did, I will be with you. I will build you a dynasty as enduring as the one I built for David and will give Israel to you (1 Ki. 11:38).

Although the Lord appears to be abandoning the Davidic monarchy in favour of a new dynasty headed by Jeroboam, his concluding words to Jeroboam indicate that he still has plans for the house of David: 'I will humble David's descendants because of this, *but not for ever*' (1 Ki. 11:39; emphasis mine). Implicit in this remark is the future restoration of the Davidic dynasty.

In spite of being chosen by God to rule over most of Israel, and conditionally offered a long dynasty, Jeroboam quickly departs from obeying the law of the Lord. Apart from setting up two golden calves, one in Bethel and one in Dan (supposedly for the worship of the Lord), he builds shrines on high places and appoints priests who are not descendants of Levi (1 Ki. 12:28–33). In these and other ways, Jeroboam distances the religious practices of his kingdom from those associated with Jerusalem and the territory controlled by Rehoboam. Although Jeroboam outwardly supports the worship of the Lord, the manner in which he promotes such worship clearly runs counter to the law of the Lord. Not surprisingly, his activities are fiercely condemned by God (1 Ki. 14:6–16). As a consequence his dynasty comes to a swift end when his son Nadab, after ruling for only two years, is killed along with all the remaining members of Jeroboam's family (1 Ki. 15:25–30).

David's dynasty survives

The total destruction of Jeroboam's family and the establishment of a new dynasty in Israel introduces an important contrast between the two kingdoms of Israel and Judah. Whereas the history of the northern kingdom of Israel is marked by the rise and fall of several dynasties, the Davidic dynasty in Judah is never brought to a complete end and replaced by another. For the narrator of 1 and 2 Kings, what distinguishes the course of history in the two kingdoms is God's promise to David that his dynasty will last for ever. This is especially noteworthy given that some of the Davidic kings are characterized as closely resembling Ahab, the worst of the northern kings.

Of the kings of Israel, the most prominent, in terms of the length of narrative devoted to him, is Ahab, the son of Omri. According to the account in 2 Kings, Ahab differs from his predecessors in that, as a consequence of his marriage to Jezebel of Sidon, he introduces into Israel the worship of Baal. Whereas Jeroboam adulterates the true way of worshipping the Lord, Ahab supports the worship of an entirely foreign god. Not surprisingly, his actions invite God's judgment, and eventually result in the throne passing to a new dynasty. Two of the Davidic kings, Jehoram and Ahaziah, however, are described as walking in the ways of the house of Ahab (2 Ki. 8:18, 27), apparently promoting Baal worship in the southern kingdom. Indeed, Jehoram marries Ahab's daughter, Athaliah. Yet, in spite of Jehoram's evil deeds, the narrator comments that 'for the sake of his servant David, the LORD was not willing to destroy Judah. He had promised to maintain a lamp for David and his descendants for ever' (2 Ki. 8:19). Not only does this underline God's special attitude towards the house of David, but it suggests that he is firmly committed, even when confronted by an evil king, to keep his covenant with David.

An excellent illustration of God's concern for the house of David comes in 2 Kings 11, which focuses on events immediately following the death of King Ahaziah. When the queen mother Athaliah, Ahab's daughter, attempts to annihilate all the remaining members of the Davidic line, one baby boy is rescued and hidden in the temple, where he remains for six years until he is publicly enthroned by the priest Jehoiada (2 Ki. 11:12). While there was good reason at this time for the Lord to establish a completely new dynasty in Judah, following the evil reigns of Jehoram and Ahaziah, he ensures that the Davidic line continues to rule in Jerusalem. The young king Joash is described as doing what is 'right in the eyes of the LORD all the years Jehoiada the priest instructed him' (2 Ki. 12:2).

Of all the kings associated with the northern kingdom, only one, Jehu, is commended; he alone rids Israel of Baal worship (2 Ki. 10:28). Nevertheless, he continues to promote the use of the golden calves set up by Jeroboam in Bethel and Dan (2 Ki. 10:29). Since Jehu represents the best in a long line of evil kings, it is hardly surprising that the northern kingdom eventually comes under God's judgment and is punished by being exiled to the land of Assyria (2 Ki. 17:3–6). To underline the reason for this, 2 Kings 17:7–23 provides a lengthy explanation. The opening sentences of this passage capture well the thrust of the whole section:

All this took place because the Israelites had sinned against the LORD their God, who had brought them out of Egypt from under the power of Pharaoh king of Egypt. They worshipped other gods and followed the practices of the nations the LORD had driven out before them, as well as the practices that the kings of Israel had introduced (2 Ki. 17:7–8).

The Lord's punishment of the northern kingdom is, according to 2 Kings, a direct consequence of the persistent failure of both kings and people to obey the law of the Lord. While the description of events in the southern kingdom occasionally gives grounds for greater optimism, here also we encounter Davidic kings who display little true allegiance to the Lord. Thus we read of Ahaz constructing a new altar in Jerusalem, fashioned after one in the city of Damascus (2 Ki. 16:10–18). This action, however, pales into insignificance when compared with those of Manasseh.

He [Manasseh] rebuilt the high places his father Hezekiah had destroyed; he also erected altars to Baal and made an Asherah pole, as Ahab king of Israel had done. He bowed down to all the starry hosts and worshipped them. He built altars in the temple of the LORD, of which the LORD had said, 'In Jerusalem I will put my Name.' In both courts of the temple of the LORD, he built altars to all the starry hosts. He sacrificed his own son in the fire, practised sorcery and divination, and consulted mediums and spiritists. He did much evil in the eyes of the LORD, provoking him to anger (2 Ki. 21:3–6).

Confronted with such activities, and in the light of his punishment of the northern kingdom, it is hardly surprising that the Lord announces that he will destroy Jerusalem:

I am going to bring such disaster on Jerusalem and Judah that the ears of everyone who hears of it will tingle. I will stretch out over Jerusalem the measuring line used against Samaria and the plumb-line used against the house of Ahab. I will wipe out Jerusalem as one wipes out a dish, wiping it and turning it upside-down. I will forsake the remnant of my inheritance and hand them over to their enemies. They will be looted and plundered by all their foes, because they have done evil in my eyes and have provoked me to anger from the day their forefathers came out of Egypt until this day (2 Ki. 21:12–15).

Such is the strength of God's feelings on this issue that even when the righteous king Josiah comes to the throne and undertakes extensive religious reforms within Jerusalem and Judah, the Lord does 'not turn away from the heat of his fierce anger, which burned against Judah because of all that Manasseh had done to provoke him to anger' (2 Ki. 23:26).

It comes as no surprise, therefore, that the concluding chapters of 2 Kings describe the capture and destruction of Jerusalem by the Babylonians. Amid the description of these events, particular attention is given to the way in which the largest of the bronze items associated with the temple are carried off to Babylon (2 Ki. 25:13–17). With this we come almost full circle since the time of David and Solomon. Having observed the establishment of the 'house' of David and the 'house' of the Lord, we now witness the removal of both from Jerusalem.

Conclusion

Against this bleak background, two apparently minor events bring the book of Kings to a conclusion. First, Ishmael, 'who was of royal blood' (2 Ki. 25:25), flees to Egypt with many others after assassinating Gedaliah, the governor appointed by Nebuchadnezzar to rule over Judah. Secondly, Jehoiachin, king of Judah, is released from prison in Babylon when Evil-Merodach becomes king. Moreover, he is given 'a seat of honour higher than those of the other kings who were with him in Babylon' (2 Ki. 25:28). In the light of God's earlier comments about maintaining 'a lamp for David and his descendants for ever' (2 Ki. 8:19), the survival of two individuals linked to the Davidic line is surely significant. That one should be in Egypt and the other in Babylon is also noteworthy, for the book of Kings contains several examples of individuals returning from exile and being enthroned in order to fulfil God's purposes.

Questions for reflection and discussion

What reasons are given by the author of Kings for the decline in the fortunes of the Israelites?

How is God's promise concerning the Davidic dynasty reported within the books of Samuel and Kings? How can we account for the tension that is created by the differing forms of the divine promise?

In what ways does the Kings narrative offer hope for the restoration of the Davidic monarchy?

12

Hope beyond judgment

Amos and Isaiah

Summary

Although the books of Amos and Isaiah proclaim at length God's judgment against the kingdoms of Israel and Judah, they nevertheless express hope in a future marked by prosperity and harmony, involving all the nations of the earth. In both books this dramatic transformation is linked to the restoration of the royal house of David.

Key texts: Amos 9:11–15; Isaiah 2:2–4; 9:1–7;
11:1–12; 65:17–25

What have we learned so far from our study of the narrative that runs from Genesis to 2 Kings? We have seen that central to the story is the line of 'seed' that descends from Abraham through his great-grandson Judah and that gives rise to the Davidic dynasty. In Genesis, God promised that this lineage would be involved in reversing the terrible consequences of Adam and Eve's disobedience and expulsion from the Garden of Eden. Furthermore, the expectation was introduced that, through a future king, God's blessing would be imparted to all the nations of the earth. A picture of this king emerged. Exalted from humble origins, empowered by the Spirit of the Lord and endowed with supreme wisdom, the divinely anointed king would bring peace, security and prosperity to those who acknowledge his authority, but would also overthrow his enemies – God's enemies. Moreover, through fully obeying the law of the Lord, this king would enjoy an especially close relationship with God; the Lord would be with him in all that he would do.

While the narrative drew attention to a king who would restore creation, it also reminded us of the alienation that exists between God and humanity. The few individuals who managed to come close to resembling God's ideal king had shortcomings which cannot be dismissed as minor flaws. David had an adulterous affair with Bathsheba which resulted in the wrongful killing of her husband. Solomon, in spite of his great wisdom, was enticed by his foreign wives into idolatry and turned away from the true worship of the Lord. In all this, there was a growing sense that the one through whom the nations would be blessed would have to be a most exceptional person.

Although Genesis to 2 Kings focuses on the importance of the house of David for the fulfilment of God's promises, it concludes with these promises still unfulfilled. The last Davidic king of Judah is carried off into exile and imprisoned in Babylon. Such an event naturally casts a shadow over the whole story. Will God, in spite of all that has happened, restore the Davidic dynasty and fulfil his earlier promises? While there are hints at such a possibility, we are left in suspense, not knowing what the outcome will be.

It is important to realize that underlying the books of Genesis to Kings is the idea that God's judgment comes upon those who disobey him. Because of their rebellious nature, the Israelites were very slow to take over the entire promised land. Then, after the reigns of David and Solomon, they gradually lost control of it due to their iniquity, eventually being expelled from the land itself. Yet, while wrongdoing is often presented as a barrier to the fulfilment of God's promises, such is his nature that he does not allow human disobedience to thwart his plans. To enable the Israelites to possess the land of Canaan, God raised up David and Solomon to deliver the people from their enemies and establish them securely in the territory promised to Abraham.

This suggests that even though David's dynasty has now gone into exile, God will ensure that his promises are fulfilled. Although the sins of David's descendants and their people provoke God to punish them, renewal will come after judgment. While this is hinted at in the books of Genesis to Kings, we shall encounter it more clearly in the writings of the prophets (to be considered next), where it forms part of a much larger picture involving the restoration of the natural environment.

Hope

The book of Amos consists almost entirely of material about the wrongdoing of the northern kingdom of Israel in the eighth century BC. But while the bulk of the book focuses on sin and punishment, its final sentences offer hope beyond judgment. This hope is introduced in Amos 9:8:

> 'Surely the eyes of the Sovereign LORD
> are on the sinful kingdom.
> I will destroy it
> from the face of the earth –

yet I will not totally destroy
the house of Jacob,'
        declares the LORD.

The book then concludes by painting a vivid picture of a revitalized and prosperous Israel.

'The days are coming,' declares the LORD,

'when the reaper will be overtaken by the ploughman
and the planter by the one treading grapes.
New wine will drip from the mountains
and flow from all the hills.
I will bring back my exiled people Israel;
they will rebuild the ruined cities and live in them.
They will plant vineyards and drink their wine;
they will make gardens and eat their fruit.
I will plant Israel in their own land,
never again to be uprooted
from the land I have given them,'

        says the LORD your God.
        (Am. 9:13–15)

A similar picture of hope comes in the book of Isaiah. Viewed as a whole, Isaiah focuses on the transformation of Jerusalem (or 'Zion'). Whereas the book opens by describing the present depravity of those living in Judah, especially Jerusalem, it concludes with a vision of the city divinely exalted above all others. The contrast between these two descriptions of Jerusalem is striking. The opening chapter of Isaiah gives a very negative depiction of the people of Judah. They are a 'sinful nation, a people loaded with guilt, a brood of evildoers, children given to corruption' (Is. 1:4). Associating them with the wicked inhabitants of Sodom and Gomorrah, God announces his complete abhorrence of the religious observances of both rulers and people; their sacrifices and prayers, intended to please God, only provoke him to greater anger. Immorality flourishes in the city (Is. 1:21–23).

Against this background, the Lord announces his intention to act.

> 'I will turn my hand against you;
>   I will thoroughly purge away your dross
>   and remove your impurities.
> I will restore your judges as in days of old,
>   your counsellors as at the beginning.
> Afterwards you will be called
>   the City of Righteousness,
>   the Faithful City'.
>
> (Is. 1:25–26)

Building on this, the text goes on to describe how in the future the nations of the earth will come to Jerusalem.

In the last days

> the mountain of the LORD's temple will be established
>   as chief among the mountains;
> it will be raised above the hills,
>   and all nations will stream to it ...
>
> The law will go out from Zion,
>   the word of the LORD from Jerusalem.
> He will judge between the nations
>   and will settle disputes for many peoples.
> They will beat their swords into ploughshares
>   and their spears into pruning hooks.
> Nation will not take up sword against nation,
>   nor will they train for war any more.
>
> (Is. 2:2–4)

Jerusalem and the nations will be radically changed in the future. The description of this transformation becomes much fuller in the concluding chapters of Isaiah. Speaking of the creation of 'new heavens and a new earth' (Is. 65:17), the Lord goes on to comment about Jerusalem:

> 'But be glad and rejoice for ever
>   in what I will create,
> for I will create Jerusalem to be a delight
>   and its people a joy ...
>
> Before they call I will answer;
>   while they are still speaking I will hear.
> The wolf and the lamb will feed together,
>   and the lion will eat straw like the ox,
>   but dust will be the serpent's food.
> They will neither harm nor destroy
>   on all my holy mountain,'
> says the LORD.
> (Is. 65:18–25)

Jerusalem will become 'the praise of the earth' (Is. 62:7) and the nations will flock to her, attracted by the light of God's glorious presence (60:1–3, 19–20; *cf.* 66:19–23). The transformation will be spectacular (62:2–4).

Yet, although the final chapters of Isaiah contain a very positive portrayal of the divinely renewed Jerusalem, attention is also given to the fate of the wicked, who will have no share in God's new creation. This is vividly illustrated in the final verses of the book:

> 'From one New Moon to another and from one Sabbath to another, all mankind will come and bow down before me,' says the LORD. 'And they will go out and look upon the dead bodies of those who rebelled against me; their worm will not die, nor will their fire be quenched, and they will be loathsome to all mankind' (66:23–24).

The contrast here between coming into the presence of the

Lord and going out to look upon the corpses of his enemies is startling. While the transforming of Jerusalem will bring great joy to the righteous, it will also involve the punishment of all who are wicked. The new Jerusalem will be inhabited only by those who know the Lord's gracious favour.

This brief survey, drawing on the books of Amos and Isaiah, reveals a strong emphasis upon hope beyond divine judgment. Moreover, the vision of the future in these passages abounds in ideas pointing to the glorious restoration of creation: the opportunity for unending communion with the Lord; land that is fertile and overflowing with produce; the inclusion of all the nations of the earth; the absolute triumph of righteousness and the total defeat of wickedness.

Hope and David's dynasty

This common vision of a renewed creation is linked to the royal line of David. Whereas Isaiah develops the connection at some length, it is mentioned only briefly in Amos. This, however, is not surprising given that only the final three verses of the book describe the divine restoration of Israel.

The link between the Davidic dynasty and the renewing of Israel is achieved in Amos by juxtaposing the relevant material. Immediately preceding the brief description of a revitalized Israel we have the following passage:

> 'In that day I will restore
>   David's fallen tent.
> I will repair its broken places,
>   restore its ruins,
>   and build it as it used to be,
> so that they may possess the remnant of Edom
>   and all the nations that bear my name,'
>   declares the LORD,
>   who will do these things.
>   (Am. 9:11–12)

Using poetic imagery, Amos envisages the royal house of David being divinely restored after lying in ruins for some time. The Davidic monarch will then exercise authority over all those who acknowledge the Lord as their God. This will involve people from all nations, including Israel's longstanding rival Edom.

The restoration of the house of David is expanded upon in Isaiah. Perhaps the most significant passage comes in chapter 11, which speaks of a shoot springing up from the stump of Jesse, a metaphor that clearly refers to the renewing of a 'chopped-down' Davidic monarchy. In the future, a Spirit-endowed descendant of David will govern with true wisdom and perfect righteousness, protecting the weak and punishing the wicked:

> A shoot will come from the stump of Jesse;
>   from his roots a Branch will bear fruit.
> The Spirit of the LORD will rest on him –
>   the Spirit of wisdom and of understanding,
>   the Spirit of counsel and of power,
>   the Spirit of knowledge and of the fear of the LORD –
> and he will delight in the fear of the LORD.
>
> He will not judge by what he sees with his eyes,
>   or decide by what he hears with his ears;
> but with righteousness he will judge the needy,
>   with justice he will give decisions for the poor of the
>   earth.
> He will strike the earth with the rod of his mouth;
>   with the breath of his lips he will slay the wicked.
> Righteousness will be his belt
>   and faithfulness the sash round his waist.
>
> (Is. 11:1–5)

This passage is followed by a dramatic vision of a renewed and harmonious creation (Is. 11:6–9). So, as in Amos, the restoration of the Davidic house is closely linked to the renewing of creation. Isaiah 11 then goes on to speak of the nations rallying to the side of the future king, and of the exiled Israelites being brought back from captivity (Is. 11:10–12).

Although the hope highlighted in this chapter of Isaiah is in keeping with what we have observed in the books of Genesis to Kings, its presence here is striking, given the terrible denunciations contained in the early chapters of Isaiah against the people of Jerusalem and particularly Ahaz, the ruling Davidic king. Isaiah wishes to affirm that, in spite of present wrongdoing, God's special role for the Davidic dynasty will ultimately be fulfilled. While Isaiah boldly proclaims that God will indeed punish the house of David, he confidently announces that the Lord will not desert it for ever. In the future it will be wonderfully restored.

This future restoration also lies at the heart of Isaiah 9, which focuses on the birth of a Davidic king who will bring both peace and justice for ever:

Nevertheless, there will be no more gloom for those who were in distress …

The people walking in darkness
  have seen a great light;
on those living in the land of the shadow of death
  a light has dawned …
For to us a child is born,
  to us a son is given,
  and the government will be on his shoulders.
And he will be called
  Wonderful Counsellor, Mighty God,
  Everlasting Father, Prince of Peace.
Of the increase of his government and peace
  there will be no end.
He will reign on David's throne
  and over his kingdom,
establishing and upholding it
  with justice and righteousness

from that time on and for ever.
The zeal of the LORD Almighty will accomplish this.

(Is. 9:1–7)

The titles used here to describe this future monarch indicate that he is no ordinary individual. Moreover, Isaiah acknowledges that the coming of this king will not occur by chance; it will be accomplished only by 'the zeal of the LORD'.

Conclusion

This material selected from the books of Amos and Isaiah provides further evidence regarding the special role which the Davidic monarchy will play in restoring harmony between God, humanity and nature. This not only supports the picture that emerges from the books of Genesis to Kings, but also suggests that the demise of the Davidic dynasty at the time of the Babylonian exile is not the end of the story. Set against a background of divine judgment, the books of Amos and Isaiah herald a glorious restoration of creation, centred on a future Davidic king and involving both Israel and the nations.

Questions for reflection and discussion

How do the books of Amos and Isaiah associate the Davidic dynasty with the renewing of creation?

What types of sins are condemned in the books of Amos and Isaiah?

What factors suggest that God's judgment and punishment of the people will not continue for ever?

13

The servant king

Isaiah

Summary

The second half of Isaiah contains several passages that focus on a 'servant' who displays royal characteristics. Taking the punishment due to others, the 'servant' plays a vital role in restoring humanity to a right relationship with God. The servant's actions are viewed as benefiting all the nations of the earth.

Key texts: Isaiah 42:1–4; 45:1–8; 52:13 – 53:12

Apart from emphasizing the coming of a future Davidic king, the book of Isaiah figures large in studies on the Messiah for another reason. Certain passages in the second half of the book focus on an individual who is often referred to as the 'servant of the LORD'. There has been much discussion concerning the relationship between this servant and the future king mentioned in the early chapters of Isaiah. Are they one and the same person?

The servant's identity

In Isaiah, the term 'servant' is used in a variety of ways. On the one hand, it designates various individuals who are clearly named: Isaiah (Is. 20:3); Eliakim (Is. 22:20); David (Is. 37:35); Moses (Is. 63:11, RSV). On the other hand, it is sometimes used of Israel as a nation (Is. 41:8–9 for example). There remain, however, a number of passages (42:1–4; 49:1–6; 50:4–9; 52:13 – 53:12), the so-called 'Servant Songs', that refer to an unnamed servant.

While some scholars have suggested that the unidentified servant is the nation of Israel, this is undermined in 49:5–6:

> And now the LORD says –
>   he who formed me in the womb to be his servant
> to bring back Jacob to him
>   and gather Israel to himself,
> for I am honoured in the eyes of the LORD
>   and my God has been my strength –
> he says:
> 'It is too small a thing for you to be my servant
>   to restore the tribes of Jacob
>   and bring back those of Israel I have kept.
> I will also make you a light for the Gentiles,
>   that you may bring my salvation to the ends of the
>   earth.'

These comments clearly distinguish the servant from the nation of Israel, for he is described here as the one through whom God will restore Israel to himself. Moreover, the servant's role is not restricted to helping only Israel; he will perform a similar duty for the nations of the earth. Yet, while the servant is someone other than the nation, a close correspondence is drawn between them; indeed, the servant is actually called 'Israel' in Isaiah 49:3. Regarding this we shall have more to say below.

Bringing salvation to the nations, the servant resembles the divinely promised future king, and several factors suggest that the servant is of royal standing.

First, although the designation 'servant' is often applied to individuals who have no royal connections, within Isaiah it is used of King David (Is. 37:35) and this reflects a common usage elsewhere in the Old Testament (*e.g.* 1 Sa. 23:10; 1 Ki. 3:6; 1 Ch. 17:4; Ps. 78:70; Je. 33:21; Ezk. 34:23).

Secondly, the servant is endowed with God's Spirit (Is. 42:1), a feature that is reminiscent of how Saul and David are empowered by the Spirit following their anointing (1 Sa. 10:10–12; 16:13; *cf.* Is. 11:1–3).

Thirdly, the servant 'will bring justice to the nations' (Is. 42:1; *cf.* 11:5). This is emphasized especially in 42:3–4:

> In faithfulness he will bring forth justice;
>   he will not falter or be discouraged
> till he establishes justice on earth.
> In his law the islands will put their hope.

The maintenance of law and justice is obviously a central aspect of royal office, although, it must be admitted, not exclusively so.

Fourthly, not only will 'the servant' be 'raised and lifted up and highly exalted' (Is. 52:13), but God promises, 'I will give him a portion among the great, and he will divide the spoils with the strong' (Is. 53:12). Elsewhere, God says 'to him who was despised and abhorred by the nation, to the servant of rulers: "Kings will see you and rise up, princes will see and bow down, because of the LORD, who is faithful, the Holy One of Israel, who has chosen you"' (Is. 49:7). The picture of the lowly servant exalted so that kings and princes bow before him is noteworthy in the light of how God elsewhere exalts individuals from humble circumstances to royal office.

These features provide grounds for believing that the servant is to be equated with the future king mentioned in the early chapters of Isaiah. An important question remains, however. Why is the servant not specifically designated a king? Several observations help answer this question.

Why a 'servant'?

A significant contrast exists in Isaiah between chapters 1 – 39 and 40 – 65. Whereas the early chapters relate to the time when the Davidic monarchy rules in Jerusalem, the later chapters focus on the period following its removal from the throne. Corresponding with this, we find that the early part of Isaiah contrasts the failure of the existing king with a future monarch. By pointing to the coming of an ideal king, the inadequacy of the present monarchy is underlined. Moreover, this contrast reveals that the shortcomings of the ruling king will not prevent God's purposes from being fulfilled; a truly righteous Davidic king will be raised up in the future. Yet, whereas the first half of Isaiah concentrates chiefly on the Davidic monarchy, the second half focuses mainly on the nation of Israel. Here also an important contrast is drawn, involving the disobedient people of Israel and one who obeys fully. While the comparison in the first half of Isaiah centres on 'royalty', in the second half a contrast is drawn between 'servants'. Thus, Israel, the disobedient servant, is contrasted with a future, dutiful servant. In this way the book of Isaiah as a whole emphasizes that king and people are equally responsible for the punishment meted out by God. The disobedience of both parties is contrasted with that of a single individual who is deliberately portrayed first as a king and then as a servant.

Several other factors shed light on the use of 'servant' in

preference to 'king'. First, throughout Isaiah great emphasis is laid upon there being only one true king, the Lord God. Even in the early chapters of Isaiah, the title 'king' is not used of the promised Davidic monarch. Although the sovereign Lord proclaims that the king will play a vital role in restoring Jerusalem and bringing God's blessing to the nations, this will be accomplished through 'the zeal of the LORD Almighty' (Is. 9:7). Moreover, while the promised ruler will play an active role in bringing God's purposes to fulfilment, he will achieve this only through obeying the Lord fully. The title 'servant' is, therefore, an important reminder of the Davidic king's position in relation to God himself.

Secondly, the servant is not called a king possibly in order to distinguish him from the Persian monarch Cyrus, whose role as a divinely appointed deliverer of Israel is described in Isaiah 44:28 – 45:13 (*cf.* Is. 41:2–7, 25; 48:14–15). Designated the Lord's anointed in Isaiah 45:1, Cyrus is a Gentile king whom the Lord raises up to deliver the nation of Israel. Although the servant is distinguished from Cyrus, parallels exist between them. Both, for example, are called and chosen by the Lord (42:6; 45:4; 49:7; 42:1), and he takes them by the hand (42:6; 45:1). What Cyrus does for Israel, the servant will do for the nations. This comparison lends further support to the idea that the unnamed servant is the future Davidic king through whom God's blessing will be mediated to the nations of the earth.

Conclusion

Having suggested why the divinely promised king in the first half of Isaiah can be identified with the Lord's servant in the second half, it is important to observe briefly how the portrayal of the servant complements and develops that of the king. In this regard, most important is the remarkable contrast between the king who judges and punishes, and the servant who is himself judged and punished. The servant is not, however, punished for his own sins; on the contrary he is described by God as righteous (Is. 53:11; *cf.* verse 9). Rather, he willingly bears the punishment due to others. This image dominates the lengthy description of the servant in Isaiah 53:2–12.

This passage emphasizes the servant's role in atoning for the sin of others by making 'his life a guilt offering'. Such an event offers hope to those who have gone astray. This, however, does not mean that each wicked person is automatically forgiven. The wider context suggests that the wicked must 'forsake his way and the evil man his thoughts' (Is. 55:6; *cf.* 1:19–20). Nevertheless, by offering himself up in place of others the servant fulfils a vital and necessary role, essential for the restoration of harmony between God and humanity.

The picture of the future king suffering for the sins of others introduces a major new dimension into the Bible's portrait of the Messiah. As we shall observe in later chapters, it is an aspect that is crucially important.

Questions for reflection and discussion

What difficulties surround the identification of the 'servant' in the second half of Isaiah?

What factors suggest that the servant may be identified with the future king mentioned in the early chapters of Isaiah?

Why is the title 'servant' an appropriate designation for the individual mentioned in the 'servant songs'?

What distinctive role is attributed to the servant in Isaiah 53?

A kingdom to replace all others

Jeremiah, Ezekiel and Daniel

Summary

Written against the background of the demise of the Davidic monarchy and the destruction of Jerusalem, the books of Jeremiah, Ezekiel and Daniel express hope in the divine restoration of the monarchy and the establishment of a kingdom that will surpass all others, lasting for ever.

Key texts: Jeremiah 33:14–26; Ezekiel 37:15–28; Daniel 7:1–28

The expectation that a Davidic king will again sit on the throne of Israel appears in two Old Testament books closely associated with the period of the Babylonian exile. The prophecies of Jeremiah and Ezekiel both contain passages which speak about God raising up a new king from the line of David. Jeremiah states:

> 'The days are coming,' declares the LORD,
>   'when I will raise up to David a righteous Branch,
> a King who will reign wisely
>   and do what is just and right in the land.
> In his days Judah will be saved
>   and Israel will live in safety.
> This is the name by which he will be called:
>   The LORD Our Righteousness.'
>
> (Je. 23:5–6)

Later, focusing once more on the Lord's promise to bring back Israel and Judah from captivity (Je. 30:3), Jeremiah quotes God as saying:

> 'I will break the yoke off their necks
> and will tear off their bonds;
>   no longer will foreigners enslave them.
> Instead, they will serve the LORD their God
>   and David their king,
>   whom I will raise up for them'.
>
> (Je. 30:8–9)

Since these promises are repeated a few chapters later (Je. 33:14–17), it is clear that Jeremiah expected the Davidic dynasty to be divinely restored to the throne.

The same expectation is also found in the book of Ezekiel, coming first in a passage that uses the image of a branch or shoot being planted on 'the mountain heights of Israel'.

This is what the Sovereign LORD says: I myself will take a

shoot from the very top of a cedar and plant it; I will break off a tender sprig from its topmost shoots and plant it on a high and lofty mountain. On the mountain heights of Israel I will plant it; it will produce branches and bear fruit and become a splendid cedar. Birds of every kind will nest in it; they will find shelter in the shade of its branches. All the trees of the field will know that I the LORD bring down the tall tree and made the low tree grow tall. I dry up the green tree and make the dry tree flourish (Ezk. 17:22–24).

While the actual dynasty is not named here, it is clear from the rest of chapter 17 that these verses refer to a future Davidic king.

A further reference to God restoring the royal house of David comes in Ezekiel 34. In a chapter that focuses on the failure of the 'shepherds of Israel' to care for God's 'sheep', Ezekiel quotes the Lord as promising, 'I will place over them one shepherd, my servant David, and he will tend them; he will tend them and be their shepherd. I the LORD will be their God, and my servant David will be prince among them' (Ezk. 34:23–24). The Lord then goes on to say:

I will make a covenant of peace with them and rid the land of wild beasts so that they may live in the desert and sleep in the forests in safety. I will bless them and the places surrounding my hill. I will send down showers in season; there will be showers of blessing. The trees of the field will yield their fruit and the ground will yield its crops; the people will be secure in their land (Ezk. 34:25–27).

Here again a close association exists between the coming of a future king and the creation of a harmonious and prosperous environment.

Similar ideas come in Ezekiel 37, where the restoration of Judah and Israel is presented first in a vision of 'dry bones' being rejuvenated through the activity of the Spirit of God (verses 1–14), and secondly through two sticks, representing the kingdoms of Judah and Israel (or 'Ephraim'), being bound together to symbolize the unification of the divided nation (verses 16–23). The chapter concludes with the Lord stressing that 'my servant David will be king over them' (verse 24; *cf.* verse 25), and that God will dwell in their midst (verses 26–28).

God's authority

These expressions of hope come during the period of the Babylonian exile. This is also the setting for the book of Daniel. The book describes events involving a handful of youths who were deported from Jerusalem to Babylon towards the beginning of the sixth century BC. Daniel affirms the supreme authority of the Lord as the one who controls everything that has occurred in the past, is presently happening, and will take place in the future. This is evident in two main ways.

First, we see God's sovereign authority reflected in the lives of the book's main characters. Although it begins by observing that 'Nebuchadnezzar king of Babylon came to Jerusalem and besieged it' (Dn. 1:1), the text immediately states that 'the LORD delivered Jehoiakim king of Judah into his hand, along with some of the articles from the temple of God' (verse 2). Nebuchadnezzar's success in taking Jerusalem is thus attributed to the Lord.

Even in distant Babylon God controls events. We see this in the progress that Daniel and his three companions make in comparison to that of the other young men (1:8–20). With the Lord's help, they become wiser than 'all the magicians and enchanters in the whole kingdom' (1:20). Also, dramatic protection is given to Shadrach, Meshach and Abednego in the fiery furnace (3:1–30) and then to Daniel in the lions' den (6:1–28). Perhaps, however, the most striking statement of God's sovereignty comes from the mouth of king Nebuchadnezzar himself. Following the restoration of his sanity after being divinely punished for seven years because of his boasting (4:1–34), he praises and honours the Most High with these words:

His dominion is an eternal dominion;
  his kingdom endures from generation to generation.
All the peoples of the earth are regarded as nothing.
He does as he pleases with the powers of heaven
  and the peoples of the earth.
No-one can hold back his hand
  or say to him: 'What have you done?'

(4:34–35)

Interestingly, similar remarks about the Lord are made later by Darius the Mede as a result of Daniel's deliverance from the lions (Dn. 6:26–27).

Secondly, God's control of events is highlighted through his revelation of what will happen in the future. Not only does the Lord direct circumstances in the present, but he also determines what will take place in the coming years. When, for example, Nebuchadnezzar has a dream about a large statue constructed of different materials, Daniel is divinely enabled both to tell the king the contents of his dream, and also to interpret its meaning. Nebuchadnezzar sees a succession of kingdoms that are eventually destroyed by a divinely established kingdom.

In the time of those kings, the God of heaven will set up a kingdom that will never be destroyed, nor will it be left to another people. It will crush all those kingdoms and bring them to an end, but it will itself endure for ever. This is the meaning of the vision of the rock cut out of a mountain, but not by human hands – a rock that broke the iron, the bronze, the clay, the silver and the gold to pieces (Dn. 2:44–45).

Nebuchadnezzar's dream anticipates the divine creation of a kingdom that will eclipse all others. Destroying great and powerful governments already in existence, this coming kingdom will last for ever. In the light of God's punishment of Israel and Judah, this picture of an everlasting kingdom must have been a source of great hope. For although Daniel 2 contains no direct reference to the house of David, the mention of a future kingdom that, established by God, will endure for ever is very much in keeping with what we have come to expect as regards the restored Davidic monarchy. Certainly, there is no compelling reason not to associate the kingdom described here with the house of David.

This picture of a future, everlasting kingdom reappears in Daniel 7. In a dream Daniel sees 'four great beasts, each different from the others' (verse 3). After seeing these four beasts, Daniel witnesses the 'Ancient of Days' taking his throne.

> Thrones were set in place,
> and the Ancient of Days took his seat.
> His clothing was as white as snow;
> the hair of his head was white like wool.
> His throne was flaming with fire,
> and its wheels were all ablaze.
> A river of fire was flowing,
> coming out from before him.
> Thousands upon thousands attended him;
> ten thousand times ten thousand stood before him.
> The court was seated,
> and the books were opened.
>
> (Dn. 7:9–10)

This description clearly refers to the Lord God.

After witnessing the punishment of the fourth beast, Daniel then sees 'one like a son of man coming with the clouds of heaven' (7:13).

> He approached the Ancient of Days and was led into his presence. He was given authority, glory and sovereign power; all peoples, nations and men of every language worshipped him. His dominion is an everlasting dominion that will not pass away, and his kingdom is one that will never be destroyed (Dn. 7:13–14).

When Daniel asks 'one of those standing there' 'the true meaning of all this', he is told, 'The four great beasts are four kingdoms that will rise from the earth. But the saints of the Most High will receive the kingdom and will possess it for ever – yes, for ever and ever' (7:17–18).

As in Daniel 2, attention is focused on the creation of a kingdom which, replacing others, will last for ever. Additional information is provided here in chapter 7 about an individual to whom 'authority, glory and sovereign power' is given. Regarding the precise identity of this 'son of man' the text is not explicit. In the light of the emphasis placed upon the creation of an everlasting kingdom, however, it seems reasonable to suppose that this kingdom is the one to be established under a future Davidic monarch. Elsewhere within the Old Testament it is clearly stated that David's throne will be established 'for ever' (2 Sa. 7:13, 16; Is. 9:7). This being so, we may deduce that the one introduced here as the 'son of man' is none other than the divinely promised Davidic king.

Conclusion

Although other material within Daniel, especially 9:24–27, may shed light on the Old Testament concept of the Messiah, we shall restrict our observations to the passages examined above. From these it is clear that the demise of the Davidic dynasty at the time of the Babylonian exile did not lessen the expectation that God would bring into being a kingdom that would surpass all others. While other 'earthly' kingdoms would continue to exist for some time, even 'waging war against the saints and defeating them' (Dn. 7:21; *cf.* verse 25), ultimately they would be defeated and replaced by a kingdom that would last for ever.

Questions for reflection and discussion

How do the books of Jeremiah and Ezekiel offer hope following the overthrow of the Davidic monarchy by the Babylonians?

In what ways does the book of Daniel emphasize the Lord's absolute sovereignty?

What factors suggest that the 'son of man' in Daniel 7 is the future king of the line of David?

15

Jesus Christ the son of David

Matthew 1 – 2

Summary

The opening chapters of Matthew's gospel emphasize in a variety of ways that the birth of Jesus Christ fulfils Old Testament expectations concerning the Davidic monarchy. The Magi's search for the 'one who has been born king of the Jews' reinforces the genealogical links between David and Jesus.

Key text: Matthew 1:1–25

Whereas the Old Testament is dominated by the lengthy narrative that runs from Genesis to Kings, pride of place within the New Testament goes to the four gospels. Focusing on the life of Jesus of Nazareth, the four gospels were brought together by the early church and accepted as being an authoritative statement of what the church believed about Jesus.

Central to the portrayal of Jesus in the four gospels is the belief that he fulfils the Old Testament expectations concerning a future Davidic king who will bring God's blessing to the nations. This belief, which lies at the heart of how the early church viewed Jesus, is reflected in the designation 'Christ'. *Christos*, meaning 'anointed one', is the Greek equivalent of the Hebrew word for Messiah. The link between these terms is explicitly made in John's gospel when, to explain the term 'Messiah', the comment is added in parenthesis: 'that is, the Christ' (Jn. 1:41). While the word 'Christ' is now commonly used as a name, it was initially used of Jesus as a title. Thus, the designation 'Jesus Christ' was probably first understood as meaning 'Jesus the anointed one.'

Son of David

Although the idea that Jesus is the divinely promised Davidic king permeates the whole New Testament, in this chapter we shall focus on the opening sections of Matthew's gospel. Here, perhaps more clearly than anywhere else, sustained attention is given to the way in which Jesus is linked to the house of David.

Matthew's gospel begins with the statement: 'A record of the genealogy of Jesus Christ the son of David, the son of Abraham' (Mt. 1:1). With this the author affirms emphatically that Jesus is both an anointed one ('Christ') and a descendant of David ('son of David'). The combination of these two ideas is significant, for an individual could be a 'son of David' without necessarily being 'an anointed one', and *vice versa*.

That Jesus is a 'son of David' is demonstrated by means of a genealogy which traces a direct line of descent from 'King

David' to Joseph. The genealogy does not, however, state explicitly that Joseph is the father of Jesus. The usual pattern of the genealogy is broken in verse 16, where we read that Joseph is 'the husband of Mary, of whom was born Jesus, who is called Christ'. This wording allows for the possibility that Joseph is not the actual father of Jesus, a fact confirmed by the immediately following account concerning Mary's conception (Mt. 1:18–25). Although the narrative affirms that Joseph is not the biological father of Jesus, it reveals that he adopts Jesus as his own son; this is indicated by the fact that Joseph names him. We have, therefore, at the start of Matthew's gospel a peculiar irony. The text, on the one hand, stresses that Jesus is 'the son of David' and, on the other hand, acknowledges that this is only so through adoption.

Messiah

Apart from emphasizing that Jesus is a 'son of David', the opening chapter of Matthew also affirms that Jesus is the Christ or Messiah. With this claim the reader is intended to understand Jesus' life as being especially significant in the working of God's purposes. This is brought out in verse 17:

Thus there were fourteen generations in all from Abraham to David, fourteen from David to the exile to Babylon, and fourteen from the exile to the Christ.

This summary of the preceding genealogy implies that the events surrounding the life of Jesus Christ will be as important as those associated with Abraham, David and the exile. By employing a pattern of fourteen generations, the narrator raises the reader's expectation that with Jesus Christ we have come to an important stage in the history of the Davidic dynasty; Jesus is no ordinary 'son of David'. Given his ancestry and the time of his coming, we are led to expect that something extraordinary is about to occur. Will the divine promises associated with the Davidic dynasty at last be fulfilled?

While the whole of Matthew's gospel spells out the significance of Jesus' role as the anointed son of David, the reader is introduced to various aspects of this in the opening two chapters. When the angel speaks to Joseph about the child to be born to Mary, he is told to 'give him the name Jesus, because he will save his people from their sins' (Mt. 1:21). Interestingly, 'Jesus' is the Greek form of the Hebrew name 'Joshua', and, as we noted earlier, Joshua was one of the most successful leaders of Israel in the Old Testament. Thus, even before he is born, there is reason to expect that Jesus will accomplish something special for his people.

This expectation is increased as we read of the visit of the Magi, who come to Jerusalem from the east in search of the 'one who has been born king of the Jews' (Mt. 2:2). Once again attention is drawn to the belief that Jesus is the heir to the Davidic throne. This idea is reinforced through the involvement of King Herod in the story. The description of his attempt to eliminate any possible rival to the throne and God's intervention to rescue Jesus is reminiscent of events in the books of Samuel and Kings when those anointed to become king are delivered from their enemies, usually the ruling monarch.

The reference to Jesus' birth in Bethlehem (Mt. 2:1) gives further weight to the idea that Jesus is the Davidic king anticipated throughout much of the Old Testament. As the birthplace of David, it is obviously significant that Jesus should also be born there. This link between Bethlehem and the Davidic kings is reinforced by the quotation given in Matthew 2:6, based on Micah 5:2:

> But you, Bethlehem, in the land of Judah,
>   are by no means least among the rulers of Judah;
>   for out of you will come a ruler
>   who will be the shepherd of my people Israel.

This is just one of several Old Testament quotations incorporated into the opening chapters of Matthew's gospel.

They are all intended to support the basic idea that Jesus' life fulfils Old Testament expectations regarding the house of David.

Thus far we have focused on the prominence given to Jesus as the anointed son of David whose birth heralds an important new phase in the working of God's purposes for humanity. By giving special attention to Jesus as the legitimate heir of the royal throne of David, the expectation is created that he will in due course come to reign. Even the account of his temporary flight into Egypt, echoing similar escapes by others destined to become kings, supports the idea that with Jesus the Davidic monarchy will soon be restored.

Blessing to the nations

In our survey of the Old Testament material we noted the importance of the idea that the divinely appointed Davidic king would mediate God's blessing to all the nations of the earth. The opening chapters of Matthew's gospel also emphasize that Jesus' coming will have a special impact on those who are non-Israelites. Three features of the narrative support this idea.

First, although prominence is given to the idea that Jesus is the son of David, he is also introduced as the 'son of Abraham'. This is stated at the outset in Matthew 1:1 and emphasized by the genealogy which begins not with David but with Abraham. While the inclusion of Abraham is obviously important in the three-fold pattern of fourteen generations, it can hardly be insignificant that the divine promise to bless all the nations of the earth was first given to him (Gn. 12:3) and afterwards linked to the line of seed descended from him through Isaac (Gn. 22:18). In the light of this promise concerning the nations, the reference to Abraham is important.

Secondly, a noteworthy feature of the genealogy is the attention given to four women. While the genealogy normally only mentions fathers and sons, this pattern is interrupted by identifying the mothers of four of those listed. Three of the mothers are named explicitly (Tamar in verse 3, Rahab in verse 5, and Ruth in verse 5), and the fourth is described as having been 'Uriah's wife' (verse 6; alluding to Bathsheba). Of all the women who might have been included in the genealogy, the presence of these four is significant for at least two reasons. For one thing, all four women have strong associations with those who are non-Israelites. Tamar and Rahab are of Canaanite birth; Ruth is a Moabitess; Bathsheba marries Uriah, a Hittite. For another, all four women are associated in the Old Testament with 'improper' sexual activities. Tamar and Ruth act in ways which could have provoked serious condemnation for lacking sexual propriety. Rahab is introduced in Joshua as a 'prostitute' (Jos. 2:1), and Bathsheba becomes involved in an adulterous relationship with king David (2 Sa. 11:1–27).

In the light of this, the inclusion of Tamar, Rahab, Ruth and Bathsheba in the genealogy of Jesus is somewhat startling. The natural inclination might have been to avoid mentioning them altogether. Yet their presence is in keeping with two themes which are important in Matthew's gospel. On the one hand, the mention of non-Israelites in the ancestry of the Davidic line provides an important reminder about the role of the Davidic king to mediate God's blessing to the nations. On the other, the inclusion of women associated with immoral sexual behaviour suggests that the unusual nature of Mary's conception should not be viewed as grounds for excluding the son born to her from the royal line of David. For this reason, the author of Matthew's gospel does not conceal Joseph's reaction to the news that Mary is pregnant and his desire to 'divorce her quietly' (Mt. 1:19).

Thirdly, of the four gospels only Matthew's gives special attention to the visit of the 'Magi from the east' (Mt. 2:1). While this episode is very much in keeping with the theme of Jesus as the new Davidic king, it also focuses on the coming of non-Israelites to 'worship' Jesus (Mt. 2:2, 8, 11). The picture of these Gentile Magi offering gold, incense and myrrh to the young child Jesus is very reminiscent of how tribute was brought by foreigners to King Solomon.

By emphasizing the role of Gentiles in its opening

chapters, Matthew's gospel introduces a theme that runs throughout the whole book. As we shall observe in a subsequent chapter, this gospel, which is commonly acknowledged to be the most Jewish of the four canonical gospels, gives special prominence to the inclusion of Gentiles within the kingdom inaugurated by Jesus Christ.

Conclusion

There can be little doubt that the opening two chapters of Matthew's gospel are designed to affirm that Jesus is the divinely intended heir to the royal throne of David. Not only are the concepts of Messiah, son of David and kingship all highlighted, but equally importantly they are presented as having their origins in the Old Testament. Moreover, there are strong hints that Jesus will be the one through whom God's blessing will be mediated to all the nations of the earth. Thus we encounter here some of the most important ideas associated with the Old Testament concept of a future, divinely anointed, Davidic king. With the opening chapters of the New Testament, the biblical portrait of the Messiah takes an important step towards completion.

Questions for reflection and discussion

In what ways do the opening chapters of Matthew's gospel affirm that Jesus is the promised Messiah?

How is the idea of 'promise and fulfilment' woven through Matthew 1 – 2?

How is Jesus associated with the 'nations' in the opening chapters of Matthew's gospel?

16

The coming of the kingdom

Matthew 3 – 13

Summary

By challenging the people to repent, John the Baptist prepares
for the coming of the kingdom of God. He anticipates the
arrival of a powerful, Spirit-endowed ruler who will support the
righteous but punish the wicked. Later, when imprisoned
without just cause, John seeks confirmation that Jesus is the
Messiah. In his parables Jesus reveals that, in order to give the
wicked an opportunity to repent, they will be judged and
punished only at the 'end of the age'.

Key texts: Matthew 3:7–12; 13:24–43

The account of Jesus' birth is probably the most familiar part of the four gospels. No doubt the celebration of Christmas has much to do with this. Yet events associated with the birth of Jesus are mentioned in only two of the gospels, and even then the content and presentation differ markedly. In terms of introducing Jesus' life, the exploits of John the Baptist are much more important. His activities are viewed by all four gospel-writers as significant because of the special way in which they prepare for Jesus' public ministry.

A way prepared

According to all four gospels John's ministry centres on two main activities, preaching and baptizing, both of which are concerned with repentance. John's preaching is summarised in Matthew in one short sentence: 'Repent, for the kingdom of heaven is near' (Mt. 3:2). Soon afterwards we read:

> People went out to him [John] from Jerusalem and all Judea and the whole region of the Jordan. Confessing their sins, they were baptised by him in the Jordan River (Mt. 3:5–6; *cf.* Mk. 1:4–5; Lk. 3:3; Jn. 1:23–28).

A further feature noted in two of the gospels is John's clothing: 'John's clothes were made of camel's hair, and he had a leather belt around his waist' (Mt. 3:4; *cf.* Mk. 1:6). Due to his unusual dress and the nature of his ministry, John is associated with the prophet Elijah (Jn. 1:21; *cf.* Mt. 11:11–14). This connection is probably influenced by the final verses of the book of Malachi, which speak of the return of the prophet Elijah:

> See, I [the LORD Almighty] will send you the prophet Elijah before that great and dreadful day of the LORD comes. He will turn the hearts of the fathers to the children, and the hearts of the children to their fathers; or else I will come and strike the land with a curse (Mal. 4:5–6).

The strong emphasis which John places upon repentance, linked to his proclamation that the kingdom of heaven is near brings to mind the pattern observed in the books of Judges and Samuel, where repentance by the people is the first step towards God's raising up a judge or deliverer. John's ministry is essentially preparatory:

> After me will come one who is more powerful than I, whose sandals I am not fit to carry. He will baptise you with the Holy Spirit and with fire. His winnowing fork is in his hand, and he will clear his threshing-floor, gathering his wheat into the barn and burning up the chaff with unquenchable fire (Mt. 3:11–12; *cf.* Mk. 1:7–8; Lk. 3:16–17; Jn. 1:26–27).

These words obviously support the expectation of a coming one, who, as a powerful, Spirit-endowed judge or ruler, will protect the righteous and punish the wicked.

Matthew's record of an encounter between Jesus and John contains several noteworthy features. First, Jesus' determination to be baptized by John underlines his humility; Jesus identifies himself with those who have confessed their sins and come to John to be ritually washed. Secondly, as Jesus emerges out of the water, 'the Spirit of God' descends upon him (Mt. 3:16). As a consequence, Jesus is empowered to fulfil his mission, a theme that is especially prominent in Luke's gospel (*e.g.* Lk. 3:21–22; 4:1, 14, 18). Thirdly, a voice speaks from heaven: 'This is my Son, whom I love; with him I am well pleased' (Mt. 3:17). The combination of these elements recalls the picture found in the books of Samuel regarding the anointing of the first Israelite kings. The coming of the Spirit of God upon Jesus reminds us of what occurred when Saul and David were first anointed. Moreover, the expression 'my son' is used in the Old Testament to describe the unique relationship which exists between the Lord and the Davidic king (*cf.* 2 Sa. 7:14; Pss. 2:7; 89:26–27).

John's doubts

Having introduced Jesus as the heir to the Davidic throne, Matthew focuses next on the reaction evoked by Jesus' teaching (Mt. 5:1 – 7:29) and miracles, mainly of healing (8:1 – 9:33). While there are indications of rising opposition (9:11, 14, 34), the predominant attitude towards Jesus in Matthew 5 – 10 is very positive.

Against this background it comes as something of a surprise to read in Matthew 11 that John sent some disciples to Jesus with the question, 'Are you the one who was to come, or should we expect someone else?' (Mt. 11:2). John's query is noteworthy because of the doubt it expresses about Jesus' identity as the promised Davidic king. Furthermore, the remainder of Matthew 11 – 12 records rising opposition to the idea that Jesus is 'the one who was to come'. Indeed, the Pharisees, an influential religious group, ascribe Jesus' power to 'Beelzebub, the prince of demons' (Mt. 12:24). Why, it may be asked, does John have doubts about Jesus, and why are some religious Jews adamant that he is not the Messiah?

Matthew addresses these questions indirectly in chapter 13. This consists of seven parables, all focusing on the nature of the kingdom of heaven. Since Jesus is presented as the promised Davidic king, it is not unexpected that he should speak about the kingdom over which he has come to rule.

First, in the parable of the different types of soil (Mt. 13:3–23), Jesus reveals that people will respond in a variety of ways when they hear the message about the kingdom. Some, due to their hardness of heart, will remain unmoved. Others, because of either the shallowness of their commitment or the ease with which other things crowd out the message, will initially display signs of life, only for this to disappear later. Finally, Jesus affirms that whoever 'hears the word and understands it' will be fruitful.

Secondly, using the parables of the hidden treasure (Mt. 13:44) and the fine pearl (Mt. 13:45–46), Jesus draws attention to the tremendous value that an individual should place upon discovering the kingdom of God. To possess it is worth all that a person has.

Thirdly, the parables of the mustard seed (Mt. 13:31–32) and yeast (Mt. 13:33) both focus on the kingdom as something small which grows slowly into something much larger. These particular illustrations must have deeply shocked Jesus' listeners. No ordinary Jew would have dared compare God's kingdom with the smallest of seeds or with yeast, something that was normally associated with evil. These images are clearly designed to challenge the contemporary conception of the kingdom of God.

Fourthly, using the parables of the weeds (Mt. 13:24–30, 36–43) and the net (Mt. 13:47–50), Jesus teaches that the righteous and the wicked will co-exist until 'the end of the age'. Then, and only then, will the wicked be removed from the kingdom. While Jesus does not deny that the coming of the kingdom will involve the punishment of the wicked, he sees this as being something which will occur only 'at the end of the age'.

Taken together, these parables reveal that the kingdom envisaged by Jesus will be established over a period of time; it will expand, although perhaps in a way that is not always easily visible. While it will begin in an exceptionally small way, real growth will occur as people respond positively, discovering its great value. Yet, although many will embrace the kingdom, others will exclude themselves from it. Consequently, the righteous and the wicked will live side by side until, at 'the end of the age', the former will be gathered in and the latter excluded.

Two aspects of this overall picture are particularly relevant for understanding the doubts of John and the hostility of the Pharisees. First, John's uncertainty appears to arise as a result of his imprisonment (Mt. 11:2). In the light of the strong Old Testament emphasis that the promised Davidic king will bring justice and righteousness, John obviously believes that the arrival of the 'coming one' will involve the immediate overthrow of the wicked. John's own comments give evidence of this expectation, for he speaks of the coming one 'gathering his wheat into the barn and burning up the chaff with unquenchable fire' (Mt. 3:12). For John, then, his unjust confinement seems incompatible with the coming of the Messiah and the establishment of the kingdom. Jesus' parables, however, reveal that initially he comes with an invitation for all to repent and accept his kingship. The wicked will ultimately be punished, but for the present they are given the opportunity to embrace Jesus as king.

Secondly, Jesus draws attention to the hostility which will exist towards the coming of the kingdom. The evil one comes and snatches away the message of the kingdom from those who do not understand it (Mt. 13:19). Jesus also speaks of the enemy sowing 'weeds among the wheat' (Mt. 13:25): 'The weeds are the sons of the evil one, and the enemy who sows them is the devil' (Mt. 13:38b–39a). By emphasizing the activity of the 'evil one', Jesus indicates that the inauguration of the kingdom will not automatically entail the removal of wickedness from the world. Rather, while the kingdom is growing, 'everything that causes sin and all who do evil' (Mt. 13:41) will continue to be active. Implicit in this comment is the suggestion that the hostility of the Pharisees is due to the 'evil one'.

Conclusion

All this sheds valuable light upon the nature of the kingdom that Jesus Christ comes to establish. It is not a kingdom created through the use of military might, but rather as the 'word' takes root in people's hearts and they submit themselves in obedience to the authority of God. Consequently, the kingdom has no geographical boundaries, but exists wherever God's reign is accepted and acted upon. As we shall observe below, this enables the coming kingdom to extend to the ends of the earth, embracing people from every nation. While the kingdom will begin small and face opposition, it will constantly grow until at the 'end of the age' the righteous will be rewarded and the wicked punished. Moreover, because it is radically different, the kingdom inaugurated through the coming of Jesus Christ will eclipse all earlier kingdoms. In the light of this it is no surprise that the New Testament writers portray King Jesus as excelling over his most famous royal predecessors. This latter emphasis will be the focus of our next chapter.

Questions for reflection and discussion

What role does John the Baptist play in preparing for the coming of the Messiah?

What light do the parables of Jesus in Matthew 13 shed upon the growth of the kingdom of God?

What are the implications of the parable of the wheat and the weeds for the Messiah's role as judge?

17

Greater than all others

Matthew and Hebrews

Summary

In a variety of passages Jesus is portrayed as surpassing some of the most important individuals mentioned in the Old Testament. These include the kingly figures of David and Solomon. Furthermore, through being compared with Melchizedek, king of Salem, Jesus is presented as a priest-king whose ministry excels that of the Aaronic high priests.

Key texts: Matthew 12:38–42; 22:41–46;
Hebrews 4:14 – 5:10

The Old Testament material relating to the coming of a future king emphasizes that his reign will be characterized by righteousness, peace, prosperity and joy. This idyllic picture owes much to the expectation that the divinely anointed king will be a perfect ruler, free from all those faults evident in other members of the royal line of David. While exhibiting all that is best in his predecessors, the Messiah will surpass them by far in all that he is and achieves.

When we turn to the New Testament, we discover that Jesus Christ is portrayed excelling all others. We have already encountered this in the comments of John the Baptist: 'After me will come one who is more powerful than I, whose sandals I am not fit to carry' (Mt. 3:11; *cf.* Jn. 3:30). John obviously considers himself quite inferior to the one for whom he prepares the way.

Greater than Solomon and Jonah

This theme is later picked up by Jesus when addressing the Pharisees as a 'wicked and adulterous generation' (Mt. 12:39). Remarking on their unwillingness to accept his teaching or acknowledge the true source of his power to perform miracles, Jesus contrasts their attitude with both the men of Nineveh and the Queen of Sheba.

> The men of Nineveh will stand up at the judgment with this generation and condemn it; for they repented at the preaching of Jonah, and now *one greater than Jonah is here*. The Queen of Sheba will rise at the judgment with this generation and condemn it; for she came from the ends of the earth to listen to Solomon's wisdom, and now *one greater than Solomon is here* (Mt. 12:41–42, emphasis mine).

The Pharisees' lack of repentance and their rejection of Jesus' teaching invite especially severe condemnation because Jesus is 'greater than' both Jonah and Solomon. In most contexts such a statement might appear exceptionally arrogant.

If, however, Jesus is the Messiah, as the New Testament documents claim, this claim to greatness is no more than we might expect. With regard to Jesus' wisdom (the characteristic for which Solomon was famous), the author of Matthew's gospel has already noted the impact that it made upon his hearers:

> When Jesus had finished saying these things, the crowds were amazed at his teaching, because he taught as one who had authority, and not as their teachers of the law (Mt. 7:28–29).

While the idea that Jesus is 'greater than Solomon' is clearly important when we think of Jesus as the promised king, a much more interesting comparison arises later. This concerns Jesus' standing in relation to that of David.

Greater than David

Shortly before his crucifixion, the Pharisees confront Jesus in order to 'trap him in his words' (Mt. 22:15). Their attempt fails, however, and, seizing the opportunity, Jesus asks them a question relating to their understanding of the Messiah: 'Whose son is he?' (Mt. 22:42). The Pharisees respond as any Jew familiar with the Old Testament would have done; they affirm that the Messiah is 'the son of David' (Mt. 22:42). On receiving this not unexpected reply, Jesus asks a further, and much more telling, question. If the Messiah is David's son, 'how is it then that David, speaking by the Spirit, calls him "Lord"?' (Mt. 22:43). In support of his question, Jesus quotes Psalm 110:1, which was composed by David: 'The Lord said to my Lord: "Sit at my right hand until I put your enemies under your feet"' (Mt. 22:44). Jesus comments, 'If then David calls him "Lord", how can he be his son?' (Mt. 22:45). The episode concludes with the observation, 'No-one could say a word in reply, and from that day on no-one dared to ask him any more questions' (Mt. 22:46).

Jesus' remarks are significant. Implicit in his comments is the idea that the Messiah is someone much greater than David. While Jesus does not immediately claim that he is the one 'greater than David', this idea does permeate the gospels. It is reflected in the unique nature of his conception by the Holy Spirit through to his extraordinary resurrection from death to life. Indeed, the gospels abound with material that points to the fact that Jesus surpasses all others: he claims to forgive sins; he performs miracles of healing, even bringing the dead back to life; he exercises control over the forces of nature. In these ways and others, the gospels indicate that Jesus is no ordinary 'son of David'.

Greater than all others

The idea that Jesus is greater than the most outstanding figures in Israel's past is not restricted to the gospels. The letter to the Hebrews emphasizes that Jesus Christ as the Son of God is superior not only to Moses and his brother Aaron, who was Israel's first high priest, but even to the angels. Opening with the remarkable claim that 'the Son is the radiance of God's glory and the exact representation of his being, sustaining all things by his powerful word' (Heb. 1:3), Hebrews proceeds to quote a number of Old Testament passages that focus on the Davidic king as the 'son of God' (Ps. 2:7; 2 Sa. 7:14; 1 Ch. 17:13; Pss. 45:6–7; 110:1). These quotations are used to demonstrate the superiority of the 'son' over the angels, who are 'ministering spirits sent to serve' (Heb. 1:14).

After stressing that Jesus is greater than the angels, Hebrews then focuses on the idea that Jesus is greater than Moses:

Jesus has been found worthy of greater honour than Moses, just as the builder of a house has greater honour than the house itself. For every house is built by someone, but God is the builder of everything. Moses was faithful as a servant in all God's house, testifying to what would be said in the future. But Christ is faithful as a son over God's house (Heb. 3:3–6).

This passage contrasts Jesus, a 'son over God's house', and Moses, a 'servant' in it.

Hebrews next compares Jesus with Aaron, the high priest. At the outset, Jesus' high-priestly nature is boldly affirmed: 'We have a great high priest who has gone through the heavens, Jesus the Son of God' (4:14). Then, in 5:4–10, a link between Jesus and the order of Melchizedek is established on the basis of Psalm 110 (which, as we have noted above, was quoted by Jesus in order to affirm that the Messiah is more than a mere 'son of David'). In the psalm, God swears an oath to the one whom David addresses as 'my Lord': God says, 'You are a priest for ever, in the order of Melchizedek' (Ps. 110:4).

Melchizedek was the king of Salem and priest of God Most High in the time of Abraham (Gn. 14:18). Since Melchizedek vanishes from the Genesis narrative almost as soon as he appears, it is remarkable that he should be mentioned in Psalm 110 in connection with the Davidic monarchy. Salem, however, is elsewhere identified with Jerusalem (*cf.* Ps. 76:2). This explains why a future Davidic king, enthroned in Jerusalem, is associated with one of its former kings, Melchizedek. For the author of Hebrews, Psalm 110:4 provides Old Testament evidence that the one greater than David will have the divinely given status of priest-king. On this basis, Hebrews affirms that the high-priestly ministry of Jesus Christ surpasses that of the high priests linked to the family of Aaron (*e.g.* Heb. 7:23–28; 9:24–28).

Conclusion

Much more could be said about the ways in which the New Testament documents underline the greatness of Jesus. From the material we have just considered, however, it is apparent that Jesus' greatness is linked to the idea that he is in a unique way 'the son of God', 'sharing' God's nature. The Son, according to the letter to the Hebrews, is 'the exact representation of his [God's] being' (1:3). The apostle Paul describes Jesus as 'the image of the invisible God' (Col. 1:15) and, in writing to the Philippians, he states that Jesus Christ, 'being in very nature God, did not consider equality with God something to be grasped' (Phil. 2:6). In the light of these statements, it is noteworthy that in the Old Testament the relationship of God to the Davidic king is sometimes presented as that of father to son (2 Sa. 7:14; Pss. 2:7; 89:26–27). Moreover, it is possible to interpret several passages as implying that the king is divine (Is. 9:6–7; Je. 23:5–6; *cf.* Ps. 45:6). While some scholars dismiss the significance of these references to the divine nature of the Davidic king as hyperbole, there can be little doubt that these passages support the New Testament belief that Jesus, as the promised Davidic king, is divine. What appear in the Old Testament as possible pointers to this reality are filled out and confirmed in the New Testament writings. With this the biblical portrait of the Messiah takes on an added dimension.

Questions for reflection and discussion

Why does Jesus suggest that the Messiah is more than a 'son of David'? What are the implications of this suggestion?

Why does the author of Hebrews associate Jesus with the priestly order of Melchizedek?

What evidence do the four gospels provide to suggest that Jesus is divine?

18

The light dawns

Matthew, Acts and Galatians

Summary

Central to the process of reconciling human beings to God are Jesus Christ's death and resurrection. As a result of these events, the way is opened for both Jews and Gentiles to enter the kingdom of God.

Key texts: Matthew 4:12–16; Acts 8:14–17; 10:9–48;
Galatians 3:6–14

Astriking feature of Matthew's gospel is the special emphasis that it gives to locating the ministry of Jesus in the region of Galilee. Attention is drawn to this shortly after Jesus is baptized by John.

> When Jesus heard that John had been put in prison, he returned to Galilee. Leaving Nazareth, he went and lived in Capernaum, which was by the lake in the area of Zebulun and Naphtali – to fulfil what was said through the prophet Isaiah: 'Land of Zebulun and land of Naphtali, the way to the sea, along the Jordan, Galilee of the Gentiles – the people living in darkness have seen a great light; on those living in the land of the shadow of death a light has dawned' (Mt. 4:12–16).

Three aspects of this link with Galilee deserve attention.

First, the quotation (from Isaiah 9:1–2) supports the affirmation that Jesus is the promised Messiah. In Isaiah, these verses introduce one of the most important passages in the Old Testament regarding the coming of a future Davidic king:

> For to us a child is born, to us a son is given, and the government will be on his shoulders. And he will be called Wonderful Counsellor, Mighty God, Everlasting Father, Prince of Peace. Of the increase of his government and peace there will be no end. He will reign on David's throne and over his kingdom, establishing and upholding it with justice and righteousness from that time on and for ever. The zeal of the LORD Almighty will accomplish this (Is. 9:6–7).

By suggesting that Jesus' arrival in the lakeside village of Capernaum fulfils the first few verses of Isaiah 9, Matthew also suggests that he is indeed the one mentioned in the next part of the chapter.

Secondly, Isaiah 9:1–2 links the region of Galilee with the nations. While most English versions read 'Galilee of the

Gentiles', the Hebrew text is best translated 'Galilee of the nations'. The significance of this can hardly be missed, for although Matthew's gospel is generally viewed as having been composed for a mainly Jewish or Jewish-Christian readership, special attention is given throughout to non-Jews. We observed this when we thought about the women listed in the genealogy that opens the gospel. Later in the narrative, Jesus commends the faith of a Roman centurion: 'I tell you the truth, I have not found anyone in Israel with such great faith' (Mt. 8:10). Possibly the most important reference to 'the nations' comes in the final verses of the gospel. Addressing his disciples in Galilee, the resurrected Jesus commands them to 'make disciples of all nations' (Mt. 28:19).

The impact of this instruction is revealed in the Acts of the Apostles, which describes how the early church expands numerically, racially and geographically. Unexpectedly, the early Jewish followers of Jesus soon find their numbers being supplemented by Samaritan and then Gentile believers. Confirmation that the nations are now included within the people of God is given when the Holy Spirit comes upon them. Like the Jewish believers in Jerusalem, Samaritans and Gentiles too experience the transforming power of the Holy Spirit. The account of this expansion ends with the apostle Paul proclaiming the good news about Jesus in Rome. What started among Jews in Jerusalem eventually reaches right to the very heart of the mighty Roman empire, embracing all nationalities.

While Acts records how the good news about Jesus is presented to those from different nations, Paul states emphatically to the Galatians that this is the fulfilment of what God originally promised Abraham:

The Scripture foresaw that God would justify the Gentiles by faith, and announced the gospel in advance to Abraham: 'All nations will be blessed through you.' So those who have faith are blessed along with Abraham, the man of faith ... Christ redeemed us from the curse of the law by becoming a curse for us, for it is written: 'Cursed is everyone who is hung on a tree.' He redeemed us in order that the blessing given to Abraham might come to the Gentiles through Christ Jesus, so that by faith we might receive the promise of the Spirit (Gal. 3:8–9, 13–14).

Although the idea is expressed in different ways, there runs throughout the New Testament the conviction that Jesus is the Messiah who mediates God's blessing to all the nations of the earth.

Reconciliation through the cross

The third aspect of the quotation from Isaiah 9:1–2 is the image of light dawning on those 'living in the land of the shadow of death'. The Matthean account of Jesus' life concludes with the risen Christ appearing to his disciples in Galilee (Mt. 28:16–20). The location of this event in Galilee is noteworthy because the preceding events, recorded in chapters 21 – 27, are located in and around Jerusalem. The reader's attention is drawn to the importance of the disciples' return to Galilee by the fact that the instruction to do so is given not once but twice, first by an angel (28:7) and then by Jesus himself (28:10). Since it is the resurrected Jesus who appears to the disciples in Galilee, the quotation from Isaiah, with its reference to the 'shadow of death', takes on added significance. Jesus' return to Galilee marks the climax of the light dawning. The completion of Jesus' mission can take place only after his death on the cross and subsequent resurrection.

In all four gospels special prominence is given to Christ's death on the cross. This is the climax towards which all the preceding events move and from which everything else flows. The gospels emphasize that Jesus anticipates his death in Jerusalem (*cf. e.g.* Mk. 8:31; 9:31; 10:33–34) and is determined not to evade the humiliation and suffering which the cross will bring.

The contrast which the gospels paint between Christ's willingness to go to the cross and the mockery that he receives as the 'king of the Jews' is significant. From his entry into Jerusalem on the back of a donkey until his execution, Jesus displays perfect humility and trust in God. For him the cross is not an unfortunate and unplanned catastrophe. On the contrary, it is the goal of his mission, for through it he enables human beings to be reconciled to God. The apostle Paul captures this well when he writes to the church at Colossae:

> For God was pleased to have all his fulness dwell in him, and through him to reconcile to himself all things, whether things on earth or things in heaven, by making peace through his blood, shed on the cross. Once you were alienated from God and were enemies in your minds because of your evil behaviour. But now he has reconciled you by Christ's physical body through death to present you holy in his sight, without blemish and free from accusation – if you continue in your faith, established and firm, not moved from the hope held out in the gospel (Col. 1:19–23).

Conclusion

Christ's death on the cross removes the alienation that exists between God and humanity, enabling human beings to enjoy God's favour. This new experience, however, is granted only to those who personally acknowledge the kingship of Jesus Christ, recognizing that through his death and resurrection he brings salvation to those who sincerely turn from their wrongdoing. For all the New Testament writers, this belief lies at the very heart of the message that they proclaim concerning the Messiah.

Questions for reflection and discussion

Why does Matthew's gospel see Galilee as an important location for Jesus' mission?

What significance do the New Testament writers give to the death and resurrection of Jesus?

Why is the inclusion of the Samaritans and of the Gentiles important for understanding Jesus' role as the Messiah?

19

Life in the kingdom

The gospels, Acts, 1 Corinthians and Galatians

Summary

Considerable attention is given in the New Testament to the
spiritual dimension of the kingdom of God. Individuals enter
the kingdom through the activity of the Spirit, and are
afterwards expected to display in their lives the fruit of the
Spirit. The moral behaviour of those within the kingdom
should distinguish them from those outside. The Spirit also
imparts spiritual gifts for the good of all.

*Key texts: Matthew 5:3–12; John 3:1–21;
1 Corinthians 12:1–31; Galatians 5:16–26*

The New Testament writers are united in their conviction that Jesus is the promised Messiah and that with his coming the kingdom of God begins. Since Jesus is the divinely anointed king, his kingdom exists wherever individuals gladly acknowledge his authority and willingly obey him. Christ's kingdom differs from every earthly kingdom, and this belief is developed in a number of significant ways within the New Testament writings.

A spiritual realm

At the outset it is important to appreciate that the kingdom of God is viewed as a 'spiritual' realm. This idea becomes clear in the discussion between Jesus and a Pharisee 'named Nicodemus, a member of the Jewish ruling council' (Jn. 3:1). Fearful perhaps of what others might think, Nicodemus comes at night, acknowledging that Jesus is a teacher 'from God'. Jesus tells Nicodemus that 'no-one can see the kingdom of God unless he is born again' (3:3). Thinking in terms of a normal, physical birth, Nicodemus asks, 'How can a man be born when he is old? … Surely he cannot enter a second time into his mother's womb to be born?' (3:4). In reply, Jesus develops what he means by being 'born again':

> I tell you the truth, no-one can enter the kingdom of God unless he is born of water and the Spirit. Flesh gives birth to flesh, but the Spirit gives birth to spirit. You should not be surprised at my saying, 'You must be born again.' The wind blows wherever it pleases. You hear its sound, but you cannot tell where it comes from or where it is going. So it is with everyone born of the Spirit (3:5–8).

Only those 'born of the Spirit' may enter the kingdom. For this reason it is a 'spiritual' kingdom.

This emphasis upon the activity of the Spirit is significant. We have already noted that only through being empowered by the Holy Spirit can the divinely anointed king fulfil his God-appointed mission. Not surprisingly, what is essential for the promised king is also necessary for the citizens of the kingdom. Thus John the Baptist stresses that, whereas he baptizes the people with water, the 'coming one' will baptize them with the Holy Spirit. Later, following the ascension of Jesus, the believers in Jerusalem undergo a profound experience when the Spirit descends upon them on the day of Pentecost:

> Suddenly a sound like the blowing of a violent wind came from heaven and filled the whole house where they were sitting. They saw what seemed to be tongues of fire that separated and came to rest on each of them. All of them were filled with the Holy Spirit and began to speak in other tongues as the Spirit enabled them (Acts 2:2–4).

This event empowers the early church for its mission to the world. The Spirit later comes upon Samaritan (Acts 8:14–17) and then Gentile believers (Acts 10:44–48). Peter's comments capture the importance of this latter event:

> As I began to speak, the Holy Spirit came on them [the Gentiles in the house of Cornelius] as he had come on us at the beginning. Then I remembered what the Lord had said: 'John baptised with water, but you will be baptised with the Holy Spirit.' So if God gave them the same gift as he gave us, who believed in the Lord Jesus Christ, who was I to think that I could oppose God? (Acts 11:15–17).

The coming of the Spirit indicates that God had 'granted even the Gentiles repentance unto life' (Acts 11:18). In the light of these events, it is evident that the Holy Spirit plays a vital role in establishing the messianic kingdom among both Jews and Gentiles.

Spiritual lives

Not only is the Holy Spirit important in bringing us into the kingdom of God, but the New Testament writers also emphasize the Spirit's ongoing role in transforming the lives of those who are within the kingdom. Two aspects of this are worth noting.

First, certain New Testament books develop the idea that the Holy Spirit imparts *gifts* for the 'common good'. The apostle Paul discusses the concept of spiritual gifts in his letter to the church at Corinth:

> There are different kinds of gifts, but the same Spirit. There are different kinds of service, but the same Lord. There are different kinds of working, but the same God works all of them in all men.
>
> Now to each one the manifestation of the Spirit is given for the common good. To one there is given through the Spirit the message of wisdom, to another the message of knowledge by means of the same Spirit, to another faith by the same Spirit, to another gifts of healing by that one Spirit, to another miraculous powers, to another prophecy, to another distinguishing between spirits, to another speaking in different kinds of tongues, and to still another the interpretation of tongues. All these are the work of one and the same Spirit, and he gives them to each one, just as he determines (1 Cor. 12:4–11; *cf.* 12:12–31; Eph. 4:7–13).

Focusing on the diversity of these gifts, Paul argues that since they come from the one Spirit they should not be a cause of division within the church. In saying this, Paul acknowledges that these spiritual gifts (*charismata*), as signs of God's grace (*charis*), are given in differing measures to different people.

Secondly, whereas the gifts of the Spirit are distributed unevenly among those within the kingdom, without any one person having all of them, all believers are intended to display in their lives all of the *fruit* of the Spirit. Once again it is the apostle Paul who provides the clearest statement as to what constitutes spiritual fruit.

But the fruit of the Spirit is love, joy, peace, patience, kindness, goodness, faithfulness, gentleness and self-control (Gal. 5:22–23).

All these qualities are present in those who 'live by' and 'are led by' the Spirit, and Paul contrasts this fruit with the behaviour produced by 'the desires of the sinful nature'. The latter are 'sexual immorality, impurity and debauchery; idolatry and witchcraft; hatred, discord, jealousy, fits of rage, selfish ambition, dissensions, factions and envy; drunkenness, orgies, and the like' (Gal. 5:19–21). Paul comments: 'I warn you, as I did before, that those who live like this will not inherit the kingdom of God' (Gal. 5:21). From these observations it is evident that entry into and life within the kingdom depends upon the enabling activity of the Holy Spirit.

The contrast which Paul makes between those who live by the Spirit and those who live according to the desires of the sinful nature highlights the distinctive moral behaviour of those in the kingdom. This emphasis is also present in the gospels. One passage that underlines this contrast is the section known as the Beatitudes (Mt. 5:3–12), part of Jesus' teaching that has special prominence in Matthew's gospel because it introduces the Sermon on the Mount (Mt. 5–7).

> Blessed are the poor in spirit,
>   for theirs is the kingdom of heaven.
> Blessed are those who mourn,
>   for they will be comforted.
> Blessed are the meek,
>   for they will inherit the earth.
> Blessed are those who hunger and thirst for
>   righteousness,
>   for they will be filled.
> Blessed are the merciful,
>   for they will be shown mercy.
> Blessed are the pure in heart,
>   for they will see God.

> Blessed are the peacemakers,
>   for they will be called sons of God.
> Blessed are those who are persecuted because of
>   righteousness,
>   for theirs is the kingdom of heaven.

Blessed are you when people insult you, persecute you and falsely say all kinds of evil against you because of me. Rejoice and be glad, because great is your reward in heaven, for in the same way they persecuted the prophets who were before you (Mt. 5:3–12).

Each statement opens with the expression, 'Blessed are ...' The repeated use of this phrase is significant, for, as the promised Messiah, Jesus comes to mediate God's blessing to others. Jesus indicates that only those who exhibit specific qualities in their lives will be blessed.

The characteristics commended by Jesus describe an individual who, conscious of his or her own spiritual poverty and personal inadequacy, is not self-assertive, but has a deep yearning that righteousness should prevail instead of wickedness. Such a person will respond positively to Jesus' call to repent. Furthermore, this person shows mercy to others, displays sincerity in everything he or she does, promotes reconciliation instead of division, and remains steadfast in the face of unwarranted opposition.

Jesus links these characteristics to ways in which God's blessing may be experienced. The repetition of 'theirs is the kingdom of heaven' (Mt. 5:3, 10) stresses that they are within the kingdom, and enjoy a special relationship with God; they will see him and be called his children. Moreover, comforted and shown mercy, they will inherit the earth, experiencing righteousness in all its fullness.

Conclusion

The New Testament writers clearly envisage the kingdom of

God as radically different from every earthly kingdom. Created through the activity of the Holy Spirit, the kingdom exists wherever individuals through repentance and faith acknowledge Jesus Christ as saviour and king. Empowered by the Spirit, those who are within the kingdom lead lives that exhibit the moral virtues of God himself. Each individual, however, experiences an ongoing conflict between his or her carnal and spiritual natures. Moreover, given humanity's inherent hostility to God, those who are within the kingdom will also face persecution and ridicule. Ultimately, however (as we shall observe in our next chapter), the divine kingdom will triumph over the powers of evil.

Questions for reflection and discussion

What is the significance of the fact that the kingdom of God is a spiritual kingdom?

How should the lives of those within the kingdom differ from those outside it?

According to Matthew 5:3–12, what personal qualities mark those who will experience God's blessing? How do these differ from those which most people today assume to be important?

20

The kingdom consummated

Matthew and Revelation

Summary

Passages in the books of Matthew and Revelation envisage a future time when the Messiah will judge all the nations, separating the righteous from the wicked. While the latter will be punished, the former will live in a transformed environment, experiencing the full blessing of God.

Key texts: Matthew 25:31–46; Revelation 20:11 – 22:5

The public ministry, death, resurrection and ascension of Jesus Christ, together with the coming of the Holy Spirit upon both Jewish and Gentile believers, mark the inauguration of the kingdom of God. With this the divine promise that the nations of the earth would be blessed through the 'seed' of Abraham begins to be fulfilled. An important distinction is drawn, however, between the present age and the age to come. This is reflected, for example, in Jesus' comments regarding the reward for those who follow him: 'I tell you the truth, no-one who has left home or wife or brothers or parents or children for the sake of the kingdom of God will fail to receive many times as much in this age and, in the age to come, eternal life' (Lk. 18:29–30). The mention of an 'age to come' reflects the fact that the completion of God's plans for the universe still lies at some distance in the future.

Judgment will come

The idea that the kingdom will be dramatically completed is also suggested, as we have already noted, in two of Jesus' parables about the kingdom in Matthew 13. In these he teaches that the righteous and the wicked will co-exist until the 'end of the age'. At that time 'the Son of Man will send out his angels, and they will weed out of his kingdom everything that causes sin and all who do evil' (13:41). 'Then the righteous will shine like the sun in the kingdom of their Father' (13:43).

A similar but fuller picture of a future judgment is recorded in Matthew 25:31–46:

When the Son of Man comes in his glory, and all the angels with him, he will sit on his throne in heavenly glory. All the nations will be gathered before him, and he will separate the people one from another as a shepherd separates the sheep from the goats. He will put the sheep on his right and the goats on his left. Then the King will say to those on his right, 'Come, you who are blessed by my Father; take your inheritance, the kingdom prepared for you since the creation of the world' (Mt. 25:31–34).

In marked contrast, the 'King' says to those on his left, 'Depart from me, you who are cursed, into the eternal fire prepared for the devil and his angels' (Mt. 25:41). As in the parables in Matthew 13, we witness here the dramatic separation of the righteous and the wicked.

The book of Revelation provides a matching picture of this future judgment.

Then I saw a great white throne and him who was seated on it. Earth and sky fled from his presence, and there was no place for them. And I saw the dead, great and small, standing before the throne, and books were opened. Another book was opened, which is the book of life. The dead were judged according to what they had done as recorded in the books. The sea gave up the dead that were in it, and death and Hades gave up the dead that were in them, and each person was judged according to what he had done. Then death and Hades were thrown into the lake of fire. The lake of fire is the second death. If anyone's name was not found written in the book of life, he was thrown into the lake of fire (Rev. 20:11–15).

These passages in Matthew and Revelation emphasize that those sentenced to punishment in the 'eternal fire' are condemned because of their wrongdoing. Revelation 21:8 states:

But the cowardly, the unbelieving, the vile, the murderers, the sexually immoral, those who practise magic arts, the idolaters and all liars – their place will be in the fiery lake of burning sulphur.

Matthew's gospel stresses the lack of compassion displayed by the wicked for the hungry, the thirsty, the stranger, the naked, the sick and the imprisoned (Mt. 25:35–44).

Just before this account of the dead being judged, the text of Revelation focuses on 'the dragon, that ancient serpent, who is the devil or Satan' (20:2). He is thrown into 'the lake of burning sulphur' to 'be tormented day and night for ever and ever' (20:10). These comments illuminate Jesus' statement about 'the eternal fire prepared for the devil and his angels' (Mt. 25:41).

The New Testament writings portray the wicked as eventually being judged and punished at 'the end of the age'. They paint a very different picture of the future of those deemed to be righteous by the 'Son of Man' or 'King'. Before focusing on the description provided in Revelation, which is by far the fullest, it is perhaps worth noting a brief comment by Jesus. Deeply impressed by the faith of a non-Jewish soldier, Jesus remarks:

> I tell you the truth, I have not found anyone in Israel with such great faith. I say to you that many will come from the east and the west, and will take their places at the feast with Abraham, Isaac and Jacob in the kingdom of heaven. But the subjects of the kingdom will be thrown outside, into the darkness, where there will be weeping and gnashing of teeth (Mt. 8:10–12).

Here, the image of a feast or banquet is used to describe the consummated kingdom. Moreover, Jesus probably hints that Gentiles from distant places will participate in the feast, whereas some Jews will not. A similar illustration is later found in another parable about the 'kingdom of heaven' involving a king who prepares a wedding banquet for his son (Mt. 22:1–14). Remarkably, some of the original wedding guests not only fail to come to the banquet, but actually kill the king's servants who are sent to remind them of their invitation. The king then says to his servants, 'The wedding banquet is ready, but those I invited did not deserve to come. Go to the street corners and invite to the banquet anyone you find' (22:8–9). Thus others are invited so that the wedding hall is 'filled with guests' (22:10). Then, in an unusual twist at the end of the story, the king commands that a guest who is present 'without wedding clothes' be tied hand and foot, and thrown outside 'into the darkness, where there will be weeping and gnashing of teeth' (22:13). As in Matthew 8:10–12, this parable points to the exclusion of some who might otherwise have been expected to participate in the consummation of the kingdom.

In the light of this final judgment, it is hardly surprising that several New Testament passages focus on Jesus Christ's future return. This is mentioned briefly at the time of his ascension into heaven.

After he [Jesus] said this, he was taken up before their [the apostles'] very eyes, and a cloud hid him from their sight. They were looking intently up into the sky as he was going, when suddenly two men dressed in white stood beside them. 'Men of Galilee,' they said, 'why do you stand here looking into the sky? This same Jesus, who has been taken from you into heaven, will come back in the same way you have seen him go into heaven' (Acts 1:9–11).

A slightly more detailed account of Christ's return comes in Paul's first letter to the church of the Thessalonians: 'For the Lord himself will come down from heaven, with a loud command, with the voice of the archangel and with the trumpet call of God' (1 Thes. 4:16; *cf.* Mt. 24:30–31). At this stage the 'dead in Christ will rise first', and then those who are still alive 'will be caught up together with them in the clouds to meet the Lord in the air'. Paul states, 'And so we will be with the Lord for ever.'

The New Testament writings give no precise indication of the time of Christ's return. It is presented as an event that will take people by surprise. Paul remarks that 'the day of the Lord will come like a thief in the night' (1 Thes. 5:2). This echoes a similar statement by Jesus (*cf.* Mt. 24:42–44) which forms part of a much longer passage that focuses on the idea that 'only the Father' knows the time when Christ will return (24:36). For this reason, Jesus encourages his followers to be prepared, remaining vigilant at all times (24:36 – 25:13).

A new heaven and earth

Christ's return will result, as we have observed, in the judgment and punishment of the wicked. The righteous, however, will enjoy the privilege of being part of the consummated kingdom. The fullest description of this resplendent kingdom comes in the last two chapters of Revelation. Here John recounts his vision of 'a new heaven and a new earth, for the first heaven and the first earth had passed away, and there was no longer any sea' (21:1). He sees in his vision 'the Holy City, the new Jerusalem, coming down out of heaven from God, prepared as a bride beautifully dressed for her husband' (Rev. 21:2). He then records this dazzling description of the new Jerusalem:

> It shone with the glory of God, and its brilliance was like that of a very precious jewel, like a jasper, clear as crystal. It had a great, high wall with twelve gates, and with twelve angels at the gates. On the gates were written the names of the twelve tribes of Israel. There were three gates on the east, three on the north, three on the south and three on the west. The wall of the city had twelve foundations, and on them were the names of the twelve apostles of the Lamb ... The wall was made of jasper, and the city of pure gold, as pure as glass. The foundations of the city walls were decorated with every kind of precious stone. The first foundation was jasper, the second sapphire, the third chalcedony, the fourth emerald, the fifth sardonyx, the sixth carnelian, the seventh chrysolite, the eighth beryl, the ninth topaz, the tenth chrysoprase, the eleventh jacinth, and the twelfth amethyst. The twelve gates were twelve pearls, each gate made of a single pearl. The great street of the city was of pure gold, like transparent glass (21:11–21).

John then comments:

I did not see a temple in the city, because the Lord God Almighty and the Lamb are its temple. The city does not need the sun or the moon to shine on it, for the glory of God gives it light, and the Lamb is its lamp. The nations will walk by its light, and the kings of the earth will bring their splendour into it. On no day will its gates ever be shut, for there will be no night there. The glory and honour of the nations will be brought into it. Nothing impure will ever enter it, nor will anyone who does what is shameful or deceitful, but only those whose names are written in the Lamb's book of life (Rev. 21:22–27).

John concludes his record by focusing on the throne of God and of the Lamb.

Then the angel showed me the river of the water of life, as clear as crystal, flowing from the throne of God and of the Lamb down the middle of the great street of the city. On each side of the river stood the tree of life, bearing twelve crops of fruit, yielding its fruit every month. And the leaves of the tree are for the healing of the nations. No longer will there be any curse. The throne of God and of the Lamb will be in the city, and his servants will serve him. They will see his face, and his name will be on their foreheads. There will be no more night. They will not need the light of a lamp or the light of the sun, for the Lord God will give them light. And they will reign for ever and ever (22:1–5).

Some of the main features of the new Jerusalem observed by John are reminiscent of the Garden of Eden mentioned in the early chapters of Genesis. Particularly striking is the reference to the 'tree of life'. Whereas Adam and Eve are expelled from Eden in order to prevent them from eating of the 'tree of life' and living for ever (Gn. 3:22), in the new Jerusalem the nations will eat of it for their healing. Likewise, whereas Adam and Eve, due to their disobedience, come under God's curse in Eden, in the new Jerusalem there will no longer be any curse. Also noteworthy is the open access to God which humanity will enjoy in the Holy City; this contrasts sharply with Adam and Eve's expulsion from Eden which brought to an end their intimate and harmonious relationship with God. Yet, while similarities exist, John's description portrays something of the greater splendour attached to the coming new Jerusalem.

Conclusion

In Revelation the arrival of the new Jerusalem is the staggering climax towards which the whole of history, and Scripture, move. With it everything is made new. As John records:

> And I heard a loud voice from the throne saying, 'Now the dwelling of God is with men, and he will live with them. They will be his people, and God himself will be with them and be their God. He will wipe every tear from their eyes. There will be no more death or mourning or crying or pain, for the old order of things has passed away.' He who was seated on the throne said, 'I am making everything new!' (21:3–5)

With this the kingdom is truly consummated.

Questions for reflection and discussion

What suggests that the New Testament writers believed the kingdom of God to be already in existence following the ascension of Jesus?

How is the consummation of the kingdom envisaged in the New Testament?

What factors determine the fate of the righteous and of the wicked?

In what ways can the 'new Jerusalem' be compared and contrasted with the Garden of Eden?

Conclusion

The purpose of this study has been to trace the development of the portrait of the Messiah through the Bible. While the specific designation Messiah is not used at the start, we noted how Genesis focuses attention on the coming of a divinely promised monarch. Beginning with the Lord God's promise to Eve concerning the defeat of the 'seed of the serpent', the Genesis narrative highlights a unique line of 'seed' which is traced firstly through Seth to Noah and then from Noah to Abraham. Against the background of humanity's existence under God's judgment, Abraham receives the promise that through this 'seed' all the nations of the earth will be blessed.

As Genesis proceeds, the line of seed is traced to Judah and his son Perez, with the expectation that a royal dynasty will be established by one of their descendants. This comes to fulfilment when David, the son of Jesse, is anointed by the prophet Samuel as king over Israel in place of Saul. The importance of this link between Judah and David is confirmed not only by the book of Ruth, but also by the way in which the narrative in the books of Joshua, Judges and Samuel prepares for and describes the establishment of the Davidic dynasty in Israel. Here we encounter for the first time a divinely chosen and empowered deliverer of the people with whom God promises to establish an everlasting dynasty. While the books of Samuel and Kings do not conceal the flaws of David, Solomon and their descendants, attention is drawn to particular qualities (*e.g.* humility and obedience) which will characterize the life of the Messiah.

Although the disobedience of successive generations of Israelites, generally involving both ruler and people, eventually leads God to punish them by removing the monarchy from Jerusalem, the hope remains that some day in the future a 'Davidic' king will be divinely restored to the throne. This hope is obviously based on the belief that God will keep his promises even when the failure of human beings presents a barrier to their fulfilment. Thus, during the Babylonian exile, the prophets Jeremiah and Ezekiel look forward to the restoration of the Davidic monarchy.

Whereas the Old Testament concludes with the promise of a future king still unfulfilled, the writers of the New Testament boldly affirm that Jesus of Nazareth is the promised Messiah. Through his public ministry, death on the cross, resurrection from the dead and ascension into heaven, he brings into being the kingdom of God, a spiritual kingdom created through the activity of the Holy Spirit. For this reason, when challenged by Pilate regarding the claim that he is 'king of the Jews', Jesus responds by saying: 'My kingdom is not of this world. If it were, my servants would fight to prevent my arrest by the Jews. But now my kingdom is from another place' (Jn. 18:36).

For the present, the spiritual kingdom consists of all those who acknowledge Christ's reign over their lives, trust in his atoning death and demonstrate in their daily living the fruit of the Holy Spirit. Drawn from the nations of the earth, Christ's subjects co-exist alongside those who, through their own unrighteousness, place themselves outside the kingdom. This situation, however, will come to an end when the Messiah returns to exercise his authority as judge, punishing the wicked and rewarding the righteous. Whereas the former will depart into eternal fire, the latter will live in a totally re-created environment, inheriting the earth and enjoying free access to the throne of God.

For his role in the accomplishment of these things, Jesus Christ will receive the adoration and worship of every creature. Something of this is captured by the apostle Paul, in words possibly drawn from an early Christian hymn:

Being in very nature God,
    [Christ Jesus] did not consider equality with God
    something to be grasped,
but made himself nothing,
    taking the very nature of a servant,
    being made in human likeness.
And being found in appearance as a man,
    he humbled himself
    and became obedient to death –
    even death on a cross!
Therefore God exalted him to the highest place
    and gave him the name that is above every name,
that at the name of Jesus every knee should bow,
    in heaven and on earth and under the earth,
and every tongue confess that Jesus Christ is Lord,
    to the glory of God the Father.

                                     (Phil. 2:6–11)

A much fuller and more vivid description comes in Revelation. There could hardly be any more appropriate words for us to end with. After describing the heavenly throne and its surroundings (4:2–11), John continues:

Then I saw in the right hand of him who sat on the throne a scroll with writing on both sides and sealed with seven seals. And I saw a mighty angel proclaiming in a loud voice, 'Who is worthy to break the seals and open the scroll?' But no-one in heaven or on earth or under the earth could open the scroll or even look inside it. I wept and wept because no-one was found who was worthy to open the scroll or look inside. Then one of the elders said to me, 'Do not weep! See, the Lion of the tribe of Judah, the Root of David, has triumphed. He is able to open the scroll and its seven seals.'

Then I saw a Lamb, looking as if it had been slain, standing in the centre of the throne, encircled by the four living creatures and the elders. He had seven horns and seven eyes, which are the seven spirits of God sent out into all the earth. He came and took the scroll from the right hand of him who sat on the throne. And when he had taken it, the four living creatures and the twenty-four elders fell down before the Lamb. Each one had a harp and they were holding golden bowls full of incense, which are the prayers of the saints. And they sang a new song:

'You are worthy to take the scroll
  and to open its seals,
because you were slain,
  and with your blood you purchased men for God from
    every tribe and language and people and nation.
You have made them to be a kingdom and priests to
    serve our God,
  and they will reign on the earth.'

Then I looked and heard the voice of many angels, numbering thousands upon thousands, and ten thousand times ten thousand. They encircled the throne and the living creatures and the elders. In a loud voice they sang:

'Worthy is the Lamb, who was slain,
to receive power and wealth and wisdom and strength
and honour and glory and praise!'

Then I heard every creature in heaven and on earth and under the earth and on the sea, and all that is in them singing:

'To him who sits on the throne and to the Lamb
be praise and honour and glory and power,
      for ever and ever!'

The four living creatures said, 'Amen', and the elders fell down and worshipped (Rev. 5:1–14).

Further reading

The following bibliography is intended to guide those who may wish to explore in more detail the topics covered in this book. The bibliography consists of four sections: general introductions to the books of the Old and New Testaments; commentaries on biblical books; special studies; recent books on the Messiah. The works in the third section have been chosen because they expand helpfully upon the approach adopted above; they also provide further bibliographical information.

General introductions to the books of the Old and New Testaments

Issues relating to the authorship, date of composition and general contents of the biblical books are helpfully discussed in the following:

R. B. Dillard and T. Longman III, *An Introduction to the Old Testament* (Leicester: Apollos, 1995).
D. A. Carson, D. J. Moo and L. Morris, *An Introduction to the New Testament* (Leicester: Apollos, 1992).

Commentaries on biblical books

A great variety of commentaries exists on all the books of the Bible. At a popular level, *The New Bible Dictionary: 21ˢᵗ Century Edition* (Leicester: IVP, 1994), is an excellent, one-volume commentary on the whole Bible. A somewhat fuller treatment, but also accessible to the ordinary reader, comes in the Tyndale Commentaries published by IVP. More technical treatments are provided in the Word Biblical Commentary series. These works generally approach the text from a conservative evangelical position. Annotated surveys of almost all the Old and New Testament commentaries available are provided by T. Longman III, *Old Testament Commentary Survey* (Grand Rapids: Baker, 2nd edn, 1995), and D. A. Carson, *New Testament Commentary Survey* (Leicester: IVP, 4th edn, 1993).

Special studies

These articles and books provide more detailed treatments of specific texts and are especially relevant to the present volume.

Genesis 1–3
  H. Blocher, *In the Beginning* (Leicester: IVP, 1984).

The family line in Genesis
  T. D. Alexander, 'Genealogies, Seed and the Compositional Unity of Genesis', *Tyndale Bulletin* 44.2 (1993), pp. 225–270.
  T. D. Alexander, 'Messianic Ideology in the Book of Genesis', in P. E. Satterthwaite, R. S. Hess and G. J. Wenham (eds.), *The Lord's Anointed: Interpretation of Old Testament Messianic Texts* (Grand Rapids: Baker; Carlisle: Paternoster, 1995), pp. 19–39.
  J. Collins, 'A Syntactical Note (Genesis 3:15): Is the Woman's Seed Singular or Plural?', *Tyndale Bulletin* 48.1 (1997), pp. 139–148.

The book of Judges
  D. Gooding, 'The Composition of the Book of Judges', *Eretz-Israel* 16 (1982), pp. 70–79.
  B. G. Webb, *The Book of the Judges: An Integrated Reading* (Sheffield: JSOT Press, 1987).

The book of Ruth
  E. H. Merrill, 'The Book of Ruth: Narration and Shared

Themes', *Bibliotheca Sacra* 142 (1985), pp. 130–139.

The books of Samuel and Kings
   P. E. Satterthwaite, 'David in the Books of Samuel: A
      Messianic Hope?', in Satterthwaite, Hess and Wenham
      (eds.), *The Lord's Anointed*, pp. 41–65.
   I. W. Provan, 'The Messiah in the Book of Kings', in
      Satterthwaite, Hess and Wenham (eds.), *The Lord's
      Anointed*, pp. 67–85.

The book of Isaiah
   R. Schultz, 'The King in the Book of Isaiah', in
      Satterthwaite, Hess and Wenham (eds.), *The Lord's
      Anointed*, pp. 141–165.
   B. G. Webb, 'Zion in Transformation: A Literary Approach
      to Isaiah', in D. J. A. Clines, S. E. Fowl and S. E. Porter
      (eds.), *The Bible in Three Dimensions: Essays in Celebration of
      Forty Years of Biblical Studies in the University of Sheffield*
      (Sheffield: JSOT Press, 1990), pp. 65–84.
   B. G. Webb, *The Message of Isaiah: On Eagles' Wings* (Leicester:
      IVP, 1996).

Some recent books on the Messiah

   J. H. Charlesworth (ed.), *The Messiah: Developments in Earliest
      Judaism and Christianity* (Minneapolis: Fortress, 1992).
   G. van Groningen, *Messianic Revelation in the Old Testament*
      (Grand Rapids: Baker, 1990).
   W. C. Kaiser, *The Messiah in the Old Testament* (Grand Rapids:
      Zondervan; Carlisle: Paternoster, 1995).
   P. E. Satterthwaite, R. S. Hess and G. J. Wenham (eds.), *The
      Lord's Anointed: Interpretation of Old Testament Messianic Texts*
      (Grand Rapids: Baker; Carlisle: Paternoster, 1995).
   J. Stein, *Jesus the Messiah* (Leicester: IVP, 1996).
   N. T. Wright, *Jesus and the Victory of God* (London: SPCK,
      1996).

THE OFFICIAL
BADDIEL & SKINNER
FANTASY
FOOTBALL
Diary

LITTLE, BROWN AND COMPANY

A *Little, Brown* Book

First published in Great Britain in 1994
by Little, Brown and Company

A CIP catalogue record for this book
is available from the British Library.

Editor: Andy Jacobs
Assistant Editor: James Bobin

Printed and bound in Great Britain by
The Bath Press

Little, Brown and Company (UK) Limited
Brettenham House
Lancaster Place
London WC2E 7EN

DAVID'S FOREWORD

As you enter the New Year, I recommend you look back on the one just gone and think about all its great achievements. In 1994, for example, there was the World Cup; the election of a new Labour leader; the discovery of proto-titanium, (a revolutionary new drug in the battle against Alzheimer's disease); and the fact that I won the Fantasy League. I feel that this last fact, that *I won the Fantasy League*, has been downplayed in certain quarters, particularly those of my flatmate Mr Skinner. I remember once discussing with him, over a small Chablis – well, I had a small Chablis, he had a meat pie wrapped in some bread – the qualities that marked out each of the leading managers in the league at that time. John Motson, we decided, was a sort of sly old fox character, constantly on the lookout for bargain buys and swiftly moving should any new players enter the Premier League; Karren Brady was more of a big-money operator; Basil Brush, of course, was a puppet.

I felt, though, that in this discussion of the leading managers at that time, one name had somehow been forgotten. Not wishing to press home a point that clearly rankled, I looked distractedly away and remarked nonchalantly, 'And *me*? What about *me*? You've forgotten about *me*! Me, me, me, me, me, me! David Lionel Baddiel! The Lord of Fantasy Football! What is the essential managerial quality that has propelled ME to the dizzy heights of four points clear at the top of the table?' And Mr Skinner, who, perhaps, it is meet we should remember at this point, never got higher than seventh, said: 'Luck.'

What terrible build-up of mental scar tissue, I remember thinking; what appalling injustices in earlier life has this poor man had to suffer to build up in him such a terrible churlishness, such a large weight of grapes so horrifically sour? Of course, he comes from Birmingham; of course, life was tough in the 1930s; of course, there is a certain amount of jaundice that must I suppose accompany having a head that looks incomplete without a flat cap. But to so blatantly fly in the face of all the alternative words that must have immediately sprung to mind – 'shrewdness', perhaps, 'nous', 'footballing instinct', 'sexiness', 'an almost clairvoyant ability to read the game' – to have blocked out all these in favour of 'luck' – well, it beggars belief. Was it luck that led me to buy Martin Allen, who went on to gain me a crucial 14 points, five weeks before the end of the season? Admittedly, I did initially have him mixed up with Clive, and then Paul, and then somewhat bizarrely with Ray, but what's in a name? I'll tell you actually: three Bs in 'Babb'. I may have had no idea who Phil Babb was at the pre-season auction, but I had a hunch that a player with so many Bs in such a short space of time was gonna be the kind of player who would earn me 16 points over the course of the season. That's what I call considered judgement.

By the way, this is a real diary. If you've never owned a diary before, the way to use them is not to fill in what you've done each day before you go to bed at night. Much better to think 'Sod it, I'll write it tomorrow,' and then leave it till the end of the week, by which time last Monday will seem like some time in the Paleolithic era, and you'll end up making it up. This is good, as the point of a diary is not to record your existence, but to make sure that should someone else read it, they won't think you've got a crap life. Here, for example, are a few extracts from my 1994 diary:

14 February: Michelle Pfeiffer rang again. When will she leave me alone? Had a small party for all my friends at Wembley Stadium. While there had a quiet word with top football chiefs about successor to Graham Taylor. Suggested T.V.

2 March: Where are the snows of yesteryear? In time, the clouds may part and release their dew, the sun may break the lining of the sky, and the stars may fall, but still my inner soul yearns for the wheat-strewn land to hang asleep under a soft cape of white. Watched TV, went to bed.

13 March: Spent whole day sorting out terrible confusion after Danny La Rue is appointed England manager.

2 May: *I win the Fantasy League*. Everything is marvellous, although we may have mice, as I can hear a kind of low whining and scratching sound coming from Frank's bedroom.

Anyway. Best wishes, and here's hoping yours makes happier reading than Peter Storey's ...

David
Baddiel

FRANK'S FOREWORD

I've got about half a dozen old diaries. They're all pretty much the same. They usually begin something like:

1 January: Terrible hangover. This year I am going to learn a foreign language. I am also going to do more towards the housework. I noticed some horrible stains on the toilet when I had my head down it this morning.

2 January: Guten tag. Ich bin Frank. That's four words already. Five if you count 'Frank' said in an Erich von Stroheim sort of a way.

3 January: Oh well, I didn't want us to win it anyway. I couldn't put up with a lot of Tottenham fans saying it didn't count. Discover that my Uncle Jimmy was put in prison during the war because he spoke German in the pub one night. Decide this is too big a risk to take. Hit Statto because he refuses to clean the toilet.

I've never filled in a diary beyond 3 January in my life. I blame the fact that those little pencils with 'Letts' on them won't fit properly in a pencil sharpener so by 4 January I might just as well dip my finger in the ashtray and use that. Also, when I was 12 I sneaked a look at my elder brother's diary hoping to learn something about sex that I could impress my mates with. I only read one entry and could never bring myself to open it again. I mean, I could hardly impress my mates with '11 March: Piles still down.'

Anyway, even if you aren't keeping a record of your life beyond 3 January of any given year, it's good to fill in some crucial appointments. The first thing you should do with this diary is to fill in your team's fixtures. This will enable you to turn down invitations to all sorts of important events with a casual, 'March the third? Let me see now ... Ah, no. Sorry, Port Vale away.' The most difficult refusals tend to be funerals, but I find complaining about the short notice usually puts paid to any whining.

The next thing you should fill in are the birthdays of family and friends. Then the next time you're invited to a funeral, you can not only refuse because of a conflicting fixture, but you can ask them to remind you of the deceased's birthday, pointing out that, 'I might as well cross it out while I've got my diary open.'

Oh, and don't forget to put in televised football. I once missed a birthday dinner at a flashy restaurant on the grounds that there was a Bundesliga game on Eurosport. Unfortunately, I didn't notice that just below 'Bayern v SV Hamburg' (NB: Don't be tempted to call out in German) it said 'Frank's Birthday'. (This is 28 January and I like Dime bars and any sort of Lucozade memorabilia.) So, happy entering! Snigger.

Frank Skinner

FANTASY LEAGUE RULES

The basic rules of Fantasy League are very simple and the game gives *you* the chance to manage your very own football team.

First of all, find ten to 15 friends to become fantasy managers and form a league. Then hold an auction to enable each of you to assemble a squad of 15 players. To do this, appoint your auctioneer, who then distributes an imaginary £20 million to each manager. It's a good idea to auction off players in groups, for example, goalkeepers, strikers, full-backs, central defenders and midfielders. So if you start off with, say, the goalies, bids are made until everyone in the league has the stopper of his or her choice. Try not to spend all your money too soon, although having a good goalkeeper or an ordinary goalie in a strong defence is vital in Fantasy League.

Repeat the process, allowing about two hours, until everyone has bought 15 players. Remember that you are not allowed more than two players from any one club.

Each week you will select 11 players from your team, and you can bring in new men and buy players from other managers.

All Fantasy League points are based on players' performances in the real life Premier League.

Points are awarded as follows:

- Each goal is worth three points.

- An assist (the final pass leading to a goal) is worth two points.

- Any defender or goalkeeper keeping a clean sheet for the Premier League team scores four Fantasy League points.

- Each goal conceded by those same defenders will lose you one point.

- Each player receives a weekly score (plus or minus) and the 11 scores are totted up to give your team's weekly total.

- Whoever has the most points at the end of the season is the winner.

JANUARY

1

1965 Stanley Matthews becomes the first footballer to be knighted.

1994 Carlton Palmer and Mark Bright are thrown out of Tramp nightclub.

2

1939 Rangers and Celtic set a Scottish attendance record (118,567).

1967 Pat Jennings gets married in Frank's local church.

3

JANUARY

1987 The quickest sending-off in First Division history (85 seconds): Liam O'Brien of Manchester United against Southampton.

4

Statto.

1982 A draw with Centrax brings non-League Thurlstone Rovers their first point for two years.

1965 Vinny Jones born in Watford.

Ex-footballers read the critics' response to Tom Finney's 'balancing glass' trick.

6

1974 The first-ever professional game on a Sunday results in a 2–2 draw between Cambridge and Oldham.

7

1989 Sutton United become only the fifth non-League team to knock out First Division opposition, beating Coventry 2–1 in the FA Cup.

1955 Four players are sent off for the first time in a game between Crewe and Bradford.

1979 Charlton strikers Mike Flanagan and Derek Hales are sent off for fighting each other.
1990 Peter Storey receives a suspended sentence for attacking a traffic warden.

10

1989 Watford score from a free kick with their first touch of the ball in a Cup tie against Newcastle after United 'keeper Dave Beasant is penalised for handling the ball outside the area.

11

1961 Abolition of the maximum wage for players. Johnny Haynes of Fulham becomes the first £100-a-week footballer.

A man in a cardigan is terribly distressed to find himself mixed up in an old Blackburn Rovers team shot.

12

1963 Only four out of 44 Football League matches are played because of bad weather.

13

1993 Bolton knock out Cup-holders Liverpool at Anfield.

14

1994 BBC TV make history when they transmit the first-ever edition of *Fantasy Football*.

1971 After four draws and 21 defeats, Newport County end the worst-ever start to a season when they beat Southend 3–0.

1994 Frank and David receive a picture of Dutch international Israel (above). It stays on their coffee table for eight months.

17

1948 The record for an English League game is set when 83,260 people watch Manchester United and Arsenal at Maine Road. Urinating on the terraces becomes popular.

18

1989 Brian Clough punches a Forest fan invading the pitch in a League Cup game against QPR.

1957 18,069 people turn up for a reserve match between Wrexham and Wisford United after the Welsh club announce that tickets will be on sale for a Cup tie against Manchester United.

20

Statto.

1923 Debut of Celtic's Jimmy McGrory – the only player ever to average more than a goal a game in British football (410 goals in 408 games).

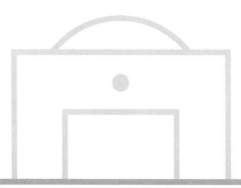

21

1992 The FA reject a £2 million offer from Bass Breweries to sponsor the FA Cup. FA chairman Bert Millichip says the FA Cup is 'sacrosanct' in terms of sponsorship.

22

1938 Barnsley's Frank Bokas scores the only documented thrown goal direct from a throw-in via the goalie's fingertips.

1953 Ipswich Town remain unbeaten for the season until this day.

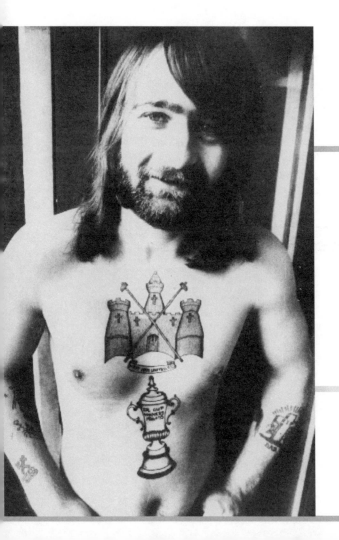

An optimistic Billy Bonds pictured just before his interview for the Millwall manager's job.

24

1994 Graham Taylor comes out with the immortal phrase 'Do I not like that' in Channel 4's *Dispatches* documentary.

25

1942 Portuguese star Eusebio, thought by some to be the second finest player of all time, is born.

1976 Kettering Town become the first English club to carry shirt sponsorship – Kettering Tyres.

1993 Gazza belches into a microphone during an Italian television interview.

*West Bromwich
Albion hear that Frank
Skinner is about to come onstage.*

27

1993 FIFA propose that throw-ins should be replaced by kick-ins.

28

1980 Granada TV's *World in Action* produces a controversial programme probing the affairs of Manchester United and chairman Louis Edwards.

Frank's birthday.

1990 Publication of the Taylor Report advocating all-seater stadia.
1994 Alex Ferguson calls Jimmy Hill a 'prat'.

Billy Bonds' CV.

30

1965 BBC cancel *Match of the Day* because of Winston Churchill's funeral.

31

1987 Goalkeeper Chris Woods of Rangers breaks the British clean-sheet record at 1,196 minutes.

1

1971 Graziano Ladoni of Palermo is fined £670 for refusing to say goodbye to his manager.

2

1991 Arsenal suffer their only defeat (2–1 to Chelsea) in their Championship-winning season.
1994 Maradona shoots at journalists outside his home with an air-rifle.

3

1990 Ally McCoist scores against Dundee United to become Rangers' leading post-war goalscorer.

4

1992 By beating Arsenal 2–1, Wrexham become the first team finishing bottom of the Football League the previous season to knock out the reigning champions.

1972 Ronnie Radford scores a memorable goal in Hereford's shock 2–1 win over Newcastle.

Proof that even doing the most mundane things, Jimmy Hill still looks ridiculous.

6

1994 Justin Fashanu claims to have had sex with two cabinet ministers.

7

1994 Stephen Milligan MP dies.

1994 Justin Fashanu denies having had sex with two cabinet ministers.

1994 Justin Fashanu decides that a holiday abroad might be a nice idea.

10

1975 Defender Dave Bassett's own goal against Leeds ends non-League Wimbledon's Cup run.

11

1994 Basil Brush makes his debut on *Fantasy Football*, his first BBC television appearance for 13 years.

Basil Brush.

1989 The Scottish FA agree to pay each player a £30,000 bonus should Scotland win the 1990 World Cup.

13

1972 Fourth Division Colchester beat Don Revie's mighty Leeds side 3–2 in the FA Cup.

14

1994 Sir Stanley Matthews agrees to do a 'Phoenix From the Flames'.

1994 Sir Stanley sees video of 'Phoenix From the Flames'.

Statto.

1994 Sir Stanley Matthews turns down 'Phoenix From the Flames'.

17

1990 Steve Bould of Arsenal scores the fastest own goal in First
Division history – 16 seconds against Sheffield Wednesday.

18

1882 England beat Ireland 13–0 to set a new British international
scoring record.

1994 Ruel Fox is granted a Royal decree declaring that he shall
always be referred to by both names.

1992 Bass Breweries agree a £12 million sponsorship of the FA Premier League, henceforth to be known as the Carling Premiership.

1994 John Motson gets over-excited on *Match of the Day* and says 'Oh! The goalkeeper pepodlecock' during his commentary.

The bloke who always played the undertaker in cowboy films kicks off at Selhurst Park.

20

FEBRUARY

1992 The FA Council approves the formation of the new Premier League.

21

1993 Two Czech goalkeepers, Ludek Miklosko and Pavel Srnicek, in opposition for the first time in the Premier League.

1956 The first game under floodlights, between Portsmouth and Newcastle at Fratton Park.

1926 All 11 Division 1 home teams win.

24

1993 England's World Cup-winning skipper Bobby Moore dies.

25

1982 Bobby Charlton opens his soccer school in Manchester.

1972 Chelsea release the record 'Blue is the Colour'.
1993 Tony Adams falls downstairs at Pizza Hut.

Bobby Charlton.

27

1994 Aston Villa goalkeeper Mark Bosnich saves three penalties in
the League Cup semi-final against Tranmere.
Karren Brady appears in a negligée in the *News of the World*.

28

1953 Charlie Tully of Celtic scores direct from a corner twice in the
same game. The first goal is disallowed because of fans
spilling on to the pitch.

MARCH

1

1992 A terrorist bomb at White Hart Lane delays the start of the League Cup semi-final between Spurs and Nottingham Forest.

2

1963 Halifax Town make history during the great freeze when they become the first club to open their ground to a paying public as an ice rink.

3

1962 Three Wrexham players – Barnes, Ambler and Davies – score hat-tricks in same game against Hartlepool.

1975 Richard Keys has his first shave. 11 am Richard Keys has his second shave.

4

1899 The first English-based League players play for Ireland.

1994 *Fantasy League* does a joke about Ossie Ardiles and any transfers at this stage in the season being irrelevant, and then cuts to some elephants playing football.

1993 *Sunday Sport* publisher David Sullivan is confirmed as the new owner of Birmingham City.

An angry Jimmy Hill removes an anonymous 'You look ridiculous' sticker from his car. Meanwhile, passers-by notice that his car aerial also looks ridiculous.

6

1993 Andy Savile's goal for Hartlepool ends the club's longest goal famine in League history (1,227 minutes).

7

1993 Manchester City are fined £50,000 for the pitch invasion during the FA Cup tie against Spurs. Four police horses are given a suspended sentence.

8

1924 Crewe are awarded four penalties in a match against Bradford Park Avenue but can only manage a 1–1 draw.

9

1968 West Brom win the BBC Quizball title, beating Sheffield Wednesday 5–1.

1991 Atletico Madrid goalkeeper Abel Resino establishes a new clean-sheet record after not conceding a goal for 1,230 minutes.

10

1993 England play their first game under new coach Terry Venables. They beat Denmark 1–0.

11

1970 Chelsea release their FA Cup song, a version of 'Chirpy Chirpy Cheep Cheep' by Peter Osgood, backed by the rest of the team.
1978 Referee Alan Turvey sends off two players in the same match for the third time in three months.

1982 Ian Botham makes his full debut for Scunthorpe in a 7–2 home defeat against Wigan.

Statto.

1982 The League Cup is renamed the Milk Cup after a sponsorship deal with the Milk Marketing Board.

14

1874 Oxford become the only university side ever to win the Cup.

15

1947 Aged 52 years and 4 months, Neil McBain becomes the oldest man to play in the Football League (New Brighton v Hartlepool United, Division 3 North).

1872 The first-ever FA Cup final is contested by Wanderers FC and the Royal Engineers. Wanderers win 1–0.

1977 Peter Storey is charged with headbutting a lollipop man.
1991 Diego Maradona tests positive for cocaine use after an Italian Serie A game. He receives a 15-month ban.

1973 Maglioni of Independiente scores the fastest hat-trick on record (1 minute 50 seconds).

Bob Wilson refuses to come out of his house after being accused of bias.

19

1991 Abel Resino is finally beaten by Enrique of Sporting Gijon after 1,275 minutes.

20

1976 Aston Villa defender Chris Nicholl scores all four goals in the 2–2 draw against Leicester.

21

1970 Jimmy Greaves scores on his debut for West Ham, completing a remarkable sequence of scoring debut goals at every level of football.

22

1975 Tony Currie scores 'a quality goal by a quality player' (John Motson) against West Ham.

1878 The Cup final is refereed by Mr S.R. Bastard.

1877 Lord Kinnaird of Wanderers scores the first-ever own goal in a Cup final.

25 MARCH

1992 Aldershot FC are expelled from the Football League.

*Mrs Julia Rimet
overjoyed at finding the stolen
dog Pickles (check this – Ed).*

1979 Aberdeen beat Motherwell 8–0 to establish a new Scottish Premier League record.

1966 Pickles the dog becomes a national hero when he recovers the Jules Rimet World Cup Trophy stolen one week earlier.

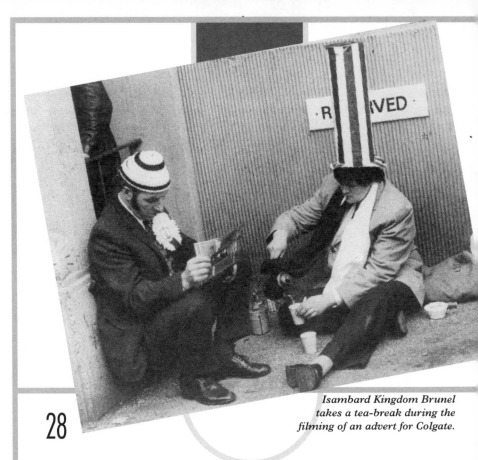

Isambard Kingdom Brunel takes a tea-break during the filming of an advert for Colgate.

28

1985 The ill-fated North American Soccer League, which originally featured stars like Pele and Cruyff, finally folds.

29

1924 Billy Meredith of Manchester City (49 years and 8 months) becomes the oldest man to play in an FA Cup tie.

30

1889 Preston North End become the first team to win the League and FA Cup double.

31

MARCH

1993 Ian Rush becomes Wales' leading scorer of all time with 24 goals.

1

1989 Manchester City win their first away game for three years and four months, 2–1 at Aston Villa.

APRIL

1887 Aston Villa beat West Brom 2–0 in the first all-Midlands Cup final. (Why did you have to bring that up? – Frank.)

1979 Sammy Nelson is suspended for two weeks after baring his behind in the 1–1 draw against Coventry.
1984 Barry Kitchener opens a trailer park and seaside souvenir shop in Great Yarmouth.

1888 West Brom beat Darwin 12–0 to establish the highest League Division 1 win, and to prove, once and for all, that the theory of evolution is nonsense.

Barry Kitchener consoles a Millwall fan by offering him a frisbee with 'Great Yarmouth' on it.

1879 James Prinsep (who?) becomes the youngest player to be capped by England at 17 years 252 days.

1992 Graeme Souness sells the story of his triple heart by-pass surgery to the *Sun*.

1994 Roy Keane grows a goatee beard.

The Three Degrees at West Brom.

7

1979 The Three Degrees appear on the pitch at West Brom.

1984 Clive Allen becomes Tottenham's record goalscorer with his 44th goal of the season (49 in total).

1986 Graeme Souness joins Glasgow Rangers as player-manager.

*Jimmy Hill shaves off
his beard and plays tennis in a sadly
miscalculated attempt to look less ridiculous.*

9

1991 Kevin Keegan is attacked in a layby by a man with a baseball bat.

1994 *Fantasy League* pokes fun at Roy Keane by comparing him to Jimmy Hill.

10

1982 The England World Cup squad release their World Cup anthem, 'This Time We'll Get it Right'.

1994 Roy Keane shaves off goatee beard.

1959 Billy Wright becomes the first player to win 100 international caps.

1970 The first Wembley Cup final not to be settled on the day, after Chelsea and Leeds draw 2–2.

1924 Everton winger Sam Chedgzoy forces a rule change for corners after dribbling the ball direct from a corner and scoring against Tottenham.

13

1936 Joe Payne hammers ten goals for Luton past Bristol Rovers, the most in one game by a single person.

14

1991 The first-ever semi-final to be played at Wembley between Spurs and Arsenal. Tottenham's Paul Gascoigne scores the 'goal of the season' in their 3–1 win.

1960 Cliff Holton of Watford becomes the only man ever to score two hat-tricks in successive days.

Statto.

1975 Malcolm Macdonald equals the England international record for goalscoring when he grabs all five against Cyprus.

17

APRIL

1888 The Football League formed.

18

1968 Jeff Astle scores the winner for West Brom in the Cup final.
1987 Glenn and Chris release 'Diamond Lights'.
1993 Millions of black butterflies invade Yaounde Stadium in Cameroon during the World Cup qualifier against Guinea.

1958 Bobby Charlton makes his debut for England, scoring the first of 49 goals.

1895 Bob Chatt of Aston Villa scores the fastest-ever goal in a Cup final (40 seconds).

21

1909 Nottingham Forest beat Leicester Fosse 12–0 to set a new Division 1 record.

1994 Bobby Tambling goes missing one week after his appearance on *Fantasy League*.

22

1959 Welshman Vic Rouse of Crystal Palace becomes the first Fourth Division player to win international honours.

1927 Cardiff City take the FA Cup out of England for the first and only time, beating Arsenal 1–0 in the final.

1915 Chelsea's Bob Thomson becomes the only one-eyed player ever to play in a Cup final.

25

1947 Dutch superstar Johan Cruyff born.

*Jimmy Hill smiles
to himself in the mistaken
belief that a man who can only see his
chin will not think he looks ridiculous.*

1968 Neil Young's goal against Leicester wins the FA Cup final for Manchester City.

1993 Crystal Palace, the team of the 80s, are relegated.

1947 The ball bursts during the Cup final between Charlton and Derby. Charlton's Bert Turner scores at both ends in the same game.

1994 Steve Heighway refuses to appear on *Fantasy League* and sing a parody of 'My Way'.

28

1973 Bobby Charlton retires.

29

1968 Manchester United defeat Benfica of Portugal 4–1 to become the first English club to win the European Cup.

1977 Man in 70s clothing paints penalty spot in game between Derby and Manchester City.

1994 The last-ever game is played in front of the Kop at Anfield.

1937 The Cup final between Preston and Sunderland is the first one ever to be televised.

2

1953 The 'Matthews' Cup final takes place. Blackpool beat Bolton 4–3. Despite a hat-trick by Stan Mortenson, the game will always be known as the 'Matthews' final.

3

1958 Bolton's Nat Lofthouse bundles Harry Gregg and the ball into the net for a controversial goal in the Cup final.

1974 Liverpool win the final trophy of the Shankly era, beating Newcastle 3–0 in the Cup final.

1928 Dixie Dean of Everton scores the hat-trick that takes his season's total to a record 60 goals.

1956 Bert Trautmann breaks his neck in the Cup final.

6

1961 Spurs beat Leicester 2–1 to become the first team to do the double this century.

1990 Tony Adams drives his Astra into an electricity pylon.

7

1921 Leicester and Stockport play out a Second Division game at Old Trafford in front of the lowest-ever recorded League attendance of 13 people. However, unofficial reports estimate the crowd to be around 2,000.

1994 David and Frank appear on *Match of the Day*.

1971 Arsenal beat Liverpool 2–1 at Wembley to clinch the first leg of the double.

1994 Frank has lunch in Portsmouth with Lorayne and Jeff Astle.

Tottenham's decision
to bring on Alfonso the Human
Cannonball goes horribly wrong.

Davros, leader of the Daleks, is found hiding in the European Cup.

9

1981 Tommy Hutchison scores for both teams in the FA Cup final between Tottenham and Manchester City. Ossie Ardiles sings 'In the Cup for Tottingham' on Chas 'n' Dave's 'Ossie's Dream'.

1977 Liverpool win the European Cup for the first time.

1987 Two ringleaders of Chelsea's notorious 'Head Hunter' gang are jailed for ten years for plotting and committing soccer violence.

12

1979 Alan Sunderland scores the last-gasp winner for Arsenal against Manchester United to win the Cup final.

13

Statto and Statto.

1994 David Baddiel wins the inaugural BBC2 *Fantasy Football League* title and receives the trophy from Anna Walker. Statto accidentally calls Basil Brush a puppet.

1966 Eddie Kavanagh becomes the first-ever football hooligan when he runs on to the pitch during the Everton and Sheffield Wednesday Cup final.

1984 Kenny Dalglish appears in a fairy outfit on *Scully*.

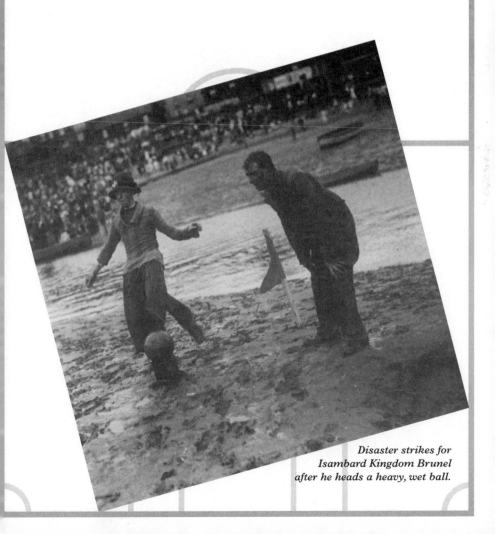

Disaster strikes for Isambard Kingdom Brunel after he heads a heavy, wet ball.

15

MAY

1984 Justin Fashanu phones Kenny Dalglish out of the blue.

16

1987 Coventry beat Spurs 3–2 to win the FA Cup for the first time.
1994 Jimmy Greaves suggests that Justin Fashanu will be 'stiffening up the back four' on Carlton TV's *Sport in Question*.

1953 The Argentina v England game is abandoned after 21 minutes due to heavy rain.

1985 Kevin Moran of Manchester United becomes the first player to be sent off in an FA Cup final.
1991 Paul Gascoigne seriously injures his knee in the Cup final.

19

MAY

1941 Harry McShane, father of Ian (Lovejoy) McShane, stars in a representative game between the Football League and an All British XI.

20

1993 By beating Sheffield Wednesday 2–1, Arsenal become the first team to win both League and FA Cups in the same season.

21

1983 Gordon Smith of Brighton misses an open goal to deny his team victory over Manchester United in the Cup final.

22

1968 With his 45th goal for England, Bobby Charlton breaks Jimmy Greaves' England international scoring record.

23

1954 Hungary complete a double over England with a 7–1 thrashing in Budapest.

24

1964 318 people are killed and 500 seriously injured in a riot during the match between Peru and Argentina. The trouble starts after an equaliser from Peru is ruled out.

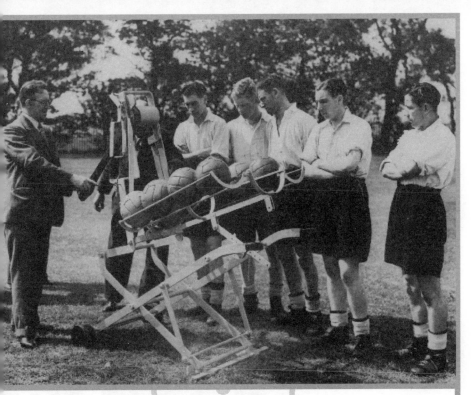

Following the Isambard Kingdom Brunel tragedy, footballers agree to play again only after the invention of a new ball-drying machine.

25

1967 Celtic become the first British club to win the European Cup by beating Inter Milan 2–1.

1970 Bobby Moore appears in court in Bogota charged with stealing a bracelet.

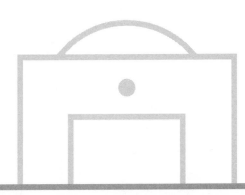

26

1989 Michael Thomas's last-gasp goal for Arsenal against Liverpool at Anfield clinches the Championship for the Gunners.

Stanley Matthews is crowned King of Ghana.

1957 Stanley Matthews is crowned King of Ghana.

1982 The lowest-ever attendance for a British international. Only 2,315 people turn up to watch Wales play Northern Ireland at Wrexham.

1959 Billy Wright makes the last of his 105 appearances for England.

David's birthday.

29

MAY

1993 Paul Gascoigne unveils a controversial protective face-mask in England's 1–1 draw in Poland.

30

1992 The new back-pass law brought in.

1986 52-year-old Pedro Gatica cycles from Argentina to Mexico for the World Cup only to find he can't afford to get in. While he is trying to barter for a ticket, thieves steal his bike.

1

1978 Poland and West Germany draw 0–0 in the fourth successive World Cup opening game to finish scoreless.

JUNE

2

1962 Chile face Italy in the battle of Santiago. Two Italians are sent off and referee Ken Aston has to be escorted off the field by police. Chile win the football bit 2–0.

3

1970 Pele attempts his famous 60-yard chip over the Czech goalkeeper Viktor in the World Cup. He misses, but Brazil win 4–1.

JUNE

4

1978 Scottish winger Willie Johnston is sent home from the World Cup after failing a routine after-match drugs test.

5

1968 Alan Mullery becomes the first England player to be sent off.

The Proclaimers brag about their best-ever chart positions.

6

1908 England play their first-ever international on foreign soil, winning 6–1 against Austria.

1970 Gordon Banks pulls off The Save from Pele's header in the England v Brazil World Cup game at Guadalajara while Jeff Astle pulls off The Miss at the other end.

1990 17-year-old Xia Qianli of China strangles his father after not being allowed to watch the opening ceremony of the World Cup.

9

1978 Referee Clive Thomas blows for full-time a fraction before Zico scores in the World Cup game between Brazil and Sweden.

1979 Kevin Keegan's record 'Head Over Heels' released.

10

1962 Brazilian star Garrincha adopts a dog after it invades the pitch and urinates on Jimmy Greaves during the World Cup.

11

1974 Sir Stanley Rous is removed as president of FIFA and replaced by Joao Havelange three days before the World Cup.

12

1938 The infamous Battle of Bordeaux between Brazil and Czechoslovakia. The final tally is a broken leg, a broken arm, a stomach injury and three sendings-off.

13

1962 Bob Wilson qualifies as a teacher.

1986 Jose Batista of Uruguay sets a new World Cup record when he is sent off after just 55 seconds.

14

1970 A nightmare for goalkeeper Peter Bonetti as West Germany overcome a two-goal deficit to beat England in the World Cup.

Muller of West Germany scores against England in the 1970 World Cup.

15

1974 Emmanuel Sannon of Haiti becomes the first player in 1,142 minutes of international play to get one past Italian goalkeeper Dino Zoff.

16

1982 Bryan Robson scores the second-fastest goal in World Cup finals history after just 27 seconds against France.

1994 Pele predicts Colombia will win the 1994 World Cup in the USA.

17

1962 Brazil clinch the second of their four World Cup triumphs with a 3–1 win over Czechoslovakia.

1994 Cardinal Basil Hume turns down the opportunity to be a manager on *Fantasy League*.

1978 Peruvian goalkeeper Ramon Quiroga is booked for a foul committed in the opposition half.

1992 The first appearance of the Turnip graphic of Graham Taylor in the *Sun*.

Graham Taylor.

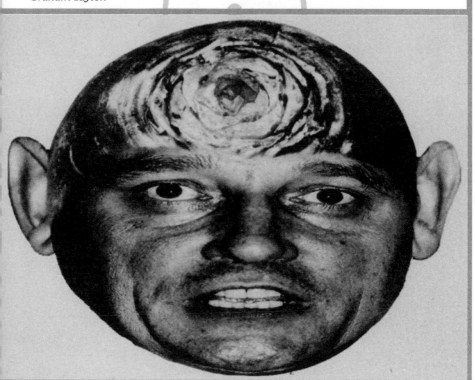

19

1958 Pele scores his first-ever World Cup goal in the 1–0 quarter-final win over Wales.

1994 David's brother Ivor's finger is broken by Hugh Grant in a celebrity charity game. Frank and David play in the same five-a-side team as Tommy Baldwin.

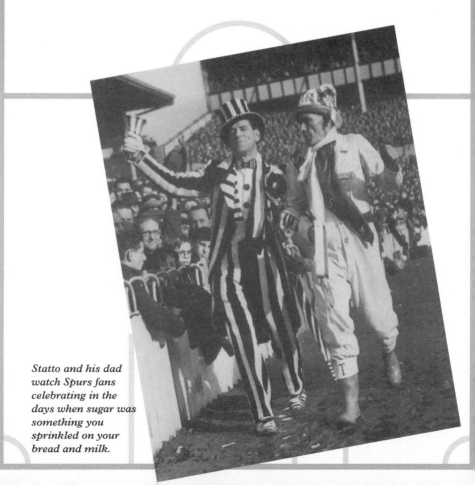

Statto and his dad watch Spurs fans celebrating in the days when sugar was something you sprinkled on your bread and milk.

1991 Terry Venables and Alan Sugar launch their ill-fated partnership at Tottenham Hotspur.

1970 Brazil, thought by many to be the greatest team of all time, beat Italy 4–1 to win the World Cup.

JUNE

1986 The infamous 'Hand of God' incident as England go out of the World Cup thanks to Diego Maradona's handiwork as well as his inspired feet.

The Hand of God.

23

1990 Cameroon become the first African team to qualify for the last eight of the World Cup finals.

24

1990 Frank Rijkaard of Holland is sent off for spitting at West Germany's Rudi Voller in the second round of the World Cup.

1982 A disgraceful day in World Cup history when West Germany and Austria contrive a convenient 1–0 result which allows both to qualify at the expense of Algeria.

Statto.

1994 Following Argentina's victory over Nigeria, Diego Maradona says he will never let his country down again.

JUNE

27

1954 Hungary beat Brazil 4–2 in an acrimonious game that becomes known as the Battle of Berne.

28

1978 Ernie Brandts of Holland achieves the dubious distinction of scoring an own goal, knocking out his own goalkeeper and scoring the equaliser in the 2–1 win over Italy that earns his country a place in the final.

29

1950 The USA defeat England 1–0 in one of the biggest World Cup shocks of all time.

30

1954 Sandor Kocsis of Hungary scores his 11th goal of the World Cup to set a new tournament scoring record.

1994 Diego Maradona tests positive for a cocktail of drugs and is banned from USA '94.

FACSIMILE COVER SHEET

MESSAGE:

NO. OF PAGES: 1
(Including this one)

DATE: July 26, 1994

Dear Mr. Jacobs:

I am sorry to regret that Dr. Kissinger will not be available to appear on the "Fantasy Football League" television program.

Thank you for your interest.

Sincerely,

Diana K. David

Dear Andy,

Many thanks for sending me the tape about your series. Unfortunately I will be unable to take part in one of your programmes. I am very sorry for any inconvenience caused to you and your company but would like to wish you every success with the series.

Yours sincerely.

Ron Radford.

10 DOWNING STREET
LONDON SW1A 2AA

Dear Mr Jacobs,

Thank you for your letter of 22 October 1993 inviting the Prime Minister to take part in your auction on 21 December. I have been asked to reply.

The Prime Minister has to decline your invitation. As you can imagine the pressure on his time is enormous and it is simply not possible to deal with all the many requests he receives of this nature.

I am sorry to have to send such a disappointing reply.

Yours sincerely

JONATHAN HASLAM
Deputy Press Secretary

Max Bygraves.

Bournemouth.
19.6.94

Dear Jim Anderson. I am flattered to be asked for "Fantasy Football" and though a shareholder in Aston Villa I don't think I could add anything to your successful programme — after running the video you kindly sent "I would feel like Alan Clarke at a meeting of the unemployed lesbians in Armenia....."
Regards. Max Bygrave

Andy Jacobs
GRAND SLAM SPORTS LTD
Durham House
Durham House Street
London
WC2N 6HF

Dear Andy Jacobs,

RE: PHIL COLLINS – "FANTASY FOOTBALL LEAGUE"

Thank you for your letter of 13th September.

However as I have already explained, Phil Collins is about to release a new album and will also be embarking on a world tour, consequently he will be very busy during the next 12 months and will not be available for your project.

I am sorry it will not be possible for us to work together on this occasion.

Yours sincerely,

P.P. *Tony Smith*

ARCHBISHOP'S HOUSE.
WESTMINSTER. LONDON. SW1P 1QJ

Dear Mr. Jacobs,

Thank you for your letter which arrived when I was absent from the Diocese.

In many ways I would be quite attracted to being involved in your programme but I really feel I have to say 'no'. I have so many engagements in my diary and I am simply not getting through all the work in the way I should. I do hope that you will understand my regret.

With kindest regards.

Yours sincerely,

Archbishop of Westminster

SIR JOHN HARVEY-JONES MBE
CHAIRMAN

Dear Andy,

Thank you very much for your letter of the 29th September.

I hope you will forgive me if I decline to take part in your programme. I am not really a particularly knowledgable footbaii person and I don't think that the programme would be my sort of thing.

I return the video herewith and I do wish the new series every success.

Yours sincerely,

[signature]

STIEFEL · PHILLIPS
ENTERTAINMENT

Dear Jim,

Thank you for your letter regarding Rod Stewart appearing on BBC's 'Fantasy Football League'. Unfortunately, I am unable to arrange anything for you as he has no plans to be in London between December and February as he will be recording an album here in the states.

Yours sincerely,

[signature]

Annie Challis

HUTTON MANAGEMENT LIMITED
(In association with Macnaughton Lowe Representation Ltd.)

Dear Mr. Jacobs,

Maureen Lipman - Fantasy Football League

Thank you for thinking of Miss Lipman but I'm afraid this idea does not appeal to her.

I return herewith your demo tape.

Yours sincerely,

[signature]

Anne Hutton
Enc:

1

1992 AC Milan shatter the world transfer record when they pay Torino £13 million for Gianluigi Lentini.

2

1990 Geoff Hurst refers to a 'nigger in a woodpile' while on the World Cup panel with Garth Crooks.
1992 The FA decide referees in the new Premier League will wear green.

3

1994 South Africa are re-elected to FIFA after 18 years in the wilderness.

*On the left is
the man who
went on to found
the 'Kick Racism Out of Football'
campaign.*

1977 Tommy Docherty is sacked by Manchester United after running off with physio Laurie Brown's wife.

1988 The USA are awarded the 15th World Cup finals.

1994 Commentators finally stop pointing out that Jason McAteer comes from a boxing family.

1982 Italy beat Brazil 3–2 in one of the most memorable games in World Cup history.

1994 Ron Atkinson says 'situation' for the 1,000th time on network television.

6

1988 Spurs sign Paul Gascoigne from Newcastle.

7

1974 Referee Jack Taylor awards Holland a penalty in the first 60 seconds of the World Cup final against Germany.

1990 Pedro Monzon of Argentina becomes the first man ever to be sent off in a World Cup final.

1916 The South American Football Federation affiliates to FIFA.

10 JULY

1989 Maurice Johnston becomes the first well-known Catholic to play for both Celtic and Rangers.

Two of the most ridiculous men in history fail to out-ridiculous Jimmy Hill.

11

1966 World Cup Willie becomes the first-ever tournament mascot.

12

1974 Bill Shankly retires.

13

1930 Lucien Laurent of France scores the first-ever World Cup goal.
1982 Statto invades the pitch at the England v India test match.
1992 The entire Barnet first-team squad slap in a mass transfer
request to club chairman Stan Flashman.

14

1977 Don Revie resigns as England manager midway through
qualifying for the 1978 World Cup, to take a job in the United
Arab Emirates.

*Rivelino swerves the Andrex puppy
past the Italian goalie Anzolin and into
the net.*

1966 Facing Brazil, Farkas of Hungary volleys in one of the most
memorable goals in World Cup history.
1968 Aston Villa sign Oscar Arce from Argentina.

16

1950 The world record attendance for any match is set when 199,854 people pack into the Maracana Stadium in Rio for the match between Brazil and Uruguay.

17

1982 Kevin Keegan appears on *Little and Large*. Syd heads a football and mimes nearly being knocked out.
1994 World Cup final at the Rose Bowl in Pasadena, USA.

1986 Sir Stanley Rous, president of FIFA, dies aged 91.

A shortage of trestle tables causes terrible problems at the first-ever Subbuteo World Cup.

19

1966 A goal by Pak Doo Ik helps tiny North Korea beat Italy 1–0 in the World Cup.

20

1991 David Platt leaves English football to join Bari in Italy for £5.5 million.

1964 Spurs' Scottish inside forward John White is killed after being struck by lightning during a golf match.

1990 Czech doctor of philosophy Josef Venglos succeeds Graham Taylor as manager of Aston Villa.

Jimmy Hill's birthday.

23

1966 England manager Alf Ramsey describes the Argentinian team as 'animals' after England's 1–0 victory in the World Cup quarter-final.

24

1986 Brighton offer Justin Fashanu six months' money to leave the club because of a knee injury.

1966 Inimitable Russian goalkeeping legend Lev Yashin makes his final World Cup appearance.

Statto.

26

1992 Alan Shearer joins Blackburn from Southampton for a then record £3.6 million.

27

1930 Both World Cup semi-finals end in 6–1 victories after Uruguay beat Yugoslavia by that score to make the final.

1958 Billy Wright marries Joy Beverley of the Beverley Sisters.

28

1985 19 years after hitting a hat-trick in the World Cup final, Geoff Hurst repeats the feat in charity match between the two 1966 squads.

1977 Eddie McCreadie leaves Chelsea because they won't give him a company car.

Eddie McCreadie, far left, weighs up his decision as six clubs vie for his services.

30

1930 The first-ever World Cup final.
1966 England beat Germany 4–2 to win the World Cup.

31

1966 Russian linesman Tofik Bakhramov is invited round to Geoff Hurst's house for tea.

1974 Brian Clough joins Leeds United for a managerial reign that is to last only 44 days.

1987 *Today* newspaper pulls out of a proposed Football League sponsorship deal only two days before the season begins.

3

1971 Pickles (the dog who discovered the missing World Cup) dies when he strangles himself on his lead while chasing a rabbit.

4

1990 The Taylor Report published.
1994 Blackpool Civic Corporation launch a new stick of rock for the summer season with Statto's name running right through it.

1968 Jimmy Five Bellies Gardner born (only two bellies at this stage).

1972 The first-ever penalty shoot-out takes place in an FA Cup third-place play-off involving Birmingham and Stoke.

Pickles' grave.

6

AUGUST

1969 Five Bellies' third belly officially launched.
1992 The Irish FA elect Harry Cavan for a world record 33rd consecutive year.

Jimmy Five Bellies Gardner.

1971 Colchester beat West Brom on penalties in the first-ever televised Watney Cup final.

1970 First airing of the familiar *Match of the Day* theme written by Barry Stroller.
1981 *Escape to Victory* released.

9

1969 Graham Taylor makes his debut for Lincoln. He scores in their 5–1 win over Notts County.

1986 Graeme Souness is sent off on the first day of the season for Glasgow Rangers.

10

1974 Kevin Keegan and Billy Bremner remove their shirts after being sent off for uncharitable behaviour in the Charity Shield.

Billy Bremner.

11

1968 ITV launch *The Big Match* with Brian Moore and Jimmy Hill.

12

1967 Pat Jennings scores a memorable goal direct from a drop-kick in the Charity Shield game between Tottenham and Manchester United.

13

1967 George Best Stylo Matchmakers launched.
1987 Barclays Bank announce a four-year sponsorship of the Football League.

1971 Leeds introduce number tabs on socks in a game against West Brom.

1990 Kenny Dalglish plays his last game for Liverpool.

1992 The first games in the new FA Premier League take place. David is asked by Nottingham Playhouse to write a play about Tommy Lawton.

16 AUGUST

1929 Albert Geldard becomes the youngest player to appear in the Football League at 15 years 158 days.

1992 Andy Gray first says the phrase 'I'll tell yer what.'

Andy Gray tries to stop saying 'I'll tell yer what.'

1992 Sky Sports transmit the first-ever Monday-night live game, between Manchester City and QPR.

1980 Steve Murray joins Forfar Athletic as manager, only to resign three days later.
1992 Andy Gray's Boot Room first broadcast.

19

1975 Manchester United goalkeeper Alex Stepney dislocates his jaw shouting at a team-mate.

20

206 BC First recorded mention of the Chinese kicking game Tsu Chu, believed to be the forerunner of the modern game.

1965 Keith Peacock (Gavin's dad) becomes the first player to appear as a substitute, for Charlton against Bolton.

Statto.

22

1964 The BBC broadcast the first-ever edition of *Match of the Day*.

23

1953 A stadium in Romania is named after the anniversary of the day the country was liberated from German rule.

24

1992 Terry Phelan joins Manchester City for £2.5 million, a record for a full-back.

*West Bromwich Albion get increasingly
desperate to lure Eddie McCreadie into
the manager's job.*

1928 Numbered shirts are worn in the League for the first time, by
Arsenal and Chelsea.

26

1986 Luton play their first home game after banning away supporters.

27

1952 Harry Bell of Middlesbrough scores a goal against Cardiff from his own goal-line.

AUGUST

28

1992 Peter Shilton is sent off for the first time in his career in his 971st League game, for Plymouth v Hull.

29

1936 A match between Arsenal and Everton is the first complete game to be televised.

30

1924 A goalie makes a save at an old football match. Beginning of a new age.

1991 Ghana beat Spain 1–0 to win the Under-17s World Cup.

31

1974 Spurs manager Bill Nicholson retires after 16 years of unparalleled success.

SEPTEMBER

1

1906 George Hilsdon scores five goals, the highest number on a League debut, for Chelsea against Glossop.

2

1972 Two East London streets are named after Bobby Moore and Trevor Brooking respectively.

3

SEPTEMBER

1955 Wolves equal the Division 1 scoring record for an away game when they beat Cardiff 9–1.

Eddie McCreadie during his playing days.

1960 Real Madrid beat Penarol 5–1 on aggregate to win the first-ever World Club Championship.

1992 Dean Saunders of Liverpool makes a tackle on Chelsea's Paul Elliot that ends his career.

6

1992 Hereford United are the first team to have four players sent off in one game. They still draw 1–1 with Northampton.

7

1991 The lowest attendance recorded since the war: 3,231 watch Wimbledon beat Luton.

1888 The inaugural day of the Football League.

1981 An ultra-patriotic Norwegian commentator goes mad as Norway beat England 2–1 in a World Cup qualifier.

10

SEPTEMBER

1972 Brian Bason makes his first appearance for Chelsea.
1985 Celtic manager Jock Stein dies.

11

1895 The original FA Cup is stolen from a shop in Birmingham and never recovered.

1885 Arbroath beat Bon Accord 36–0 to set a record for the highest score in a first-class match.

1993 Bob Monkhouse gives Frank a Seiko watch.

13

1979 Geoff Hurst is appointed caretaker manager of Chelsea.

1980 ITV broadcast the first-ever *Play Your Cards Right*.

14

1891 The first-ever penalty is taken in the Football League.

1971 Graeme Souness makes his only appearance for Spurs, appearing as a substitute in a UEFA Cup tie.

15

1980 Arsenal and England defender Peter Storey is jailed for three years for planning to manufacture fake gold coins.

1972 Jimmy Hill makes history when he takes over from injured linesman Denis Drewitt in a match between Arsenal and Liverpool at Highbury.

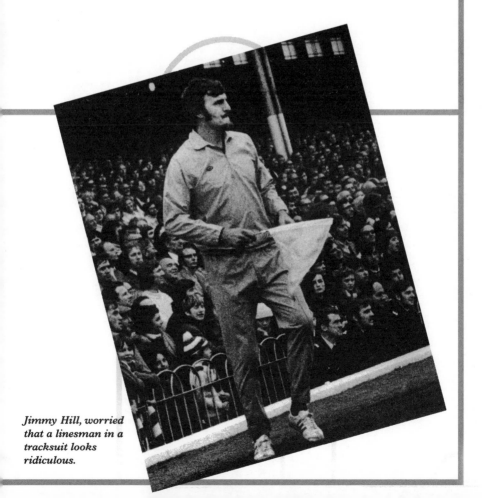

Jimmy Hill, worried that a linesman in a tracksuit looks ridiculous.

17

SEPTEMBER

1974 Nine of Liverpool's ten outfield players score in an 11–0 Cup-Winners' Cup win over Stromsgodset of Norway.

18

1948 Nine out of 11 First Division games end in draws to set a new record.
1965 Gary Lineker and Willie Thorne meet for the first time.

SEPTEMBER

1946 Barnet make history when their game against Tooting and Mitcham is the first game televised live.
1990 George Best says 'shit' on Wogan (on, not of? – Ed).
1993 The *Sunday Mirror* publish a story about Brian Clough being found in a ditch at a local cricket club.

1991 Spurs defender Terry Fenwick is jailed for four months on a drink-driving charge.

21

1949 The Republic of Ireland beat England 2–1 in their first international on English soil.

1969 Peter Knowles announces his intention to become a Jehovah's Witness.

22

1976 Willie Johnston kicks the referee up the arse in West Brom's 2–0 League Cup defeat by Brighton.

1993 Albanian players are banned from swapping shirts with their opponents, Spain, after a match because their FA cannot afford to buy replacements.

1992 Paul Gascoigne makes his long-awaited debut for Lazio.

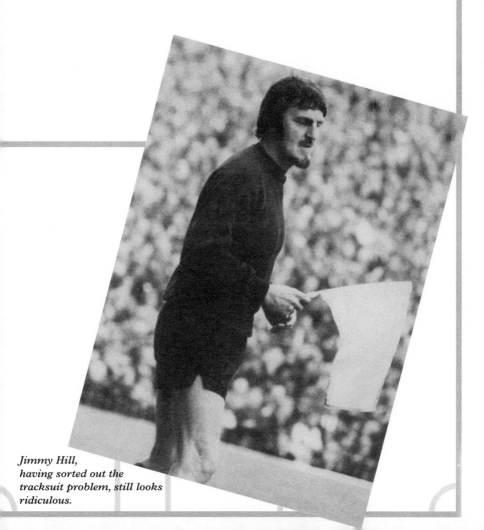

*Jimmy Hill,
having sorted out the
tracksuit problem, still looks
ridiculous.*

24

SEPTEMBER

1976 The first World Cup match to be played on artificial turf is Canada v USA.

1978 The BBC broadcast *Albion in The Orient*. Sightseeing around the Great Wall of China, John Trewick says 'When you've seen one wall, you've seen 'em all.'

25

1980 Peter Shilton crashes into a lamp-post with a strange woman.

1991 Ian Wright scores on his debut for Arsenal.

SEPTEMBER

26

1962 Arthur Rowley becomes the leading goalscorer in English League history.

Statto.

27

1986 Forest manager Brian Clough gives a V-sign salute to his own fans after they cheer an opposing player being stretchered off.

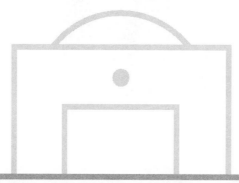

28 SEPTEMBER

1991 Paul Gascoigne, recovering from knee surgery, falls over in a Newcastle nightclub, setting his recovery back a further two months.

Two years after Edinburgh's only sign-writing company goes bust, men arrive from Glasgow with the letters E, A, R, T, O, F, M, I, D, L, O, T, H, I, A, N, F and C.

1971 Chelsea beat Jeunesse Hautcharage 13–0 to establish a record score for British clubs in Europe.

1981 Liverpool legend Bill Shankly dies.

1992 Vinny Jones is charged by the FA for misconduct after releasing a video called *Soccer's Hard Men*, which extols the virtues of foul play.

1

OCTOBER

1977 Pele retires after a 22-year career.

2

1976 Red and yellow cards are introduced to the Football League. George Best receives the day's first red card.

1970 Ernie Hunt scores a controversial goal for Coventry against Everton from Willie Carr's donkey-kick.

1913 Stockport's Norman Wood scores an own goal, concedes a spot-kick and misses a penalty in the 3–1 defeat against Fulham.

5

1946 Newcastle hammer Newport 13–0 to establish the highest-ever Second Division score.

6

1888 James Ross scores seven goals to set a First Division scoring record that still stands today.

1980 Everton become the first team to play 3,000 games in the First Division when they beat Brighton 3–1.

1990 Pele comes out of retirement at the age of 50 to play in a friendly international against Italy.

9

1993 Pop Robson goes into a restaurant where David's girlfriend works as a waitress.

10

1987 Andy Awford (now of Portsmouth) becomes the youngest man ever to play in an FA Cup tie at 15 years 88 days. The match is Worcester City v Borehamwood.

1924 Huddersfield's Billy Smith scores the first-ever goal direct from a corner.

Celebrations after the men from Glasgow finally turn up at Highbury.

12

1993 Paul Gascoigne manages to upset an entire nation by telling the whole of Norway to f*** off.

13

1993 German referee Herr Assenmacher fails to send off Ronald Koeman in the crucial World Cup qualifier against England. Koeman scores the first goal in a 2–0 victory.

1878 The first-ever experimental floodlit game takes place at Bramall Lane.

Mr Barry Mortimer, winner of the award for Best Euphemism For Anal Sex on a Hat, 1938.

15

1887 Preston establish a record score in an FA Cup tie by overwhelming Hyde 26–0.

16

1922 Max Bygraves born.
1992 Gordon Durie is the first player to be found guilty of feigning injury. He is given a three-match ban, later rescinded on appeal.

1987 Aston Villa score against Bournemouth and become the first club to register 6,000 goals in League competition.

Statto.

1980 John Trollope of Swindon sets a record for League appearances for one club with 765.

19

1968 Geoff Hurst scores six as West Ham thrash Sunderland 8–0.

20

1961 Liverpool and Wales striker Ian Rush born.

1936 Five penalties are awarded in the FA Cup second
qualifying-round match between Ipswich and Lowestoft.

1988 Three Wallace brothers, Danny, Rod and Ray, become the first
triple siblings to play in the same team for 68 years.

Pele.

23

1940 Edson Arantes de Nascimento (a poor boy from Brazil etc.) born. Has some success after changing his name to Pele.

OCTOBER

24

1857 Formation of Sheffield FC, the oldest football club in the world.

25

1980 Chris Waddle makes his debut for Newcastle in a 6–0 defeat by Chelsea.

26

OCTOBER

1863 The Football Association is formed.

27

1990 Substitute Ben Rowe of Exeter City is sent off while sitting in the dugout.

28

1972 Martin Peters scores all four goals in Tottenham's 4–1 away win at Manchester United.

29

1969 Aston Villa sign Fred Mwilla and Emmet Kapngwe from Uganda.

30

1960 Diego Maradona born.

31

1984 Liverpool lose their first League Cup tie for 25 rounds, 1–0 to Spurs.

NOVEMBER

1

1906 England beat France 15–0 in an amateur international.

1971 Jeff Astle releases his single 'Sweet Water'. The B side is called '"Summer Sadness" by The Piano of Jeff Astle'.

2

1991 Only nine goals are scored in 11 First Division games.

3

1993 Manchester United crash out of the European Cup to Galatasary.

4

1992 Rangers win the so-called Battle of Britain, knocking Leeds out of the European Cup.

Robert Maxwell.

5

1991 Boardroom caterers around Britain breathe a sigh of relief as Oxford chairman Robert Maxwell goes overboard for the final time.

6 NOVEMBER

1957 Northern Ireland record their first-ever win at Wembley.

*'Chopper' Harris looking very
out of place in the Chelsea back four.*

1931 Billy 'Ginger' Richardson fires home four goals in the first five minutes for West Brom against West Ham.

1888 George Cox of Aston Villa scores the League's first-ever own goal for Wolves.

9

1992 Leeds beat Stuttgart in a replayed European Cup tie after FIFA find the Germans guilty of fielding four foreign players.

10

1979 Chelsea beat Orient 7–3 to record their 1,000th League victory.

1871 Jarvis Kenrick becomes the first player ever to score in the FA Cup.

A confused Alf Sedgewick after spending his £100 Boots voucher.

12

1904 Sheffield Wednesday recover to draw 5–5 at home to Everton after trailing 5–0.

13

1985 Soren Lerby becomes the first man to play for two different teams (Bayern Munich and Denmark) in two different countries on the same day.

1934 Arsenal supply seven of the England team which beats Italy
3–2 at Highbury.

Statto.

1969 *Match of the Day* is screened in colour for the first time.

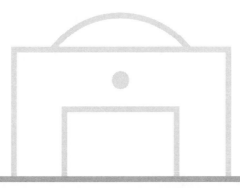

16

1938 Willie Hall scores the fastest British international hat-trick with three in three and a half minutes.

17

1993 England go one down to San Marino after just nine seconds and, despite going on to win 7–1, are eliminated from the World Cup.

18

1979 Fog is to bla
Wembley in

1981 Ron Greenwood's England qualify for the 1982 World Cup by
beating Hungary 1–0.

19

1979 Glenn Hoddl
1985 Ken Bailey is
Court.

1981 Fulham manager Malcolm Macdonald becomes the first
football club director to be paid.

1969 Pele
agai

Peter Storey comes face to face with the two sides of his nature.

23

1990 Peter Storey is charged with smuggling pornography in his tyres.

1991 Five players from America Tres Rios of Brazil are sent off in the first ten minutes of a game.

Statto's birthday.

1953 Hungary's great team featuring Ferenc Puskas defeats England 6–3 at Wembley.

26

1991 The first FA Cup tie to be decided by a penalty shoot-out takes place when Rotherham beat Scunthorpe 7–6 on penalties.

27

1989 FA fine Norwich and Arsenal £50,000 and £20,000 respectively for a brawl at Highbury on 4 November.

1989 The first FA Cup match to be played under floodlights is between Newcastle and Carlisle.

1977 Viv Anderson becomes the first black footballer to represent England in a full international.

30 NOVEMBER

1872 The first-ever England v Scotland game takes place.

Having realised that when he does mundane things he looks ridiculous, Jimmy Hill does a ridiculous thing, but still looks ridiculous.

DECEMBER

1

1990 The Tottenham team coach is towed away en route to a game with Chelsea. Spurs are fined £20,000 (that makes a change) for their late arrival.

2

1993 Dalian Atkinson is involved in a car accident and subsequently banned from driving for two years for being uninsured.

3

DECEMBER

1962 Mansfield Town purchase the old stand at Hurst Racecourse at auction.

4

1965 Frank Saul becomes the first Tottenham player to be sent off for 60 years.

1970 George Best scores his 100th goal for Manchester United and Jimmy Greaves his 351st goal in 500 League games.

1882 The Rules of Association Football are formalised.

7

1990 Only 625 people turn up for Scarborough's home game
against Wrexham, the lowest ever in the Fourth Division.

*A confused
Mahatma Gandhi after
spending his £100 Boots
voucher.*

1979 Colin Cowperthwaite scores a goal for Barrow against Kettering Town within 3.58 seconds of the kick-off.

1978 Liverpool end Nottingham Forest's 42-match unbeaten run, which spanned two seasons.

10

1987 After being sent off for the 11th time in his career, QPR defender Mark Dennis receives a 53-day suspension.

1993 Super-supporter and patriot Ken Bailey dies in his Union Jack waistcoat.

11

1909 Vivian Woodward scores all six goals in England's victory against Holland.

DECEMBER

1896 Arsenal suffer their worst-ever defeat, an 8–0 thrashing by Loughborough Town.

1989 Bryan Robson, playing for England against Yugoslavia, scores the fastest-ever goal at Wembley in a first-class game.

14

DECEMBER

1991 Torquay defender John Uzell's career comes to an end after he sustains facial damage in a controversial elbowing incident with Brentford's Gary Blissett.

15

1990 Clydebank goalkeeper Jim Gallacher equals Sandy Jardine's Scottish appearance record of 634.

1983 The BBC broadcast the first-ever live *Match of the Day*.

1955 Dennis Evans of Arsenal scores an own goal after a whistle blown by a spectator leads him to believe the game is over.

An ITV hitman is suspected of trying to nobble future BBC football presenters.

1968 Tommy Docherty takes over his third club in just six weeks when he becomes manager of Aston Villa.

1990 Matthias Sammer becomes the first East German to represent the newly unified Germany.

20

DECEMBER

1985 Live soccer returns after a long-running battle between television companies and the Football League is resolved.

21

1979 Peter Storey is charged with running a brothel.
1993 The first-ever *Fantasy Football League* auction is held at FA headquarters.

1963 The start of the big freeze that prevents a full League
programme for nearly four months.

Charlie George,
superstar, selects his outfit for
the PFA Awards Dinner.

23

1945 Graham Kelly born.
1990 15 players get their marching orders in the highest number of sendings-off in a League programme.

24

1973 Former Sheffield United star Derek Dooley loses the manager's job at Sheffield Wednesday.
1990 Tony Adams crashes his Ford Sierra.

1936 Ambrose Brown of Wrexham is sent off after just 20 seconds in a Third Division South game against Hull.

Statto.

1952 Three Sheffield Wednesday players score own goals in a 5–4 defeat at the hands of West Brom.

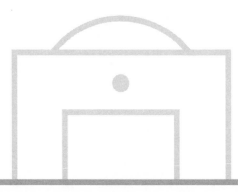

27

1949 The highest-ever total attendance for a single day: 1,272,185 watch 44 League games.

28

1990 A newspaper poll names Diego Maradona Italy's most hated man. Saddam Hussein comes second.

DECEMBER

29

1989 Bryan Robson is awarded the OBE in the New Year's Honours List.

30

1989 Brian Clough completes his 1,000th game as a League manager.

31

1993 Colombian goalkeeper Rene Higuita is freed from jail after being held without charge for over 120 days.

A dwarf.

THE TV FANTASY LEAGUE

LEAGUE TABLE

	Goals (3 Pts)	Ass. (2 Pts)	C.S. (4 Pts)	G.A (–1 Pt)	Week Total	Total
David Baddiel's The Creator Supremes	41	28	27	89	16	198
Basil Brush's PSV Boom! Boom!	26	27	36	92	9	184
John Motson's Oak Lodge Albion	41	43	25	141	6	168
Sue Johnston's Enfield Albion	37	22	28	104	12	163
Roy Hattersley's The Critics	18	29	25	59	16	153
Karren Brady's Blue Nose City	28	19	21	58	9	148
Roddy Doyle's Dublin Moenchengladbach	20	24	26	90	27	122
Lennox Lewis's Team Lennox	24	15	21	78	9	108
Eddie Large's Franny's In City	19	31	29	130	20	105
Bob Mortimer's Beg Tets	19	24	24	96	13	105
Richard Littlejohn's Garrincha's Dogs	20	20	19	88	3	88
Frank Skinner's Astle United	28	14	19	100	2	88
Mandy Smith's Muswell Babes	22	10	21	98	3	72
Andrew Ridgeley's The Beautiful Game FC	26	14	18	110	1	68
Dave Bassett's Bassett's Allsorts	19	17	12	77	1	62

BIBLIOGRAPHY

The Guinness Football Fact Book (1990), Jack Rollin

The Cassell Soccer Companion (1994), David Pickering

World Cup: A Complete Record 1930–90 (Breedon Books, 1990), Ian Morrison

More Soccer Shorts (Guinness, 1991), Jack Rollin

Rothmans Football Yearbook (1967 to 1993 editions), Jack Rollin *et al.*

The Guinness Record of the FA Cup (1993), Mike Collett

Match of the Day – The Complete Record (BBC Publications, 1992), John Motson

The Guinness Book of British Hit Singles (1992), Paul Gambaccini, Tim Rice, Jonathan Rice

The Daily Telegraph Football Chronicle (1993), Norman Barrett

News of the World Football Annual 1993–4, Bill Bateson and Albert Sewell (eds)